D11605547

WINTER BOTANY

By

WILLIAM TRELEASE

Third Revised Edition

DOVER PUBLICATIONS, INC.
NEW YORK

Published in Canada by General Publishing Company, Ltd., 30 Lesmill Road, Don Mills, Toronto, Ontario.

Published in the United Kingdom by Constable and Company, Ltd., 10 Orange Street, London WC 2.

This Dover edition, first published in 1967, is an unabridged and unaltered republication of the third revised edition of the work, published by the author in 1931.

Library of Congress Catalog Card Number: 67-19701

Manufactured in the United States of America
Dover Publications, Inc.
180 Varick Street
New York, N. Y. 10014

CONTENTS

FOREWORD

While at the University of Wisconsin, nearly forty years ago, I became interested in the differences by which woody plants may be recognized in winter—sometimes more surely than when in flower—and learned from Willkomm's excellent but inconveniently shaped book how readily these differences may be grouped for differential purposes. A large collection of winter twigs was accumulated subsequently at the Missouri Botanical Garden, and I owe a lasting debt of gratitude to many friends—among them the even then venerable Dr. Chapman of Florida—who collected such material for me.

Willkomm's book, like other contemporary publications of its kind, was confined to the commonest deciduous trees and shrubs of northern Europe. My intention at that time was to prepare a winter manual of the trees native to the Eastern United States, and illustrations of many of these were prepared by Miss Grace E. Johnson (now Mrs. George Clifford Vieh). For a variety of reasons, this undertaking was laid aside, and her skilful and expressive drawings remain unpublished except for those picturing *Acer*, *Carya*, *Juglans* and *Leïtneria*. It is a pleasure to record that though long out of practice, Mrs. Vieh has prepared for the engraver some of the simplified drawings now published.

URBANA, ILLINOIS,
August, 1918.

INTRODUCTION

When my Plant Materials pocket manual was issued, in 1917, an unusually full account was given of characters that are not mentioned in the usual handbooks, but the keys were based in large part on differences used by the old herbalists, —position and other pecularities of the foliage. The key of the present volume utilizes leaf-scar and bud differences in the same manner.

Because the keys of the first volume are as available for coniferous evergreens in winter as in summer, this important group of trees is not considered here at all; but angiospermous evergreens and the few deciduous conifers are treated now in even greater fullness. To avoid unnecessary repetition, family descriptions are not repeated here, and the generic characters are confined to the direct purpose of the book.

This purpose, naming our common trees and shrubs when without foliage, involves a close accounting for small differences between small parts, so that illustrations are more indispensable than for a Summer Manual leading to the same end with the same plants. Such illustrations are inserted in the text, where they may be used with convenience.

Even more necessary than in summer studies, is a good pocket-lens of about 12-magnification; and it should be an invariable practice to examine carefully a number of buds and leaf-scars, particularly those of ordinary branches rather than suckers or spurs, before beginning to use the key. When this practice is followed, after a few familiar species have been traced through so as to give facility, the key will be found simple, direct and conclusive in nearly every case; and native and introduced species, as well as genera, may be named for the most part.

The present volume, though conifers are excluded, deals

with 328 genera belonging to 94 families. Species and especially varieties are not differentiated to the same extent as in the earlier volume, but the keys lead to the names of about 1100 such forms.

As in the earlier volume, questions of nomenclature have been waived, and the same names are used in both books except for correction of a few oversights in the first, so that reference may be made readily to the Standard Cyclopedia for other information concerning the plants; and this is even more necessary than when names are learned from summer characters.

Though, like the "Plant Materials," appealing to only a limited number of users, the "Winter Botany" continues to prove serviceable to those who wish a simple and compact guide to the common trees and shrubs of park and garden, and the present edition is published to meet continuing demands for it. Except for corrections, few changes have been made from the second edition, published in 1925.

URBANA, ILLINOIS,
June, 1931.

USING THE KEYS

As in the Summer Manual, the keys are essentially dichotomous, bringing together in couplets alternatives with usually sharply contrasted differences. In each instance, these contrasts are grouped under a single number. A few examples will show the simplicity of using such a key, and the directness with which it leads to the name of a plant.

Caution should be observed with all alternate-leaved shrubs until the poisonous species of *Rhus* have become known.

Having a disinclination to come into unexpected contact with the poison ivy, I decide to familiarize myself with its essental winter-characters at once. Remembering where I saw it last summer, I go to a post or tree trunk over which it is climbing, and without touching it I am able to see that it climbs by the aid of numerous short roots that fasten themselves to the support, but has no tendrils, and that its leaf-scars are distributed singly along the stem, or alternate. Cautious examination under a lens, still without touching the plant, shows that these leaf-scars are half-round or somewhat shield- or heart-shaped or 3-sided, and after looking at several of them I have satisfied myself that each scar is marked by a number of dots—more or less evidently in 3 groups, each of which is a bundle-trace corresponding to one of the woody strands that passed from the stem to make up the framework of the leaf last season. Over each leaf-scar is a single bud, slightly elongated or stalked below its leaves. No sign of stipules, or scars left after their fall, is evident near any of the leaf-scars. I have noticed everything essential to naming the plant without having exposed myself to danger from its poison. Turning to the key (p. xii), I find only five contrasts—no. 1 to 140; no. 140 to 150; no. 150 to 151; no. 151 to 157—before I stop convinced that it belongs to the genus *Rhus*. Reading the winter-description of that genus on p. 189 confirms me in this conviction. The analysis of species under *Rhus* leads as directly and certainly to *Rhus radicans* (f. 4) as the name of my plant.

As I return to the house, I stop to look at a velvety vine rooted against a tree-trunk where I remember having seen something different from poison ivy last summer. Without touching this climber I look it over carefully, first with the unaided eye, then under a lens, and find that it differs from *Rhus* in a number of respects. Besides the roots by which it is fastened to its support, it produces short hand-like tendrils at many of its nodes and the fingers of these are dilated into broad adhering tips. These tendrils are opposite the half-round leaf-scars, each of which has a series of rather indistinct bundle-traces just inside its margin; and a narrow stipule-scar runs off at either side of the short round bud above each leaf-scar. The sequence in the key here is no. 1 to 140; 140 to 150; 150 to 151; 151 to 152; and 152 to 153. The disks at end of the tendril-branches satisfy me that this is a Virginia creeper, and the key to the several kinds of *Parthenocissus* (p. 227) shows that I have seen the rooting ampelopsis, *Parthenocissus quinquefolia Saint-Paulii*, which I may transplant to my house next spring without fear,—and in the certainty that it will cling closely and tenaciously to the wall.

My neighbor grows a fleecy, tall shrub that has the peculiarity of discarding many of its very slender twigs every fall, reclothing itself in a similar array the next season. I find that instead of ordinary broad leaves, this produces small scales, one at a node though often crowded close together. These scale-leaves have not fallen as most leaves do, but are present in winter. In the axil or angle over each of them is a small round bud, and the outer scales of some of these have parted, showing a nest of smaller buds. Cutting across one of the reddish branchlets, I see that its pith is toward one side rather than exactly central in the zone of wood by which it is separated from the bark. Tracing the shrub is simple:—no. 1 to 140; to 141; to 142; to 143; to 144; to 145, where I stop at *Tamarix*. The species (p. 245) are not easily distinguished, but the color of the twigs makes me believe that this is the commonly cultivated *Tamarix gallica*.

Several years ago a squirrel overlooked some sort of a nut that he had buried next a fence. It has grown into a small tree with sumach-like foliage, that must be either a hickory or black walnut or butternut. I want to know which. The twigs present many peculiarities: leaf-scars are alternate, raised above the level of the stem, shaped much as in the poison ivy, with 3 usually C-shaped or fragmented bundle-traces; over each leaf-scar are two scaly buds, one superposed above the other; and the twig, when split, shows a peculiar pith, not solid, but consisting of thin brown plates separating cavities or chambers. The key leads me from no. 1 to 140; to 150; to 172; to 202; to 203; to 219; to 224; to 225; to 227; to 255; to 256; to 259; to 260; where I decide that my tree is a *Juglans*. The characters of this genus (p. 17) satisfy me that this is right, and the short gray silky terminal bud and the absence of moustache-like velvety lines above the leaf-scars show that it was a black walnut that the squirrel planted and forgot, here as along many other fences.

A horticultural friend brings me a twig of one of the golden bells which survived the last severe winter better than the common *Forsythia viridissima*, and asks if it can be the hybrid (× *F. intermedia*) between that species and the hardier *F. suspensa*. The key (1 to 2; to 15; to 19; to 22; to 35; to 40; to 86; to 87; to 92; to 97; to 104; to 124; to 126) convinces me that what he has is really a *Forsythia*. Turning to p. 310 I find that the twig has the solid tissue at its nodes characteristic of *F. suspensa* (f. 3), but the thin plates or their remains between the nodes characteristic of *F. viridissima* (f. 1); for the hybrid × *Forsythia intermedia* (f. 2) is intermediate between the parent species in this as in other characters.

KEY TO GENERA.

1. Leaves solitary (alternate) at each node. 140.
   Leaves 2 or more at each node. 2.
   (Leaves may be represented by scales or spines or by scars from which they have fallen, in either of the groups).
2. Leaves characteristically 2 at each node. 15.
   Leaves characteristically 3 or more at each node. 3.
   (Exceptional branches may have 3 instead of 2, or 2 instead of the customary 3 leaves).

LEAVES WHORLED.

3. Leaves reduced to small thin scales. 3a.
   Ordinary leaves or their scars present. 4.

3a. Twigs finely striate. p. 6. Ephedra.
   Twigs few-grooved. p. 9. Casuarina.

4. Leaves persistent and green (evergreen). 5.
   Leaves absent (deciduous), or dried. 10.
5. Leaves small, narrow, revolute: low shrubs. 6.
   Leaves larger, broad, flat: sap milky. 9.
6. Leaves terete: aromatic. p. 183. Ceratiola.
   Leaves broader than thick. 7.
7. Leaves 3 or 4 in a whorl: plants erect. p. 301. Erica.
   Leaves about 5 in a whorl: plants matted. 8.
8. Leaves flat above, not toothed. p. 182. Empetrum.
   Leaves biconvex, microscopically toothed. p. 181. Corema.
9. Stipules present: leaf-scars not fringed. p. 326. Allamanda.
   Stipules lacking: leaf-scars fringed at top. p. 328. Nerium.
10. Twigs stout: leaf-scars large. p. 343. Catalpa.
    Twigs slender. 11.
11. Buds small, often sunken in the bark. p. 346. Cephalanthus.
    Buds moderate or very evident. 12.
12. Bundle-trace 1: pods long, slender. p. 342. Chilopsis.
    Bundle-traces several. 13.
13. Pith spongy or excavated: buds acute. p. 79. Deutzia.
    Pith continuous. 14.
14. Two or four hairy lines below each node. p. 350. Diervilla.
    Without hairy ridges: buds short, blunt. p. 83. Hydrangea.

LEAVES OPPOSITE.

15. Leaves represented by small persistent scales. 16.
    Ordinary leaves or petioles, or their scars, present. 19.
16. Twigs often ending in spines. 17.
    Twigs not sharp and pungent. p. 6. Ephedra.
17. Spines much flattened. p. 216. Colletia.
    Twigs cylindrical (terete). 18.
18. Spines rather long: no stipules. p. 243. Koeberlinia.
    Spines 2 cm., outcurved: stipules minute. p. 223. Adolphia.
19. Leaf-scars and buds in 2 vertical ranks. 20.
    Leaf-scars in 4 ranks unless on climbers. 22.
20. Deciduous: without stipules or stipule-scars. 21.
    Evergreen: stipules persistent. p. 161. Guaiacum.
21. Not aromatic: buds elongated. p. 44. Buckleya.
    Aromatic: buds round. p. 69. Meratia.
22. Climbing or scrambling. 23.
    Not climbing. 35.
23. Climbing by coiling leaf-organs (tendrils). 24.
    Climbing by aerial roots. 25.
    Twining or scrambling, without aerial roots or tendrils. 28.
24. Wood showing a cross in section. p. 340. Bignonia.
    Wood not showing a cross: stem angled. p. 53. Clematis.
25. Evergreen: leaves rather small. p. 197. Evonymus.
    Deciduous. 26.
26. Leaf-scars half-round: bundle-trace 1. p. 341. Campsis.
    Leaf-scars cresent-shaped. p. 83. Hydrangea.
    Leaf-scars U-shaped or horseshoe-shaped: pith spongy. 27.
27. Leaf-scars U-shaped, bundle-traces 5. p.80. Schizophragma.
    Leaf-scars horseshoe-shaped. p. 81. Decumaria.
28. Pith continuous. 29.
    Pith spongy: evergreen: sap milky. 30.
    Pith chambered or excavated. 32.

29. Twigs acutely 4-lined. p. 322. Jasminum.
Twigs terete and not ribbed. p. 332. Petraea.
30. Leaves rounded at ends. p. 330. Stephanotis.
Leaves acute at both ends. 31.
31. Leaf-scars transversely connected. p.327. Trachelospermum.
Leaf-scars without connecting lines. p. 326. Allamanda.
32. Sap milky: leaf-scars raised, shriveled. p. 329. Periploca.
Sap not milky. 33.
33. Bundle-trace 1. 33a.
Bundle-traces 3: twining. p. 355. Lonicera.
33a. Evergreen. 34.
Deciduous. p. 310. Forsythia.
34. Twining: stems 4-lined: leaves simple. p. 334. Gelsemium.
Scrambling: stems not lined. p. 322. Jasminum.
35. With spines ending some twigs or in the axils. 36.
Without spines or prickles. 40.
36. Scurfy with shield-shaped (peltate) scales. 37.
Without such scales. 38.
37. Evergreen: buds naked: leaves lanceolate. p. 320. Olea.
Deciduous. buds scaly. p. 250. Shepherdia.
38. Spines forking: evergreen. p. 325. Carissa.
Spines unbranched, often blunt: foliage deciduous. 39.
39. Buds several, superposed, small. p. 318. Forestiera.
Buds not superposed, relatively large. p. 222. Rhamnus.
40. Bundle-traces 3 or more, separate, in an open series. 41.
Bundle-trace 1; or many traces scattered or in an ellipse, or nearly confluent in a straight or curved line. 86.
(This group includes cases in which the bundle-traces are indistinguishable in a shriveled scar).
41. Leaf-scars large and broad: twigs stout. 42.
Leaf-scars small or narrow. 43.
42. Buds solitary, the terminal enlarged. p. 209. Aesculus.
Buds multiple. 42a.
42a. Bundle-traces 3-7. p. 361. Sambucus.
Bundle-traces many. p. 312. Fraxinus.

43. Leaf-scars linear or U-shaped. 75.
    Leaf-scars horseshoe-shaped. 85.
    Leaf-scars not as above unless by tearing. 44.
44. Evergreen. 45.
    Deciduous. 48.
45. Leaves pinnate, frequently alternate. p. 145. Sophora.
    Leaves simple. 46.
46. Bundle-traces three. 47.
    Bundle-traces 7: stipules forming a sheath. p.347. Gardenia.
47. Pith uniform and continuous. p. 351. Viburnum.
    Pith gritty, finally chambered. p. 366. Aucuba.
48. Pith spong or finally excavated. 49.
    Pith characteristically continuous and persistent. 53.
49. Leaf-scars raised, or else buds superposed. 50.
    Leaf-scars little raised: buds not superposed. 52.
50. Buds sessile. 51.
    Buds slightly stalked. 50a.
50a. Tender: small. shrub. p. 358. Leycesteria.
    Hardy: larger. p. 264. Cornus.
51. Buds never superposed. p. 354. Symphoricarpos.
    Buds often superposed. p. 355. Lonicera.
52. Pith spongy, or lower bud-scales short. p. 78. Deutzia.
    Pith excavated: lower scales as long as bud. p.349. Dipelta.
53. Buds behind a persistent petiole-base. p. 264. Cornus.
    Buds covered by a broad membrane. p. 76. Philadelphus.
    Buds exposed. 54.
54. Buds enclosed in a single outer scale or sac. 55.
    Buds naked, or with separate scales. 57.
55. Scale 1, split in front. p. 51. Cercidiphyllum.
    Scales 2, united in a closed sac. 56.
56. With evident stipule-scars. p. 203. Staphylea.
    Without stipule-scars. p. 351. Viburnum.
57. Most leaf-scars alternate: buds silvery. p. 150. Laburnum.
    Without this combination of characters. 58.

58. Leaf-scars ciliate at top. 59.
    Leaf-scars not ciliate. 61.
59. Buds solitary over each leaf-scar. 60.
    Buds often collaterally multiplied. p. 114. Rhodotypos.
60. Buds essentially sessile. p. 204. Acer.
    Buds slightly but evidntly stalked. p. 351. Viburnum.
61. Twigs with 2 or 4 often hairy raised lines. p. 350. Diervilla.
    Twigs not ridged when fresh. 62.
62. Buds without scales: stellate-scurfy. p. 351. Viburnum.
    Buds with scales. 63.
63. Visible scales 1 or 2 pairs. 64.
    Visible scales more than 2 pairs. 70.
64. Buds stalked: scales meeting at their edges. p. 204. Acer.
    Buds not stalked. 65.
65. Leaf-scars distinctly raised. 66.
    Leaf-scars low. 68.
66. Aromatic: lateral bundle-traces very small. p. 69. Meratia.
    Not aromatic: bundle-traces 3, nearly equal. 67.
67. Leaf-scar on a finally torn membrane. p. 76. Philadelphus.
    Leaf-scar not on an articular membrane. p. 355. Lonicera.
68. Leaf-scar thin and tearing at top. p. 76. Philadelphus.
    Leaf-scar not on an articular membrane. 69.
69. Glabrate: with stipule-scars. p. 203. Staphylea.
    Velvety: without stipule-scars. p. 164. Evodia.
70. Buds sometimes superposed. 71.
    Buds not superposed. 72.
71. Leaf-scars raised. p. 355. Lonicera.
    Leaf-scars low. p. 350. Diervilla.
72. Bark exfoliating: traces subconfluent. p. 359. Kolkwitzia.
    Bark not exfoliating, or else bundle-traces separated. 73.
73. Buds nearly globose or else plants pithy. p. 83. Hydrangea.
    Buds conical. p. 204. Acer.
    Buds ovid or oblong. 74.
74. Buds branching or else leaf-scars meeting. p. 204. Acer.
    Buds remaining solitary. p. 351. Viburnum.

75. Bud-scale 1, forming a closed sac. 76.
    Bud-scales several or indistinct, or lacking. 77.
76. Buds gummy within. p. 351. Virburnum.
    Buds not gummy when opened. p. 12. Salix.
77. Twigs with many ridges. p. 78. Fendlera.
    Twigs without such ridges. 78.
78. Very woolly: savory: small. p. 336. Rosmarinus.
    Neither very woolly nor savory. 79.
79. Buds quite sessile. 80.
    Buds somewhat stalked. 83.
80. Pith continuous. 81.
    Pith spongy: often stellately pubescent. p. 79. Deutzia.
    Pith excavated: twigs slender. p. 360. Abelia.
81. Evergreen: leaf-scars at first raised. p. 269. Garrya.
    Deciduous. leaf-scars low. 82.
82. Leaf-scars meeting. p. 77. Jamesia.
    Leaf-scars not meeting. 82a.
82a. Buds superposed. p. 68. Calycanthus.
    Buds not superposed. p. 204. Acer.
83. Leaf-scars for a time raised: scales valvate. p. 264. Cornus.
    Without this combination of characters. 84.
84. Leaf-scars meeting in a point. p. 204. Acer.
    Leaf-scars not meeting. 84a.
84a. Twigs bright-colored. p. 264. Cornus.
    Twigs not bright-colored. p. 351. Viburnum.
85. Aromatic: buds closely superposed. p. 68. Calycanthus.
    Not fragrant: buds solitary. p. 167. Phellodendron.
86. Leaf-scars fringed: evergreen: sap milky. p. 328. Nerium.
    Without this combination of characters. 87.
87. Soft pithy half-shrubs: buds superposed. 88.
    Without this combination of characters. 92.
88. Peppery-aromatic: leaf-scars U- or C-shaped. p. 335. Vitex.
    Not peppery-aromatic. 89.
89. Leaf-scar subelliptical. 90.
    Leaf-scar triangular or crescent-shaped. p. 323. Buddleia.
    Leaf-scar or bundle-trace C-shaped. p. 333. Callicarpa.

90. Leaf-scars of each pair connected. p. 344. Tecoma.
    Leaf-scars not connected by a downy line. 91.
91. Leaf-scars straight at top. p. 334. Caryopteris.
    Leaf-scars notched. p. 331. Clerodendron.
92. Bundle-traces many in a compound or elliptical series. 93.
    Bundle-traces few (often 3), rather distinct. 95.
    Bundle-trace 1, sometimes obscure. 97.
93. Sap milky: bud-scales striated. p. 37. Broussonetia.
    Sap not milky: but-scales 2 or four, not ribbed. 94.
94. Pith chambered: leaf-scars elliptical. p. 339. Paulownia.
    Pith continuous: scars shield-shaped. p. 312. Fraxinus.
95. Aromatic: middle bundle-trace largest. p. 69. Meratia.
    Not aromatic. 96.
96. Stipules persistent: buds silvery-hairy. p. 150. Laburnum.
    Stipules lacking: buds gray-velvety. p. 359. Kolkwitzia.
97. Heath-like or trailing, with small evergreen leaves. 98.
    Not heath-like or trailing and also evergreen. 104.
98. Delicate trailing rooting vine. p. 357. Linnaea.
    Heath-like or moss-like. 99.
99. Leaves auricled at base and sessile. p. 300. Calluna.
    Leaves neither auricled nor sessile. 100.
100. Leaves overlapping like fleshy scales. p. 284. Cassiope.
    Leaves not overlapping. 101.
101. Leaves very revolute. p. 279. Loiseleuria.
    Leaves narrowly if at all revolute. 102.
102. Leaves finely toothed. p. 200. Pachistima.
    Leaves entire. 103.
103. Leaves with distinct dots beneath. p. 278. Leiophyllum.
    Leaves not or very indistinctly dotted. p. 280. Kalmia.
104. Evergreen. 105.
    Deciduous. 124.
105. Leaves of 2 leaflets: odoriferous. p. 162. Covillea.
    Leaves pinnately divided. p. 322. Jasminum.
    Leaves simple, not divided. 106.

106. Aromatic. 107.
Not aromatic. 112.
107. Leaves narrowly lanceolate: shrub. p. 254. Myrtus.
Leaves broad. 108.
108. Leaves several-nerved, rather ovate. p. 71. Cinnamomum.
Leaves 1-nerved, elliptical or falcate. 109.
109. Leaves white-woolly beneath. p. 256. Feijoa.
Leaves glabrous. 110.
110. Leaves of mature growth alternate. p. 259. Eucalyptus.
Leaves all opposite and elliptical. 111.
111. Bark shredding: buds solitary. p. 252. Punica.
Bark not shredding: buds superposed. p. 257. Pimenta.
112. Leaves and buds gray- or golden-scurfy. p. 320. Olea.
Not scurfy. 113.
113. Pith spongy. 114.
Pith continuous. 117.
114. Sap milky: pith round. p. 326. Allamanda.
Sap not milky: pith usually 4-angled. 115.
115. Pubescent: pith brown. p. 255. Psidium.
Glabrous: pith green or white. 116.
116. Leaves very small (5-8×15-20 mm.). p. 200. Pachistima.
Leaves distinctly larger. p. 197. Evonymus.
117. Buds not superposed. 118.
Buds often superposed. 120.
118. Leaves small (2 cm.). 119.
Leaves larger: stipules sheathing. p. 348. Coffea.
119. Leaves blunt. p. 179. Buxus.
Leaves acute. p. 246. Daphne.
120. Bundle-trace at top of the leaf-scar. p. 180. Simmondsia.
Bundle-trace in the middle of the leaf-scar. 121.
121. Leaf-scars relatively large (3 mm.), p. 317. Osmanthus.
Leaf-scars smaller, elevated. 122.
122. Leaves elliptical. p. 280. Kalmia.
Leaves ovate or lanceolate. 123.

123. Leaves entire, lance-ovate. p. 321. Ligustrum.
Leaves toothed or else not ovate. p. 316. Phillyraea.
124. Pith spongy. 125.
Pith finally chambered or excavated. 126.
Pith continuous and persistent. 130.
125. Leaf-scars round: bark flaking. p. 251. Lagerstroemia.
Leaf-scars crescent-shaped. p. 197. Evonymus.
126. Buds slender, finally much multiplied. p. 310. Forsythia.
Buds only 1-3 in each axil. 127.
127. Leaf-scars shield-shaped. p. 314. Schrebera.
Leaf-scars triangular or lens- or crescent-shaped. 128.
128. Leaf-scars raised, shriveled. p. 354. Symphoricarpos.
Leaf-scars low. 129.
129. Leaf-scars triangular. p. 238. Ascyrum.
Leaf-scars triangularly lens-shaped. p. 239. Hypericum.
130. Twigs rather sharply 4-ridged. 131.
Twigs at most angular or grooved below the nodes. 132.
131. Leaf-scars ciliate or fringed at top. p. 311. Fontanesia.
Leaf-scars not ciliate. p. 252. Punica.
132. Leaf-scars transversely broad (3 mm.). 133.
Leaf-scars often minute (scarcely 2 mm.). 135.
133. Buds superposed. 134.
Buds not superposed. p. 315. Syringa.
134. Bud-scales stiff-pointed. p. 319. Chionanthus.
Bud-scales not pungent. p. 312. Fraxinus.
135. Leaf-scars low. 136.
Leaf-scars elevated. 137.
136. Buds several, superposed, separated. p. 318. Forestiera.
Buds collaterally multiplied. p. 184. Coriaria.
Buds usually solitary: bark not shredding. p. 246. Daphne.
137. Leaf-scars shriveled. p. 354. Symphoricarpos.
Leaf-scars distinctly outlined. 138.
138. Bushy. 139.
With a tendency to climb. p. 322. Jasminum.

139. With a stipular line. 139a.
Without stipular vestiges. p. 321. Ligustrum.
139a. Buds conspicuous. p. 345. Pinckneya.
Buds minute. p. 346. Cephalanthus.

LEAVES ALTERNATE

140. Leaves represented by small scales, or by spines. 141.
Ordinary leaves, or scars, or petioles, present. 150.
141. Wood-strands scattered through the stem. p. 7. Ruscus.
Wood in a zone between pith and bark. 142.
142. Leaves persistent in the form of scales. 143
Leaves or their axes persistent as spines. 146.
143. Scales and buds minute: twigs spiny. p. 243. Koeberlinia.
Scales and buds evident, though small: not spiny. 144.
144. Percurrent tree: twigs slender. p. 5. Taxodium.
Openly branched small tres or shrubs. 145.
145. Pith central in the branches. p. 240. Myricaria.
Pith toward one side of the branches. p. 240. Tamarix.
146. Twigs, as well as leaves, becoming spines. p. 151. Ulex.
Only the leaves becoming spines. 147.
147. Spines without leaflet-scars. 148.
Spines with leaflet-scars. 149.
148. Spines unbranched: stems rather fleshy. p.241. Fouquieria.
Spines commonly branched. p. 59. Berberis.
149. Buds with evident scales. p. 156. Caragana.
Bud scales indistinct: tender. p. 143. Parkinsonia.
150. Climbing or scrambling. 151.
Not climbing. 172.
151. Climbing by tendrils. 152.
With aerial roots but no tendrils. 157.
Twining or scrambling, without roots or tendrils. 158.
152. Tendrils on the persistent leaf-base. p. 8. Smilax.
Tendrils opposite the leaf-scars. 153.
153. Tendrils often ending in disks. p. 227. Parthenocissus.
Tendrils not enlarged into disks. 154.

154. Pith continuous. 155.
Pith sub-chambered. p. 224. Ampelopsis.
155. Stems rather fleshy, terete. p. 225. Cissus.
Stems firm. 156.
156. Bark not flaking: pith not firmer at nodes.
p. 227. Parthenocissus.
Bark flaking and pith firmer at nodes except in one.
p. 226. Vitis.
157. Evergreen: leaves simple, usually angular. p. 260. Hedera.
Deciduous. *Poisonous.* p. 189. Rhus.
158. Leaf-scars U-shaped or linear. 159.
Leaf-scars neither U-shaped nor linear. 160.
159. Buds solitary, scaly: stem often prickly. p. 125. Rosa.
Buds superposed, pubescent, indistinct. p. 46. Aristolochia.
160. Some twigs spinescent. 161.
Entirely unarmed. 162.
161. Twigs 5-ridged, pale. p. 337. Lycium.
Twigs not ribbed. p. 48. Bougainvillea.
162. A knob or spur at each angle of the leaf-scar.
p. 153. Wisteria.
Leaf-scars without knobs at their angles. 163.
163. Buds small or sunken or covered by the leaf-scar. 164.
Buds moderately large, evident. 167.
164. Bundle-trace 1: stems not corrugated. p. 234. Actinidia.
Bundle-traces 3-7: stems corrugated. 165.
165. Stem hairy: stone of fruit crescent-shaped. p. 63. Cocculus.
Stem becoming nearly or quite glabrous. 166.
166. Stem finally glabrous. p. 63. Menispermum.
Stem somewhat pubescent. p. 63. Calycocarpum.
167. Buds oblong, appressed. p. 219. Berchemia.
Buds round or ovoid, not appressed. 168.
168. Bundle-trace 1. 169.
Bundle-traces several. 170.

169. Bud-scales glabrous, acute. p. 201. Celastrus.
Bud-scales pubescent, blunt. p. 338. Solanum.
170. Pith excavated: leaf-scars low. p. 67. Schizandra.
Pith continuous: leaf-scars raised. 171.
171. Deciduous: leaf-scars much raised. p. 57. Akebia.
Evergreen: leaves digitately compound. p. 56. Stauntonia.
172. With spines (pungent twigs or stipules). 173.
With prickles (superficial outgrowths). 197.
Without either spines or prickles. 202.
173. Scurfy with silvery or brown scales. 174.
Not scurfy with such scales. 175.
174. End-bud often present: twigs moderate. p. 249. Elaeagnus.
Twigs ending in spines, very slender. p. 248. Hippophäe.
175. Spines at side of the leaf-scar, (stipules). 176.
Spines representing leaves. See 146.
Spines ending the twigs, or axillary (stem). 181.
176. Only the stipules pungent. 177.
Pungent leaves also present. See 146.
Pungent twigs also present. See 181.
Prickles also present. See 186.
177. Leaf-scars on a finally torn membrane. p. 159. Robinia.
Leaf-scars small, not on an articular membrane. 178.
178. Bundle-trace one. 179.
Bundle-traces three. 178a.
178a. Buds red-hairy. p. 163. Zanthoxylum.
Buds not red. p. 137. Prosopis.
179. Slender branchlets from the nodes: fruit fleshy. p. 214. Zizyphus.
Without this combination of characters. 180.
180. Leaf-scars low: fruit umbrella-shaped. p. 215. Paliurus.
Leaf-scars raised: fruit a legume. p. 135. Acacia.
181. Wood appearing "endogenous": a supra-axillary spine present. p. 48. Bougainvillea.
Wood distinctly in a zone between pith and bark. 182.

182. Pith chambered or excavated. p. 133. Prinsepia.
Pith spongy: spine by side of bud. p. 337. Lycium.
Pith continuous. 183.
183. Aromatic: evergreen or with green twigs. 184.
Not aromatic: evergreen: leaves simple. p.101. Pyracantha.
Neither aromatic nor evergreen nor green-twigged. 186.
184. Deciduous: spines strong. p. 171. Poncirus.
Evergreen: leaves compound. 185.
185. Leaflets 3: spines needle-like. p. 169. Triphasia.
Leaflet 1, but disarticulating from its stalk. p. 170. Citrus.
186. Sap more or less milky. 187.
Sap not milky. 188.
187. Without stipule-scars: bundle-traces 3. p. 304. Bumelia.
With stipule-scars: bundle-traces more. p. 36. Maclura.
188. Leaf-scars on finally torn membranes. 189.
Without such articular membranes. 190.
189. Spines branched, often clustered. p. 141. Gleditsia.
Spines unbranched. p. 145. Sophora.
190. Branches very green, terete. p. 144. Cercidium.
Branches gray-green, flat-ribbed. p. 199. Glossopetalon.
Branches very gray or white: Southwestern. 191.
Branches neither conspicuously green nor white. 192.
191. Twigs terete. p. 218. Microrhamnus.
Twigs 5-angled. p. 217. Condalia.
192. With clustered stipules in the axils. p. 137. Prosopis.
Without bristly dwarf-branches. 193.
193. Spines very pungent, beside the buds. 194.
Spines less specialized twigs or branch-tips. 195.
194. Bud-scales fleshy: twigs terete. p. 113. Crataegus.
Bud-scales dry: twigs angular. p. 105. Chaenomeles.
195. Bundle-trace 1: Western. p. 221. Ceanothus.
Bundle-traces 3. 196.
196. Leaf-scars linear or U-shaped. p. 106. Pyrus.
Leaf-scars broader: with stipule-scars. 196a.

196a. Leaf-scars half-elliptic. p. 129. Prunus.
Leaf-scars triangular. p. 105. Chaenomeles.
197. Leaf bases persistent and torn at top. p. 117. Rubus.
With clean-cut though sometimes shriveling leaf-scars. 198.
198. Leaf-scars on articular membranes. p. 159. Robinia.
Leaf-scars relatively broad. p. 163. Zanthoxylum.
Leaf-scars small, elliptical or shriveled. p. 135. Acacia.
Leaf-scars linear or U-shaped. 199.
199. Leaf-scars nearly encircling the thick stem. p. 262. Aralia.
Leaf-scars shorter: twigs not excessively stout. 200.
200. Buds elongated and stalked: pith spongy. p. 84. Ribes.
Buds round-ovoid: pith continuous. 201.
201. Leaf-scar U-shaped: bundle-traces 5. p.261. Acanthopanax.
Leaf-scar nearly straight: bundle-traces 3. p. 125. Rosa.
202. Bundle-traces 2: dwarf-twigs abundant. p. 3. Ginkgo.
Without this combination of characters. 203.
203. Creeping or matted or heath-like evergreens. 204.
Not evergreen, or else not matted or heath-like. 219.
204. Leaves revolute nearly or quite to the midrib. 205.
Leaves not revolute to the midrib. 208.
205. Twigs and revolute leaves terete. p. 183. Ceratiola.
Twigs flat-ribbed below the leaves. 206.
206. Leaves quite entire: twigs glabrescent. p. 182. Empetrum.
Leaves microscopically toothed. 207.
207. Twigs downy in the grooves. p. 181. Corema.
Twigs glabrous. p. 281. Phyllodoce.
208. Delicate, trailing, the leaves not crowded. 209.
Not loosely trailing or else the leaves crowded. 210.
209. Stems chaffy: leaves not white beneath. p. 299. Chiogenes.
Stems not chaffy: leaves white beneath. p.297. Vaccinium.
210. Leaves very narrow: plants small, moss-like. 211.
Leaves broader: plants not at all moss-like. 212.
211. Leaves glabrous. p. 284. Cassiope.
Leaves white-hairy. p. 242. Hudsonia.

212. Not forming distinct leaf-scars. 213.
Leaves finally falling from clean-cut scars. 214.
213. Leaves obtuse, spatulate, outcurved. p. 302. Diapensia.
Leaves acute, oblanceolate. p. 303. Pyxidanthera.
214. With stipules. p. 102. Cotoneaster.
Without stipules. 215.
215. Leaves neither toothed nor dotted. 216.
Leaves minutely toothed, or else dotted beneath. 217.
216. Leaves densely woolly beneath. p. 282. Daboecia.
Leaves not woolly. p. 294. Arctostaphylos.
217. Leaves elongated or else pungent. p. 293. Pernettya.
Leaves relatively broad, not pungent. 218.
218. Leaves broadest below the middle. p. 296. Gaylussacia.
Leaves broadest above the middle. p. 297. Vaccinium.
219. Without leaf-scars. 220.
With large leaf-scar on deciduous sheath. p. 47. Coccoloba.
With leaf-scars on stem or on leaf cushion or petiole. 224.
220. Trailing hairy evergreen: leaves elliptical. p.291. Epigaea.
Not trailing. 221.
221. Leaf-bases not overlapping: petiole torn. p. 117. Rubus.
Persistent leaf-bases overlapping at least on spurs. 222.
222. Evergreen: leaflets numerous. p. 58. Nandina.
Deciduous or else without many leaflets. 223.
223. Petiole sometimes elongated: deciduous. p. 119. Potentilla.
Petiole not elongated: subevergreen. p.62. ×Mahoberberis.
224. Bundle-traces 3 or more, separate, in an open line. 225.
Bundle-trace 1; or traces scattered or in an ellipse, or nearly confluent in a straight or curved line. 344.
(This group includes cases in which the bundle-traces are indistinguishable in a shriveled scar).
* *Caution.* Learn the poisonous species of *Rhus.**
225. Evergreen, with small finely compound leaves. 226.
Leaves not small and fern-like if evergreen. 227.
226. Leaves scarcely twice pinnate. p. 98. Chamaebatiaria.
Leaves nearly thrice pinnate. p. 124. Chamaebatia.

227. Leaf-scars linear or narrowly U-shaped. 228.
Leaf-scars C-shaped or horseshoe-shaped, or ring-like and encircling the bud. 248.
Leaf-scars not of the preceding types. 255.
228. Stipule-scars encircling the twig. p. 65. Magnolia.
Stipule-scars, if any, not encircling the twig. 229.
229. Leaf-scars fully half-encircling the twig. 230.
Leaf-scars shorter. 231.
230. Evergreen: leaves pinnately compound. p. 61. Mahonia.
Deciduous: twigs yellow when cut. p. 53. Zanthorhiza.
231. Bud-scale distinctly 1, forming a sac. p. 12. Salix.
Bud-scales several or else indistinct. 232.
232. Pith spongy: buds acute. 232b. p. 84. Ribes.
Pith chambered: buds obtuse. 232a.
Pith continuous. 233.
232a. With stipule-scars. p. 40. Celtis.
Without stipule-scars. p. 127. Osmaronia.
232b. Buds sessile. p. 107. Aronia.
Buds stalked. p. 84. Ribes.
233. Aromatic: twigs slender: buds superposed. p.74. Benzoin.
Without this combination of characters. 234.
234. Buds round-ovoid with resinous or fleshy scales. 235.
Buds usually indistinct: bark green. p. 144. Cercidium.
Without either of these combinations of characters. 237.
235. Buds imbedded in gum or resin. 236.
Buds not resinous, fleshy. p. 113. Crataegus.
236. With stipule-scars: pith flat or 3-sided. p. 24. Betula.
No stipule-scars: pith round. p. 362. Baccharis.
237. Leaf-scars low, almost straight. p. 125. Rosa.
Leaf-scars more or less raised if straight. 238.
238. Lateral buds short-ovoid or bluntly conical or oblong. 239.
Lateral buds elongated-ovoid or conical. 243.
239. With stipule-scars. 240.
No stipule-scars. 242.
240. Pith minute, flat or 3-sided. p. 24. Betula.
Pith rounded. 241.
241. Twigs hairy. bud-scales overlapping. p. 104. Cydonia.
Glabrous: buds ovoid, scales subvalvate. p. 244. Stachyurus.

242. Twigs slender (1 mm.). 242a.
 Twigs stouter: usually with end-bud. p. 106. Pyrus.
242a. With end-bud. p. 100. Exochorda.
 Without end-bud. p. 111. Photinia.
243. Pith 5-angled: bud-scales twisted. p. 112. Amelanchier.
 Without this combination of characters. 244.
244. Pith minute, green, flattened or 3-sided. p. 24. Betula.
 Pith not 3-sided if small. 245.
245. Bark exfoliating. 245a.
 Bark not exfoliating. 246.
245a. Pith small. p. 100. Exochorda.
 Pith large, brown. p. 117. Rubus.
246. Buds woolly or gummy, ovoid-oblong. p. 108. Sorbus.
 Buds neither woolly nor gummy. 247.
247. Buds narrowly oblong. p. 107. Aronia.
 Buds acutely ovoid: bark bitter. p. 129. Prunus.
248. Stipule-scars encircling the twig. p. 92. Platanus.
 Stipule-scars not encircling the twig. 249.
249. Leaf-scar from the first nearly encircling the bud. 250.
 Leaf-scar at first on an articular membrane. 252.
250. Sap milky or flowing freely: pith continuous. p. 189. Rhus.
 Without this combination of characters. 251.
251. Pith continuous: nodes not swollen. p. 146. Cladrastis.
 Pith spongy: junctures swollen. p. 247. Dirca.
252. Somewhat aromatic: twigs dotted. p. 166. Ptelea.
 Not aromatic: end-bud lacking. 253.
253. With small stipules or stipule-scars. 254.
 Without stipules or stipule-scars. p. 141. Gleditsia.
254. Nodes usually swollen: buds distinct. p. 145. Sophora.
 Nodes neither swollen nor buds large. p. 159. Robinia.
255. Leaf-scars enlarged on trunk: sap milky. p. 245. Carica.
 Without this combination of characters. 256.
256. Pith spongy between the nodes. 257.
 Pith chambered, at least at some nodes. 259.
 Pith continuous. 262.

257. Leaf-scars 2-ranked. p. 41. Zelkova.
Leaf-scars in more than 2 ranks. 258.
258. Lowest bud-scale in front. p. 10. Populus.
Scales otherwise disposed. p. 87. Liquidambar.
259. Buds naked: bundle-traces large. p. 20. Pterocarya.
Buds scaly. 260.
260. Twigs coarse: leaf-scars large. p. 17. Juglans.
Twigs slender: leaf-scars small. 261.
261. Buds triangular, appressed, solitary, 2-ranked. p.40. Celtis.
Buds globose, superposed: twigs green. p. 82. Itea.
262. Pith with firmer plates at intervals. 263.
Pith without firmer diaphragms. 266.
263. Evergreen: very rusty-hairy. p. 66. Michelia.
Deciduous. 264.
264. Buds solitary or not forming spurs. p. 268. Davidia.
Buds superposed or else forming dwarf branches. 265.
265. Buds with scales, not red-hairy. p. 267. Nyssa.
Buds red-hairy, the terminal without scales. p.69. Asimina.
266. Evergreen or largely so. 267.
Deciduous. 281.
267. Leaves compound. 268.
Leaves simple. 274.
268. Peppery-aromatic. p. 187. Schinus.
Not peppery. 269.
269. Buds superposed. p. 210. Sapindus.
Buds not superposed. 270.
270. Twigs greenish. p. 145. Sophora.
Twigs brown. 271.
271. Twigs warty. 272.
Twigs not warty: leaflets small, blunt. p.138. Tamarindus.
272. Leaflets large and pointed. 273.
Leaflets small, very numerous. p. 136. Leucaena.
273. Bark papery-exfoliating. p. 173. Bursera.
Bark not papery. p. 174. Swietenia.

274. Leaves with several nectar-glands beneath. p. 129. Prunus.
Leaves without such glands. 275.
275. Leaf-scars with acute angles: hairy. p. 110. Eriobotrya.
Leaf-scars transversely elliptical. p. 253. Rhizophora.
Without either of these combinations of characters. 276.
276. Leaf-scars at first raised and minute. p. 122. Cercocarpus.
Leaf-scars from the first low. 277.
277. Leaves large (15 cm. or more long). 278.
Leaves distinctly smaller (scarcely 10 cm.). 279.
278. Leaves oblanceolate. p. 231. Theobroma.
Leaves lance-oblong. p. 185. Mangifera.
279. Leaves with resin-glands, crenate or lobed. p. 14. Myrica.
Leaves not resin-dotted, entire or serrate. 280.
280. Glabrous: buds acute. p. 109. Raphiolepis.
Somewhat hairy: buds rather obtuse. 280a.
280a. Odoriferous. p. 86. Pittosporum.
Scentless. p. 111. Photinia.
281. Buds small, superposed, in silky pits. p. 142. Gymnocladus.
Buds at first under a membrane. 281a.
Buds neither sunken in pits nor covered if superposed. 282.
281a. Buds evident. p. 141. Gleditsia.
Buds indistinct. p. 159. Robinia.
282. With free-flowing gum or sap. 283.
Sap not flowing freely when twigs are cut. 286.
283. Pith angular: twigs often corky-ridged. p. 87. Liquidambar.
Pith not angular. 284.
284. Bundle-traces 3, or in 3 groups. 285.
Bundle-traces or groups more than 3. p. 189. Rhus.
285. Odoriferous: bud-scales 2. p. 188. Cotinus.
Not odoriferous: bud-scales several. p. 35. Morus.
286. Exuding a sweet gum: pith angled. p. 87. Liquidambar.
Not exuding a sweet gum if pith is angular. 287.
287. Lowest scale central over the leaf-scar: pith 5-angled, sometimes spongy. p. 10. Populus.
Without this combination of characters. 288.

288. With resin-glands or blisters, at least in sheltered places. 239.
Not resinous-glandular. 290.
289. Stipule-scars elongated: resin in blisters. p. 24. Betula.
Stipule-scars minute or lacking. p. 14. Myrica.
290. Buds distinctly stalked below their lowest scales. 291.
Buds not stalked except as they begin to develop. 295.
291. Leaf-scars 2-ranked: buds pubescent. 293.
Leaf-scars in more than 2 ranks. 292.
292. Spicy-aromatic. p. 74. Benzoin.
Not aromatic. p. 26. Alnus.
293. Bark flaking: buds often black. p. 88. Parrotia.
Bark not exfoliating. 294.
294. Fruit in elongated clusters. p. 89. Fothergilla.
Partly developed fruit in sessile groups. p. 90. Hamamelis.
295. Pith 3-sided or much flattened. 296.
Pith neither 3-sided nor greatly flattened. 297.
296. Bud-scales scarcely meeting. p. 26. Alnus.
Bud-scales overlapping. p. 24. Betula.
297. Twigs 3-ribbed below the (usually stipulate) leaf-scars. 298.
Twigs not sharply 3-ribbed from the leaf-scars when fresh. 307.
298. Twigs green or red, slender: small shrubs. 299.
Without this combination of characters. 300.
299. Twigs green: buds solitary. p. 115. Kerria.
Twigs red: buds superposed. p. 95. Stephanandra.
300. Leaf-scars fringed: buds superposed. p. 139. Cercis.
Leaf-scars not fringed or else buds not superposed. 301.
301. Buds superposed. 302.
Buds not superposed. 303.
302. Bark not exfoliating. p. 162. Amorpha.
Bark quickly exfoliating. p. 94. Neillia.
303. Buds appressed: bark exfoliating. p. 93. Physocarpus.
Without this combination of characters. 304.

304. Leaf-scars notched: bark shredding. p. 116. Neviusia.
Without this combination of characters. 305.
305. Stipules falling from the twig. p. 152. Amorpha.
Stipules or their scars, if any, on a leaf-cushion. 306.
306. Leaf-cushion gland-fringed. p. 154. Colutea.
Leaf-cushion not glandular. p. 129. Prunus.
307. Buds long and spine-like: stipule-scars long. p. 28. Fagus.
Without this combination of characters. 308.
308. Twigs very stout: leaf-scars large: buds short. 309.
Without this combination of characters. 310.
309. Bundle-traces 5: end-bud present. p. 175. Cedrela.
Bundle-traces 9; end-bud fallen. p. 172. Ailanthus.
310. Buds small and appressed. 311.
Buds scarcely appressed. 314.
311. Trunk smooth and green. p. 144. Cercidium.
Trunk not green. 312.
312. Leaf-scars on raised leaf-cushions. p. 129. Prunus.
Leaf-scars low. 313.
313. Twigs zig-zag, gray: pith small. p. 40. Celtis.
Twigs straight, brown: pith larger. 313a.
313a. With stipule-scars. p. 244. Stachyurus.
Without stipule-scars. p. 70. Asimina.
314. Buds very large, acute, warty-wrinkled. p. 55. Decaisnea.
Without this combination of bud-characters. 315.
315. Bundle-traces 5 or 7 in 1 series. 316.
Bundle-traces 3 or in 3 groups. 317.
Bundle-traces grouped about a central one. p. 52. Paeonia.
316. Buds solitary: leaf-scars ciliate. p. 49. Euptelea.
Buds superposed: scars not ciliate. p. 16. Platycarya.
317. Leaf-scars rounded. bundle-traces 3. p. 99. Sorbaria.
Without this combination of characters. 318.
318. Buds superposed. 319.
Buds not superposed. 320.
319. Leaf-scars somewhat 3-lobed. p. 134. Albizzia.
Leaf-scars not lobed. p. 220. Hovenia.

320. Twigs warty: bud-scales fringed. p.213. Xanthoceras.
Without this combination of characters. 321.
321. Twigs warty: end-bud lacking. p. 128. Maddenia.
Without this combination of characters. 322.
322. Stipules persistent: leaf-scars raised. p. 150. Laburnum.
Stipules lacking: leaf-scars raised. 322a.
Without either of these combinations of characters. 323.
322a. Buds naked. p. 222. Rhamnus.
Buds with scales. 322b.
322b. With end-bud. p. 213. Xanthoceras.
Without end-bud. p. 111. Photinia.
323. Pith 5-sided: twigs often corky-ridged. p. 87. Liquidambar.
Pith not sharply 5-angled. 324.
324. Leaf-scars often 2-ranked. 325.
Leaf-scars in more than 2 ranks. 332.
325. Bud-scales several in 2 ranks. 326.
Bud-scales not evidently in 2 ranks. 328.
326. Bud-scales acute. p. 42. Aphananthe.
Bud-scales obtuse. 327.
327. Buds ovoid, moderate or else twigs gray. p. 39. Ulmus.
Buds round, small: twigs cherry-colored. p. 40. Planera.
328. End-bud present. p. 91. Corylopsis.
End-bud lacking. 329.
329. Bud-scales striate: bark of trunk scaly. p. 23. Ostrya.
Without this combination of characters. 330.
330. Bud-scales 2. p. 228. Tilia.
Bud-scales about half-a-dozen. 331.
331. Buds nearly globose: twigs often bristly. p. 21. Corylus.
Buds ovoid: not bristly: tree. p. 22. Carpinus.
332. Visible bud-scales two. 333.
Exposed-scales more than two or buds naked. 334.
333. Scales valvate: end-bud present. p. 264. Cornus.
Scales overlapping: end-bud lacking. p. 146. Cladrastis.
334. Without stipules or stipule-scars. 335.
With stipule-scars or persistent stipules. 338.

335. Aromatic: twigs green, mucilaginous. p. 73. Sassafras.
 Not aromatic. 336.
336. Buds with red fleshy scales. p. 113. Crataegus.
 Bud-scales not fleshy. 337.
337. Buds woolly or gummy: no catkins. p. 108. Sorbus.
 Buds not woolly or gummy. p. 15. Leitneria.
338. Stipule-scars rather elongated. 340.
 Stipule-bases present, or their scars short. 339.
339. Stipule-scars or bases on a leaf-cushion. p. 129. Prunus.
 Stipule-scars not on a leaf cushion. 341.
340. Pith round: buds often superposed. p. 94. Neillia.
 Pith 3-sided: buds not superposed. p. 24. Betula.
341. Leaf-scars somewhat raised. 341a.
 Leaf-scars low. 342.
341a. Bud scales 2. p. 244. Stachyurus.
 Scales more than 2. p. 229. Rhamnus.
342. Buds nearly globose. p. 152. Amorpha.
 Buds ovoid. 343.
343. Bundle-traces confluent or twigs hairy. p. 222. Rhamnus.
 Bundle-traces separate or twigs glabrous. p. 129. Prunus.
344. Stipule-scars nearly or quite encircling the twig. 345.
 Stipule-scars not nearly encircling the twig. 349.
345. Buds pointed and spike-like. p. 28. Fagus.
 Buds not sharp and hard. 346.
346. Sap milky. p. 38. Ficus.
 Sap not milky. 347.
347. Very rusty-hairy. p. 66. Michelia.
 Without long rusty hairs. 348.
348. Buds terete. p. 65. Magnolia.
 Buds flattened. p. 64. Liriodendron.
349. Leaf-scar nearly encircling the twig. p. 123. Purshia.
 Leaf-scar not at all nearly encircling the twig. 350.
350. Bundle-traces crescent-shaped: pith chambered. p. 20. Pterocarya.
 Without this combination of characters. 351.

351. Bundle-traces many, mostly in 3 groups: leaf-scars lobed. 352.
    Without this combination of characters. 358.
352. Pith chambered and angular. p. 17. Juglans.
    Pith continuous. 353.
353. Evergreen: buds solitary: leaves fern-like. p. 43. Grevillea.
    Deciduous. 354.
354. With terminal bud: buds ovoid: pith angled. p. 19. Carya.
    Without terminal bud. 355.
355. Buds half-ellipsoid: leaf-scars raised. p. 211. Koelreuteria.
    Buds globose. 356.
356. Buds solitary. 357.
    Buds superposed. p. 210. Sapindus.
357. Twigs glabrous: lenticels conspicuous. p. 176. Melia.
    Twigs dingy-tomentulose. p. 212. Ungnadia.
358. Bundle-traces many in a long series, or scattered. 359.
    Bundle-trace 1, not ring-like, barely broken into 3 or 5 if divided. 370.
359. Leaf-scars large, subelliptical: buds not superposed. 360.
    Leaf-scars small if they are elliptical. 361.
360. Tree: twigs green: pith continuous. p. 232. Sterculia.
    Shrub: twigs buff or gray. p. 224. Ampelopsis.
361. CAUTION. (See *Rhus.*). Sap milky or gummy. 362.
    Sap neither milky nor gummy. 365.
362. With stipule-scars. 363.
    Without stipule-scars. *Sometimes very poisonous.* p. 189. Rhus.
363. Pith with thin diaphragms at nodes. p. 37. Broussonetia.
    Pith without firm nodal diaphragms. 364.
364. Buds ovoid. p. 35. Morus.
    Buds depressed-globose. p. 36. Maclura.
365. Without stipules or stipule-scars. 366.
    With stipules or stipule-scars. 367.
366. Small and soft-wooded: twigs stout. p. 52. Paeonia.
    Large and woody: twigs rather slender. p. 236. Gordonia.

367. Pith, and usually twigs, grooved. 368.
Pith nearly or quite round: end-bud lacking. 369.
368. Bud-scales numerous: end-bud present. p. 30. Quercus.
Bud-scales 2 or 3; end-bud often lacking. p. 29. Castanea.
369. Buds evident, with 2 broad scales. p. 228. Tilia.
Buds naked except for stipules. p. 229. Grewia.
Buds not discernible. p. 230. Hibiscus.
370. Leaf-scars minute, on ridges. fruit a cone. 371.
Without this combination of characters. 372.
371. Buds rounded: cone-scales persistent. p. 4. Larix.
Buds more elongated: cone-scales falling. p. 4. Pseudolarix.
372. Pith chambered. 373.
Pith spongy. 379.
Pith continuous. 388.
373. Leaf-scars large and saucer-like. p. 233. Cola.
Leaf-scars not dish-like if large. 374.
374. Buds round-conical: subevergreen. p. 309. Symplocos.
Buds ovoid or triangular. 375.
375. Bud-scales 2, overlapping. p. 305. Diospyros.
Bud-scales several. 376.
376. Leaves evergreen, pellucid-punctate. p. 168. Skimmia.
Leaves deciduous. 377.
377. Buds deltoid, closely appressed. p. 40. Celtis.
Buds ovoid. 378.
378. Leaf-scars notched at top. p. 306. Halesia.
Leaf-scars not notched. p. 50. Eucommia.
379. Evergreen: leaves simple. 380.
Deciduous. 384.
380. Leaves entire. 381.
Leaves more or less toothed. 382.
381. Leaves flat, glabrous. p. 258. Tristania.
Leaves revolute, woolly beneath. p. 273. Ledum.
382. Leaves distinctly serrulate: aromatic. p. 292. Gaultheria.
Leaves somewhat crenate. 383.
383. Leaves flat, not pellucid-punctate. p. 237. Thea.
Leaves revolute, pellucid-punctate. p. 168. Skimmia.

384. Buds very small: twigs angled, pale. p. 337. Lycium.
Buds of moderate size: twigs not angled. 385.
385. Bud-scales numerous. 386.
Exposed bud-scales two or three. 387.
386. Leaf-scars low: no stipules. 386a.
Scars raised: stipules persistent. p. 119. Potentilla.
386a. Bundle-trace C-shaped. p. 165. Orixa.
Bundle-trace round. p. 45. Pyrularia.
387. Buds triangular-ovoid with 2 scales. p. 305. Diospyros.
Buds subfusiform, sometimes multiple. p. 235. Stewartia.
388. Pith with firmer plates at intervals. p. 202. Tripterygium.
Pith without firmer plates. 389.
389. Leaf-base for a time persistent, torn at top. 390.
Leaf-scar clean-cut even if on a raised base. 391.
390. Twigs few-ribbed, gray-green. p. 199. Glossopetalon.
Twigs finely corrugated: rush-like. p. 147. Spartium.
Twigs neither green nor sculptured. 395a.
391. Bundle-trace frequently broken into three. 392.
Bundle-trace undivided, or else of many fragments. 396.
392. Twigs aromatic, green, mucilaginous. p. 73. Sassafras.
Twigs neither aromatic nor green. 393.
393. Buds solitary. 394.
Buds superposed. 395.
394. Leaf-scars raised, with stipules. p. 150. Laburnum.
Leaf-scars without conspicuous stipules. p. 222. Rhamnus.
395. Buds subglobose. p. 193. Ilex.
Upper buds oblong. 395a.
395a. Buds appressed. p. 308. Styrax.
Buds not appressed. p. 117. Rubus.
396. Leaf-scars fringed at top, shield-shaped. 397.
Leaf-scars not fringed. 398.
397. Evergreen: leaves thick and not veiny. p. 191. Cliftonia.
Deciduous, or leaves very veiny if present. p. 192. Cyrilla.
398. Aromatic: evergreen. 399.
Not both aromatic and evergreen. 403.

399. Leaves compound: resin flowing freely. p. 186. Pistacia.
Leaves simple. 400.
400. Leaves with several nerves. p. 71. Cinnamomum.
Leaves with only 1 principal vein. 401.
401. Leaves sickle-shaped: buds naked. p. 259. Eucalyptus.
Leaves lanceolate: buds with scales. 402.
402. Glabrous: leaves not whitened or veiny. p. 75. Laurus.
Pubescent or else leaves whitened or veiny. p. 72. Persea.
403. Leaf-scars on dilated or ribbed leaf-cushions. 404.
Leaf-scars not on dilated or ribbed leaf-cushions. 421.
404. Evergreen: leaves compound or serrate or glandular or varnished. 405.
Deciduous or else leaves not as above. 407.
405. Leaves at most finely toothed. p. 122. Cercocarpus.
Leaves with about 5 revolute lobes. 406.
406. Bud-scales 2: stipules lacking. p. 120. Fallugia.
Forming spurs with leaf-bases. p. 121. Cowania.
407. With bud-like axillary spurs. 408.
Not producing such dwarf-branches. 410.
408. Twigs hairy but not glandular. p. 135. Acacia.
Twigs at first glandular-bristly: bark exfoliating. 409.
409. Stipules small (scarcely 1 mm. long). p. 123. Purshia.
Stipules large (fully 5 mm. long). p. 157. Calophaca.
410. Buds globose, thicker than twig. p. 155. Halimodendron.
Buds ellipsoid: twigs rounded. p. 119. Potentilla.
Without either of these combinations of characters. 411.
411. Twigs essentially terete. 413.
Twigs evanescently angled at the nodes. 412.
Twigs conspicuously corrugated or angled or ribbed. 417.
412. With persistent stipules. p. 102. Cotoneaster.
Without persistent stipules. p. 96. Spiraea.
413. Low, compact and spreading. p. 295. Arctous.
Not matted or spreading on the ground. 414.
414. Leaf-cushion equaling the bud. p. 154. Colutea.
Leaf-cushion much shorter than the bud. 415.

415. Without persistent stipules. 416.
     Stipules persistent. 415a.
415a. Bud-scales striate. p. 136. Lespedeza.
     Scales not striate. p. 102. Cotoneaster.
416. Bud-scales indistinct. p. 148. Cytisus.
     Bud-scales evident. p. 96. Spiraea.
417. Twigs corrugated: rush-like. p. 147. Spartium.
     Twigs strongly angled or ribbed: not rush-like. 418.
418. Twigs with narrow low ribs. 419.
     Twigs deeply corrugated or grooved. 420.
419. Twigs sharply zig-zag. p. 154. Coronilla.
     Twigs not conspicuously zig-zag. p. 156. Caragana.
420. Leaf-cushion without prominent ribs. p. 148. Cytisus.
     Leaf-cushion 3-ribbed. p. 149. Genista.
421. Freely resiniferous when cut. p. 186. Pistacia.
     Without free-flowing sap or resin. 422.
422. Scales 2: bundle-trace C-shaped. p. 305. Diospyros.
     Without this combination of characters. 423.
423. Buds not scaly: leaf-scars round. p. 140. Ceratonia.
     Without this combination of characters. 424.
424. Leaf-scars usually deltoid, as high as broad. 425.
     Leaf-scars usually broader than high. 432.
425. End-bud not enlarged if present. 426.
     End-bud distinctly larger than the lateral buds. 430.
426. Twigs glabrescent. 427.
     Twigs sparingly pubescent. 429.
427. Buds slightly glaucous: twigs red. p. 271. Elliottia.
     Buds not glaucous. 428.
428. Twigs reddish, becoming buff. p. 272. Zenobia.
     Twigs brown: buds very glossy. p. 290. Oxydendrum.
     Twigs gray. p. 288. Pieris.
429. Twigs moderate: everygreen or deciduous. p. 288. Pieris.
     Twigs very slender: evergreen. p. 293. Pernettya.
430. Outer scales of end-bud shorter than the bud. 431.
     Outer scales as long as the bud. p. 270. Clethra.

431. Bark shredding: capsules bristly. p. 277. Menziesia.
Without this combination. p. 274. Rhododendron.
432. Soft-wooded or aromatic, deciduous, quickly branching. 433.
Without this combination of characters. 435.
433. Buds solitary. 434.
Buds often superposed: with stipules. p. 178. Securinega.
434. Not aromatic: with stipule-vestiges. p. 221. Ceanothus.
Aromatic. without stipule-scars. p. 73. Sassafras.
435. Leaf-scars often opposite or in whorls of three. 436.
Leaf-scars at most crowded toward the end. 437.
436. Deciduous: fruit of long slender capsules. p. 342. Chilopsis.
Evergreen: capsules short. p. 280. Kalmia.
437. Evergreen: leaves white or scurfy or woolly beneath. 438.
Leaeves different if evergreen. 441.
438. Leaves whitened beneath but not dotted or scurfy. 439.
Leaves scurfy beneath. 440.
439. Capsules often present. p. 286. Andromeda.
Fruit (berry-like) not present. p. 297. Vaccinium.
440. Leaves lanceolate: capsule 2-bracted. p.287. Chamaedaphne.
Leaves oblanceolate: capsule bractless. p. 289. Lyonia.
441. Evergreen: 442.
Deciduous. 448.
442. Leaves peltate-scurfy. p. 249. Elaeagnus.
Leaves without peltate scales. 443.
443. With minute stipules or stipule-scars. p. 193. Ilex.
Without any trace of stipules. 444.
444. Leaf-scars large, acute at sides. p. 236. Gordonia.
Leaf-scars small, not laterally produced. 445.
445. Fruit of small capsules. p. 285. Leucothöe.
Fruit (berry-like) not present in winter. 446.
446. Leaves broadest above the middle. p. 297. Vaccinium.
Leaves broadest at or below the middle; 447.
447. Glabrous: leaves blunt. p. 296. Gaylussacia.
Pubescent: leaves acute. p. 293. Pernettya.

448. Twigs rather stout: leaf-scars large. p. 236. Gordonia.
Twigs slender. leaf-scars usually small. 449.
449. With stipules or stipule-scars. 450.
Without stipules or stipule-scars. 455.
450. Stipule-scars narrow but elongated. p. 160. Erythroxylon.
Stipule-scars or stipules minute. 451.
451. Buds often superposed. 452.
Buds not superposed. 453.
452. Pith small: fruit berry-like. p. 193. Ilex.
Pith large, twigs slender. p. 178. Securinega.
453. Buds with several scales: twigs very slender. 454.
Buds ovoid, with 2 scales. p. 263. Helwingia.
454. Leaf-scars slightly raised. p. 96. Spiraea.
Leaf-scars not at all raised. p. 177. Andrachne.
455. Bud-scales 2: twigs glaucous. p. 196. Nemopanthus.
Without this combination of characters. 456.
456. Leaf-scars 2-ranked: end-bud naked. p. 307. Pterostyrax.
Leaf-scars in more than 2 ranks. 457.
457. Buds ovoid or oblong. 458.
Buds subglobose. 461.
458. Fruit of small round capsules. p. 289. Lyonia.
Fruit (berry-like) absent in winter. 459.
459. Scurfy with peltate scales. p. 249. Elaeagnus.
Not peltate-scurfy. 460.
460. Twigs green or warty, or buds round. p. 297. Vaccinium.
Twigs not green or warty: buds ovoid. p. 296. Gaylussacia.
461. Tree: buds glossy red. p. 290. Oxydendrum.
Shrubs. 462.
462. Branches almost in whorls at tip. p. 283. Enkianthus.
Branches not clustered at end of the season's growth. 463.
463. Leaf-scars crescent-shaped. p. 285. Leucothöe.
Leaf-scars rather 3-sided. p. 272. Zenobia.

WINTER CHARACTERS OF WOODY PLANTS
SYSTEMATICALLY ARRANGED
WITH KEY TO SPECIES UNDER EACH GENUS

GINKGOACEAE.

GINKO. Maidenhair Tree.

(Family Ginkgoaceae).

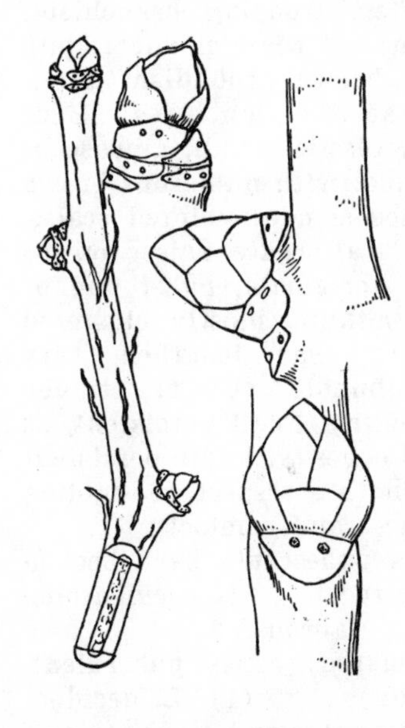

Gray-barked trees of rather conical habit but usually with irregularly placed exceptionally large branches: deciduous. Twigs moderate, rounded, with quickly shredding outer bark: pith rather small, somewhat 3-sided, brownish, spongy. Buds solitary, moderate, sessile, round-ovoid or hemispherical, with about 3 exposed scales, usually developing into blunt spurs. Leaf-scars alternate, crowded on the spurs but separated elsewhere, crescent-shaped or transversely elliptical, low, moderately small: bundle-traces 2: stipule-scars lacking. (*Salisburia.*)

The maidenhair tree possesses peculiar interest as the sole representative of its family, and in being essentially a species which has been preserved only through cultivation. Except for the even more primitive cycads, of which several genera are to be found in greenhouses and are used for formal effects in the warmer parts of the world, it is the only Spermatophyte which possesses ciliated male gametes,—a character common to all fernworts and mossworts.

Winter-character references:—Blakeslee & Jarvis, 333, 382, pl.; Bösemann, 68; Otis, 2; Schneider, f. 57, 64; Shirasawa, 265, pl. 9. The contrast between long shoots and spurs is discussed by Collins in the sixth volume of The Plant World.

Twigs buff or gray: buds light brown. G. biloba.

LARIX. Larch. Tamarack.
(Family Pinaceae).

Percurrent scaly-barked trees with often drooping branchlets: deciduous. Twigs slender: pith minute, brown, roundish, interrupted at the junctures. Buds solitary, sessile, small, globose or short-ovoid, with numerous brown sometimes slender pointed scales. Leaf-scars alternate, raised on decurrent sterigmata, half-round or 3-sided, minute, mostly clustered on spurs that lengthen very slowly: bundle-trace 1: stipule-scars lacking. Fruit persistent, as ellipsoid cones with thin persistent scales, in this respect resembling the spruces and hemlock.

1. Twigs pubescent: bark becoming red. L. occidentalis.
   Twigs glabrous. 2.
2. Bark dark gray: twigs straw-colored: cones puberulent, large (2-4 cm. long). (European). (1). L. decidua.
   Bark red-brown: twigs rather orange: cones glabrous and often glaucous, small (under 2 cm. long). (2). L. laricina.

PSEUDOLARIX. Golden Larch.

The golden larch (*Pseudolarix Kaempferi*, sometimes called *Laricopsis Kaempferi*), sometimes seen in cultivation, differs from the true larches in that the scales of its cones fall off at maturity, as, for example, in the firs (*Abies*).

Winter-character references:—*Larix decidua*, Blakeslee & Jarvis, 335, 365; Bösemann, 70; Schneider, f. 141; Ward, 1, frontispiece and f. 105. *L. laricina*. Blakeslee & Jarvis, 335, 365; Otis, 16. *Pseudolarix Kaempferi*. Schneider, f. 141.

TAXODIUM. Bald Cypress.
(Family Pinaceae).

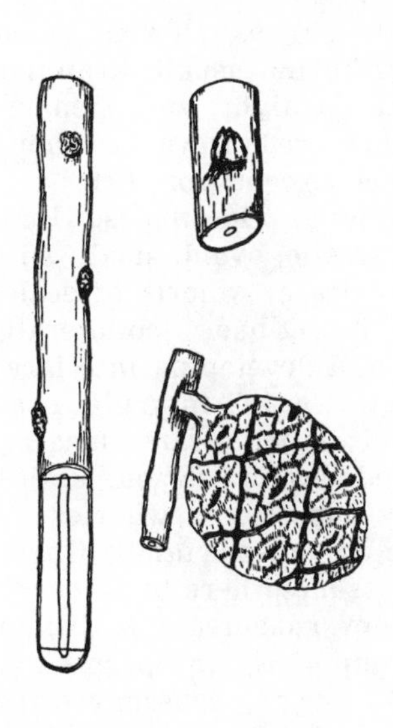

Percurrent, somewhat shredding-barked trees, when large often buttressed, and in very wet places surrounded by large conical "knees" developed from the roots: deciduous. Twigs slender: pith minute, brown, roundish, rather spongy. Buds sessile, minute, subglobose, with few scales, commonly indistinct and very frequently represented by round scars from which transient foliage-sprays of the season have fallen, solitary unless developing into flower-clusters. Leaf and stipule-scars lacking, the buds subtended by minute scales or their vestiges. Fruit, when persistent, in the form of small ellipsoid cones with thickened scales.

The conical form of the bald cypress is very different in appearance from the open-topped tree of cypress swamps: but young trees about the borders of the swamps are usually of this form. The very high knees of old trees in some localities correspond to a former high-water level. An interesting account of the tree in its various forms, by Wilson, is to be found in the first volume of Biological Lectures of the Marine Biological Laboratory at Wood's Hole.

The Montezuma cypress of Mexico is evergreen through persistence of its foliage-shoots.

With flat open top. T. distichum.
Conical: the usual cultivated form. T. distichum pyramidatum.

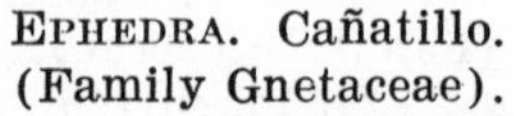

EPHEDRA. Cañatillo.
(Family Gnetaceae).

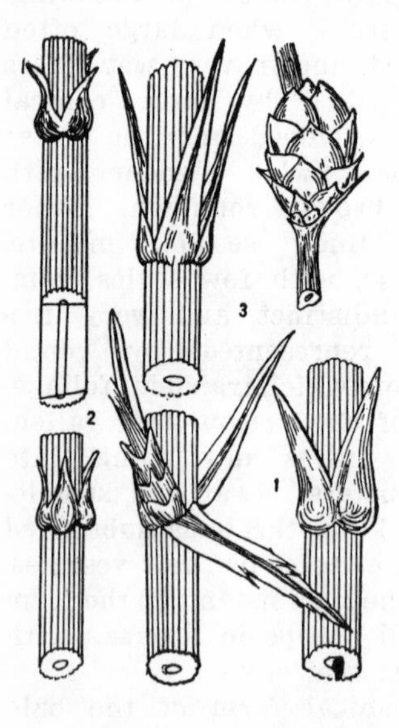

Scraggly shrubs. Twigs green, finely striate and usually granular, elongated, straight and slender; pith round, red-brown, resinous, continuous except for firm pale diaphragms at the nodes. Buds solitary, sessile, ovoid, small, with about 3 pairs or whorls of scales or the flower-buds collaterally multiple and developing into large thin-scaled "cones" in fruit. Leaf-scars and stipule-scars lacking. Leaves reduced to scarious scales, connately opposite or whorled.

The heterogeneous family Gnetaceae, represented here by *Ephedra*, though now considered to belong to the group of Gymnosperms was long held to be angiospermous, and it combines the characters of these superior groups in so puzzling a way that its present taxonomic location is more tenable on grounds of embryogenesis than for other reasons. Like the Angiosperms, its secondary wood produces true vessels, the other Gymnosperms containing tracheids only.

1. Leaf-scales opposite in pairs, ovate, brown, soft. 2.
   Leaf-scales in whorls of three. 3.
2. Scales very short (1-2 mm.). E. viridis.
   Scales moderate (4-5 mm.). (1). E. antisyphilitica.
3. Scales short (3 mm.), soft. (2). E. Torreyana.
   Scales elongated (10 mm.), subpungent. (3). E. trifurca.

RUSCUS. Butcher's Broom.
(Family Liliaceae).

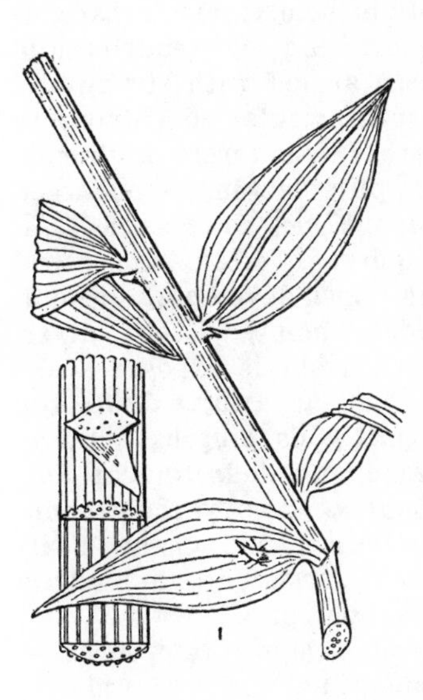

Shrubs, sometimes scrambling: appearing to possess evergreen foliage because of the peculiar leaf-like branches. Stems green: pith lacking,—the wood "endogenous" as in a corn-stalk. Buds scarcely evident, developing immediately into often pungent striate leaf-like branches. Leaf-scars lacking, the true leaves represented by persistent scales from the axils of which the leaf-like branches arise. On the backs or margins of some of these, other scales appear, and flowers are borne in the axils of these.

Except in greenhouses, *Ruscus* is grown only in the warmer parts of the world where some of the species are sometimes used to cover trellis-work. It illustrates the leaf-like branches called cladodia or cladophylls, familiar in the Boston vine or "smilax" of florists. Though rarely seen growing, it will be recognized (dyed red) as an occasional component of Christmas decorations.

Other examples of cladodia or phyllocladia are afforded by *Muhlenbeckia and Phyllanthus.* A superficially comparable appearance of *Helwingia* results from the adnation of an inflorescence-branch to the subtending leaf.

1. Stems round: flowers dorsal on the flat branches. 2.
   Stems deeply fluted: flowers marginal. R. androgynus.
2. Stems smooth: cladophylls large. R. Hypoglossum.
   Stems striate: leaf-like branches small. (1). R. aculeatus.

SMILAX. Greenbrier.
(Family Liliaceae).

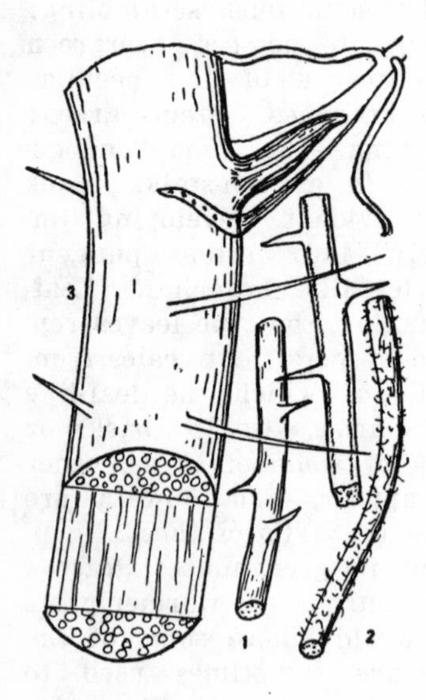

Woody or sometimes herbaceous plants climbing by tendrils and commonly armed with strong and often large prickles: deciduous in the North. Stems terete or sharply angled: pith lacking,—the wood "endogenous" as in a corn-stalk. Buds moderate, often superposed with the upper developing promptly, 3-sided, pointed, very divergent, with a single exposed scale. Leaves tearing away above the dilated partly clasping base, therefore leaving no definite scar, but with about a dozen vascular bundles: stipules, or their near-equivalent, persistent as tendrils on the leaf-bases.

Winter-character references:—*S. hispida.* Brendel, 27, pl. 4; Hitchcock (3), 20, (4), 139. f. 121-2. Velenovsky, in volume 68 of the journal Flora, discusses the anomalous position of the bud-scales in this genus.

The tender vine so much grown by florists as "smilax" belongs to another genus (*Asparagus*).

1. Evergreen: leaves elliptical to oblong (1). S. laurifolia.
   Deciduous. 2.
2. Stems woolly, not prickly. (2). S. pumila.
   Stems glabrous, usually with prickles. 3.
3. Stems glaucous. S. glauca.
   Stems not glaucous. 4.
4. Prickles needle-like, black. (3). S. hispida.
   Prickles dilated or flattened at base. (4). S. rotundifolia.

Casuarina. Australian "Pine."
(Family Casuarinaceae).

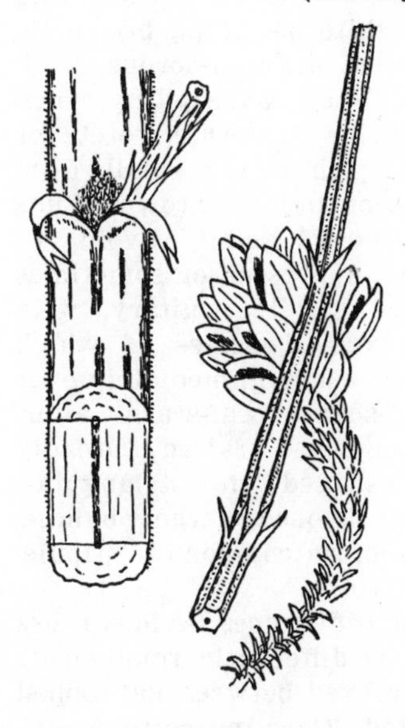

Trees of pine- or spruce-like habit of growth. Twigs blue-green, very slender, easily broken at the nodes, 6-to 8-grooved and granular, elongated; pith minute, pale, angular, continuous. Buds solitary, sessile, ellipsoid, with several pale scales, quickly elongating. Leaf-scars and stipule-scars lacking. Leaves reduced to scarious scales, velvety or glabrate, in whorls of 6-8 alternating with the grooves of the twig. Fruit in cone-like clusters, the 1-seeded dehiscent carpels in about a dozen vertical rows. The tree sometimes called beef-steak tree, is very tolerant of salt air and of poor soil.

Though Casuarina is treated commonly as primitive among the Dicotyledoneae, it presents characters that are scarcely primitive.

Fruit-clusters brown, round-ellipsoid. (1). C. equisetifolia.

POPULUS. Poplar. Aspen.
(Family Salicaceae).

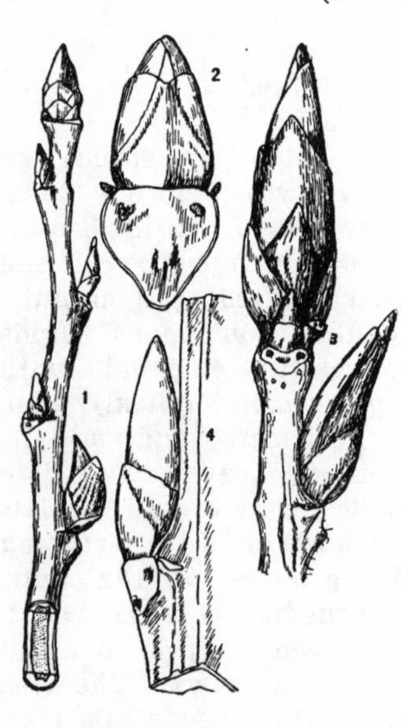

Trees: deciduous. Bark at first usually smooth and green or whitish or orange, gray and often deeply fissured in age. Wood rather soft, white becoming brownish, minutely diffused-porous with fine medullary rays, satiny when split. Twigs moderate, terete or 5-angled: pith rather small, 5-angled, subcontinuous, brown. Buds moderately small, ovoid or elongated, appressed or sometimes outcurved, sessile, solitary, with several exposed scales of which the lowermost is immediately over the leaf-scar. Leaf-scars alternate, somewhat raised, broadly crescent-shaped to triangular, somewhat 3-lobed, large: bundle-traces, 3, often compound: stipule-scars narrow.

The poplars possess many winter differences besides those used in the present key. The bark is differently roughened: in the native cottonwood gray and grooved between flat-topped ridges, while in the commonly planted "Carolina cottonwood" (× *P. Eugenei*), as in the Lombardy poplar which is one of the parents of this, it is dark with pale fissures between rather sharp ridges. On young trunks, and the branches of older trees, the smooth bark is colored in a characteristic fashion: olive in the Lombardy poplar, orange in many "Carolina" poplars, greenish-white in the large-toothed aspen, and sometimes almost chalky white in the silver poplar and our native aspen.

1. Weeping. P. Tremula pendula.
   Fastigiate. 2.
   Neither weeping nor fastigiate. 3.
2. Twigs and plump buds woolly.
   (Bolles' poplar). P. alba Bolleana.
   Twigs and slender buds glabrous.
   (Lombardy poplar). P. nigra italica.
3. Lateral buds plump, with more exposed scales. 4.
   Lateral buds often elongated, mostly with 3 exposed scales. (Cottonwoods and Balsams). 8.
4. Buds glabrous or glabrate. 5.
   Buds persistently silky or tomentose. 6.
5. Buds glabrous, somewhat gummy.
   (American aspen). (1). P. tremuloides.
   Buds somewhat downy. (European aspen). P. Tremula.
6. Twigs glabrous. (Large-toothed aspen). P. grandidentata.
   Twigs tomentose. 7.
7. Tomentum gray. (Gray poplar). P. canescens.
   Tomentum white. (Silver poplar). P. alba.
8. Buds short and broad, dark and brown.
   (Swamp cottonwood). (2). P. heterophylla.
   Buds elongated, often gummy. 9.
9. Twigs green or gray or buff, glabrate. (Cottonwoods). 10
   Twigs brown or red-brown, somewhat villous.
   (Balm-of-Gilead). (3). P. candicans.
10. Trees oblong, with ascending branches.
    ("Carolina cottonwood"). × P. Eugenei.
    Trees ovoid or open. 11.
11. Of moderate growth: twigs rather slender.
    (European black poplar). P. nigra.
    Large: twigs rather stout: native. 12.
12. Buds glabrous. (Common eastern cottonwood).
    (4). P. deltoides monilifera.
    Buds minutely velvety: Western.
    (Plains cottonwood). P. Sargentii.

SALIX. Willow.
(Family Salicaceae).

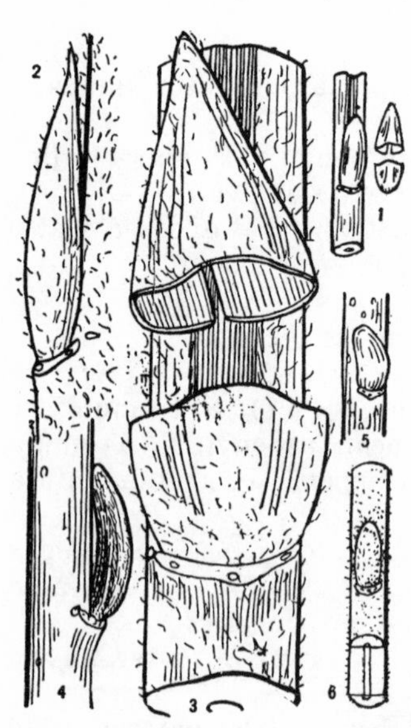

Shrubs or trees: deciduous. Bark at first usually smooth and green, gray and more or less fissured in age. Wood soft, white becoming brown, minutely diffused-porous with fine medullary rays, satiny when split. Twigs mostly slender, terete: pith rather small, roundish, continuous, white. Buds mostly small, oblong, appressed, sessile, solitary, with a single exposed scale standing immediately over the leaf-scar, or collaterally multiple, the end-bud absent. Leaf-scars alternate or exceptionally opposite, low, U-shaped: bundle-traces 3: stipule-scars short, often absent.

Willows are particularly difficult to name at any time of the year by characters which may be put in words, but the comparatively few species that enter into landscape use to any considerable extent usually differ in habit, color of bark, etc., characters which one gardener points out to another.

They illustrate particularly well a type of elongation in which each season's growth is made by the development of an axillary bud of the preceding year, the end of the twig dying back in winter, as it commonly does in *Salix*, or falling early in the season by a clean-cut abscission-scar, as in *Ulmus*, *Tilia* and many other trees, where the scar is small and often pushed to one side so as to be likely to be overlooked, and in *Ailanthus*, where it is particularly large and evident.

What is called the weeping willow here is really a complex including not only *Salix babylonica* but a series of usually hardier hybrids of that species.

1. Weeping. 2.
   Not markedly weeping. 4.
2. Twigs very slender, glabrous. 3.
   Twigs stout: villous.
   (Kilmarnock willow). S. caprea pendula.
3. Buds alternate. (Weeping willow). (1). S. babylonica.
   Buds open opposite. (Purple willow). S. purpurea.
4. Buds large (5 × 10 mm.). 5.
   Buds moderate (4-6 mm. long). 7.
   Buds small (scarcely 3—rarely 4-5—mm. long). 9.
5. Buds plump or rather sharply 2-winged. 6.
   Buds plano-convex. (2). S. missouriensis.
6. Buds green-and-red: planted.
   (Goat willow). (3). S. caprea.
   Buds blackish: native. (Pussy willow). S. discolor.
7. Buds frequently opposite. S. purpurea.
   Buds always alternate. 8.
8. Twigs glossy olive, glabrous. (Shining willow). S. lucida.
   Twigs dull, velvety. S. incana.
9. Trees: Twigs mostly glabrescent. 10.
   Shrubs: twigs gray-velvety. 13.
10. Twigs olive-green. 11.
    Twigs golden. (Golden willow). S. vitellina.
    Twigs red. (Red-twigged willow).
    S. vitellina Britzensis.
11. Large open trees. 12.
    Slender, pole-like. (Sand-bar willow). S. longifolia.
12. Trunks mostly clustered. (Black willow). S. nigra.
    Trunk single: twigs sometimes velvety.
    (White willow). S. alba.
13. Buds 3 mm. long. (Prairie willow). S. humilis.
    Buds 2 mm. long. (Dwarf gray willow). (6). S. tristis.

MYRICA. Bayberry. Wax Myrtle.
(Family Myricaceae).

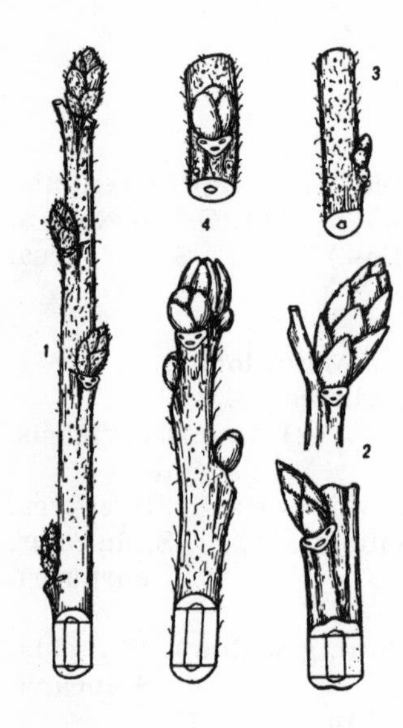

Shrubs or very small trees, aromatic: deciduous in the North. Twigs rounded or angular, slender, resinous-dotted when young: pith small, somewhat angled, continuous, green. Buds small, solitary, sessile, subglobose or ovoid, with 2 or about 4 exposed scales, the end-bud absent. Leaf-scars alternate, half-elliptical or somewhat 3-sided, more or less raised: bundle-traces 3: stipule-scars small if present.

The sweetfern is considered sometimes to represent a distinct genus (*Comptonia*), of which it is the only representative. A readable account of its ancestry is given by Berry in volume 40 of The American Naturalist. The sweet-gale also has been held apart under the generic name *Gale*.

1. With stipule-scars. (Sweetfern). M. asplenifolia.
   Without stipule-scars. 2.
2. Buds conical-ovoid or oblong, no end bud. (2). M. Gale.
   Buds subglobose, obtuse: fruit encrusted with wax. 3.
3. Buds hairy: fruit moderate (4 mm.). M. californica.
   Buds glabrate. 4.
4. Buds small (about 1 mm.), glandular-dotted: lenticels very conspicuous: fruit small (3 mm.). (3). M. cerifera.
   Buds larger (1.5 mm.), soon glandless: fruit larger. 5.
5. Fruit moderate (4 mm.): leaves veiny. (4). M. carolinensis.
   Fruit larger (6×8 mm.): leaves smooth. M. inodora.

LEITNERIA. Corkwood.
(Family Leitneriaceae).

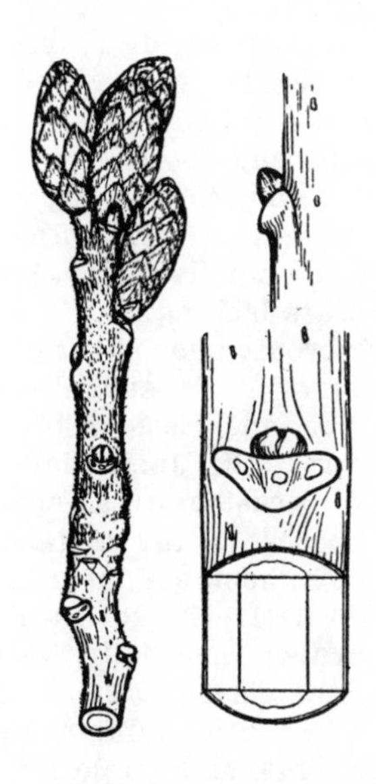

Little-branched tree-like shrubs with very soft and light wood: deciduous. Twigs round, rather stout: pith moderate, rounded, continuous, white. Buds solitary, sessile, rather small, ovoid, with about 3 exposed scales, or the upper (floriferous) enlarged, oblong, or ellipsoid, and with a dozen or more exposed scales. Leaf-scars alternate, half-elliptical or somewhat 3-lobed, slightly raised: bundle-traces 3: stipule-scars lacking.

The North American corkwood, apart from the fact that its wood is very much lighter than that of any other native shrub or tree, is interesting in that it is the only representative of its family, not very closely related to any other group, and that it occurs locally in swamps from western Florida, where it was first found, to southern Missouri, apparently surviving from a time when the Missisipi carried much more water and spread over a greater delta than at present. Like the bald cypress, though occurring naturally in swamps, it is capable of successful cultivation in soil of ordinary dryness.

On anatomical grounds, Van Tieghem and Lecomte, in the Bulletin de la Société botanique de France, 33:181, ally Leitneria with Dipterocarpaceae. Dr. Pfeiffer, in the Botanical Gazette, 53:119, finds in it a suggestion of derivation of catkin-bearing angiosperms from gymnosperms.

Loosely gray-hairy: twigs purplish. L. floridana.

PLATYCARYA.

(Family Juglandaceae).

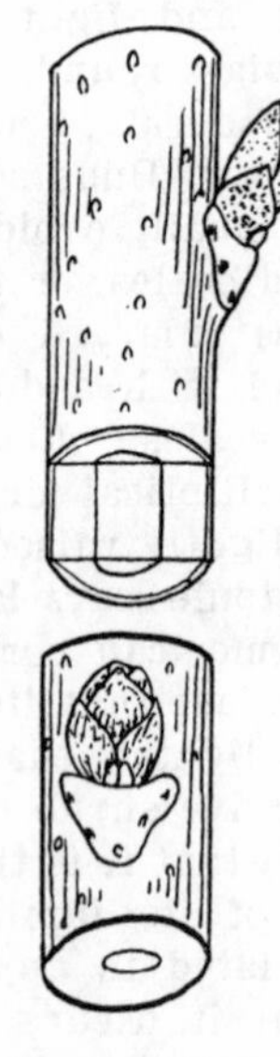

Trees: deciduous. Twigs moderate or rather slender, terete, with fine lenticels: pith rounded, moderate, pale, continuous. Buds rather small, superposed, sessile, ovoid, with some 4 or 5 exposed scales. Leaf-scars alternate, shield-shaped: bundle-traces 5 or 7: stipule-scars lacking.

Twigs glabrous: buds puberulent or glandular. P. strobilacea.

Though not much used in decorative planting, the Juglandaceae are effective occasionally as specimens or massed in the distance, and some of them are of rapid growth. The native hickories and walnuts furnish especially valuable wood, the former almost indispensable in the manufacture of farm implements, and the latter—at one time the most used cabinet wood—the main reliance for gunstocks. An interesting popular account of the geological history of the family, by Berry, is to be found in volume fifteen of The Plant World.

Winter-character references: — *Platycarya strobilcea.* Schneider, f. 135; Shirasawa, 257, pl. 6.

Winter references to the principal Juglandaceae—*Juglans* and *Carya*—are collected between the discussion of these two genera. The family is interesting anatomically because of the marked and characteristic differences between the solid pith of this genus and *Carya* in contrast with the chambered pith of *Juglans* and *Pterocarya.*

JUGLANS. Walnut.
(Family Juglandaceae).

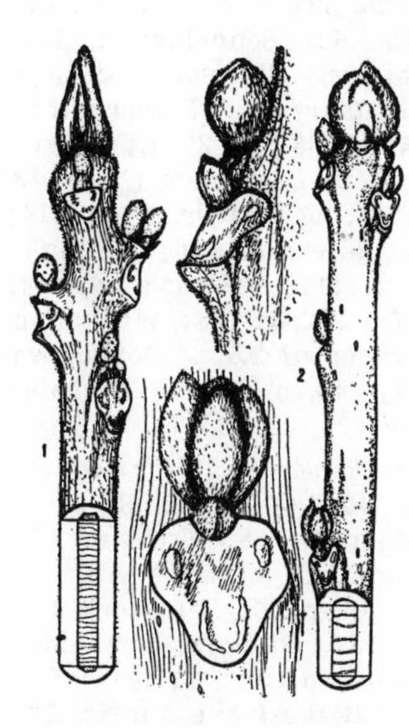

Usually trees, sometimes of large size: deciduous. Twigs rather stout, more or less fluted: pith moderate, brown, angular, chambered with rather close thin plates. Buds moderate, with several scales, superposed and often developing into catkin rudiments, the terminal much larger and with more or less lobed scales. Leaf-scars alternate, shield-shaped or 3-lobed, large, raised: bundle-traces in 3 compound groups: stipule-scars lacking.

Of recent years black walnut has been planted in some quantity for its wood; and the European walnut furnishes one of the important Californian crops, and in more hardy forms it is recommended for other regions. Hybrids are known between the European walnut and the black walnut, and *Juglans rupestris* has been thought (undoubtedly wrongly) to hybridize with the California live-oak.

1. Terminal bud elongated: leaf-scar downy at top. 2.
   Terminal bud short: leaf-scar without a downy line. 3.
2. Leaf-scars not notched at top. (Butternut). (1). J. cinerea.
   Leaf-scars notched: twig very stout. J. Sieboldiana.
3. Twigs gray-pubescent: buds canescent: pith-diaphragms close together (18 to 1 cm.). (Black w.). (2). J. nigra.
   Twigs and lateral buds glabrescent: bark smooth: pith diaphragms 8 to 1 cm. (European walnut). J. regia.

Winter-character references to *Juglans*:—*J. californica*. Trelease (1), 43, pl. 24. *J. cinerea*. Beal, American Naturalist, 1881, p. 36, f.; Blakeslee & Jarvis, 324, f. 6, 331, 398, pl.; Bösemann, 60; Brendel, pl. 2; Otis, 62; Schneider, f. 114; Trelease (1), 42, pl. 24. *J. cordiformis*. Shirasawa, 232, pl. 1; Trelease (1), 43, pl. 25. *J. mandshurica*. Trelease (1), 43, pl. 25. *J. nigra*. Beal, Amer. Nat., 1881, p. 36, f.; Blakeslee & Jarvis, 331, 400, pl.; Brendel, pl. 2; Hitchcock (1), f. 13, (3), 17, (4), 138, pl. 99, 101; Otis, 64; Schneider, f. 49, 114; Trelease (1), 44, pl. 24. *J. regia*. Bösemann, 60; Malpighi, Opera Omnia, 22, pl. 9; Schneider, f. 114; Trelease (1), 44; Ward, 1:69, f. 48, 70, f. 49, 118, f. 59, 212, f. 108; Willkomm, 6, 27, f. 30; Zuccarini, 7, pl. 4. *J. regia sinensis*. Shirasawa, 232, pl. 1. *J. rupestris*. Trelease (1), 43, pl. 24. *J. Sieboldiana*. Shirasawa, 231, pl. 1; Trelease (1), 42, pl. 25.

Winter-character references to *Carya*:—*C. alba* (*C. tomentosa*). Blakeslee & Jarvis, 337, 404, pl.; Brendel, pl. 2; Hitchcock (1), 6; Otis, 72; Schneider, f. 168; Trelease (1), 38, pl. 14, 15, *C. cordiformis* (*C. amara; C. minima*). Blakeslee & Jarvis, 332, 337, 408, pl.; Brendel, pl. 2; Hitchcock (1), 6, f. 16, 17, (3), 18, (4), 138, f. 102-103; Otis, 78; Schneider, f. 88; Trelease (1), 35, pl. 13. *C. acquatica*. Trelease (1), 34, pl. 13. *C. glabra* (*C. porcina*). Blakeslee & Jarvis, 337, 406, pl.; Hitchcock (1), 6; Otis, 76; Schneider, f. 39, 88; Trelease (1), 36, pl. 14. *C. laciniosa* (*C. sulcata*). Hitchcock (1), 6; Otis, 70; Schneider, f. 168; Trelease (1), 40, pl. 15. *C. mexicana*. Trelease (1), 39. *C. myristicaeformis*. Trelease (1), 34, pl. 13. *C. ovalis* (under various names). Bailey, American Garden, 11:381, 385-8; Otis, 74; Trelease (1), 36-37, pl. 14. *C. ovata* (formerly called *C. alba*). Blakeslee & Jarvis, 402, pl.; Brendel, 29, 30, pl. 2; Hitchcock (1), 6, f. 18, (3), 18; Otis, 68; Schneider, f, 168; Trelease (1), 41, pl. 15. *C. Pecan*. Brendel, 31, pl. 2; Hitchcock (1), 6; Trelease (1), 32, pl. 13. *C. villosa*. Trelease (1), 37, pl. 14.

CARYA. Hickory.
(Family Juglandaceae).

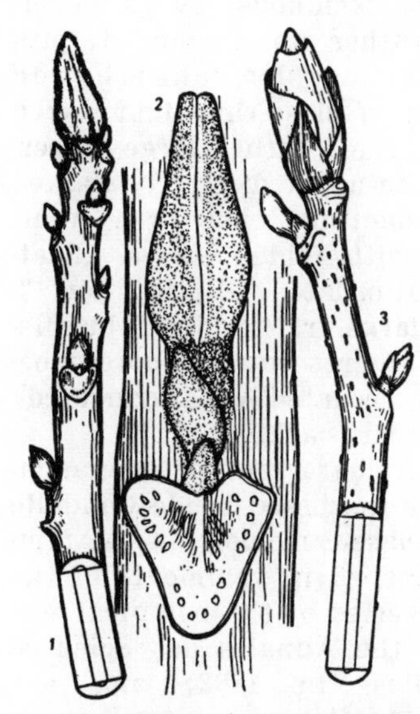

Trees: deciduous. Twigs moderate, terete: pith moderate, angled, often brown, continuous, or broken at the nodes. Buds rather large, sometimes stalked or superposed, the terminal larger, ovoid or oblong, apparently naked or with 1 or several exposed scales. Leaf-scars alternate, shield-shaped or 3-lobed, large, low: bundle-traces numerous in 3 or 4 more or less definite groups; stipule-scars lacking. (*Hicoria; Scoria*).

1. Bud-scales in pairs. 2.
   Bud-scales not opposite. 3.
2. Yellow-glandular: fruit bitter. (2). C. cordiformis.
   Scarcely glandular: fruit sweet. (Pecan). (1). C. Pecan.
3. Terminal bud large (usually over 10 mm.). (Hickories). 4.
   Terminal bud small (scarcely 10 mm.). (Pignuts). 7.
4. Outer bud-scales falling earl. (Mockernut). C. alba.
   Outer scales persistent, pointed. (Shagbarks). 5.
5. Twigs buff or orange: fruit very large. C. laciniosa.
   Twigs gray or red-brown: fruit smaller. 6.
6. Twigs glabrate. (Shagbark). (3). C. ovata.
   Twigs hairy. (Hairy Shagbark). C. ovata hirsuta.
7. Bark very rough, broken into squares. C. villosa.
   Bark rather smooth or flaking. 8.
8. Husk of fruit not splitting far. (Eastern). C. glabra.
   Husk splitting nearly to base. (Western pignut). C. ovalis.

PTEROCARYA.
(Family Juglandaceae).

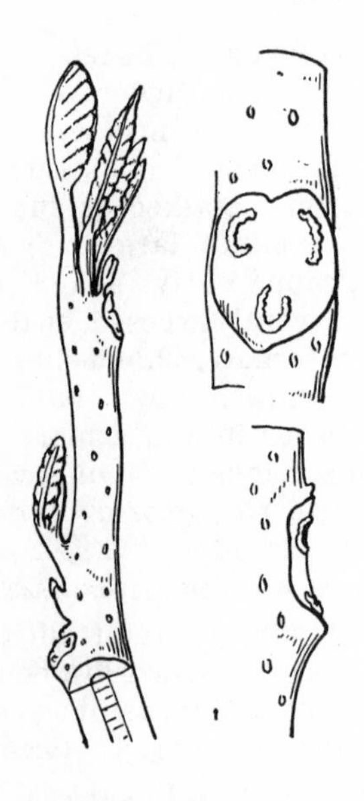

Trees: deciduous. Twigs moderate or rather stout, rounded: pith moderate, angular, chambered with rather close thin light brown plates. Buds rather large, superposed, the upper distinctly stalked or elongating the first year, naked, with folded leaves. Leaf-scars alternate, elliptical or 3-lobed, large, rather low: bundle-traces 3, crescent- or horseshoe-shaped, crenated or fragmented: stipule-scars lacking.

Winter-characters of Juglandaceae are discussed by de Candolle in his classic memoir on the family published in volume 18 of the fourth series of the botanical section of the Annales des Sciences Naturelles, in 1862; and are shown in Michaux' Sylva.

References to *Pterocarya*:—*P. fraxinifolia.* Leavitt, Outlines of Botany, 31, f. 22; Schneider, f. 5, 86. *P. rhoifolia.* Leavitt, Outlines of Botany, 29, f. 18; Shirasawa, 232, pl. 1, *P. stenoptera.* Schneider, f. 86.

Like the other Juglandaceae, and particularly *Juglans*, *Pterocarya* well illustrates distinct superposed buds, of which the uppermost is largest. This is the usual condition in such cases.

1. Twigs distinctly pubescent and glandular. P. stenoptera.
   Twigs essentially glabrous and glandless. 2.
2. Twigs and buds red-brown. (1). P. fraxinifolia.
   Twigs and buds gray-brown. P. rhoifolia.

CORYLUS. Hazel. Filbert.
(Family Betulaceae).

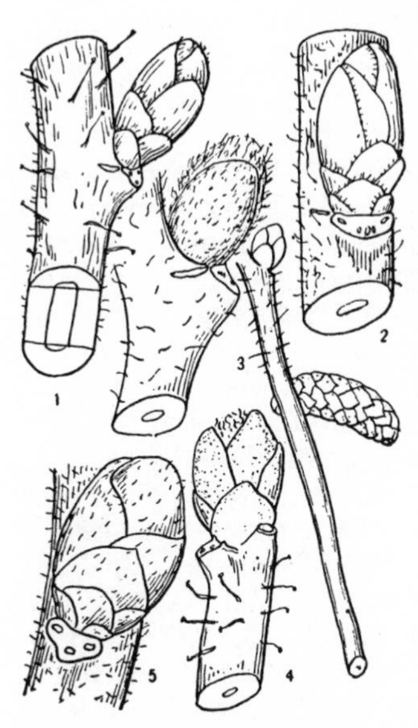

Shrubs: deciduous. Twigs moderate or rather slender, zig-zag, round; pith somewhat 3-sided, continuous, pale. Buds solitary, obliquely sessile, round or ovoid and obtuse with some 4-6 exposed scales, or early developing into ashen catkins, the end-bud lacking. Leaf-scars alternate, 2-ranked, half-round or triangular, somewhat raised, rather small: bundle-traces 3, or multiplied and finally obscure: stipule-scars elongated.

Winter-character references: — *C. americana.* Brendel, pl. 2; Hitchcock, (3), 18; Foerste, Bull. Torr. Bot. Cl. 20: 164, f.; Schneider, f. 165.—*C. Avellana.* Bösemann, 68; Fant, 12, f. 3; Schneider, f. 164; Ward, 1:185. f. 92; Willkomm, 4, 25, f. 26; Zuccarini, 5, pl. 3.—*C. Colurna.* Schneider, f. 164; Willkomm, 8, 9, 26, f. 28.—*C. heterophylla.* Shirasawa, 263, pl. 8.—*C. maxima.* Bösemann, 68; Schneider, f. 164; Willkomm, 26, f. 27.—*C. rostrata.* Schneider, f. 165; Shirasawa, 264, pl. 8.

1. Buds glabrescent but with ciliate scales. 2.
   Buds gray-pubescent. 3.
2. Buds small (scarcely 4 mm.). (1). C. Avellana.
   Buds large (6 mm. long): twigs olive. (2). C. pontica.
3. Outer scales elongated, quickly falling. (3). C. rostrata.
   Scales persistent, the lower short. 4.
4. Buds rather small (4 mm.): native. (4). C. americana.
   Buds larger (often 5 mm. long). (5). C. maxima.

CARPINUS. Hornbeam.
(Family Betulaceae).

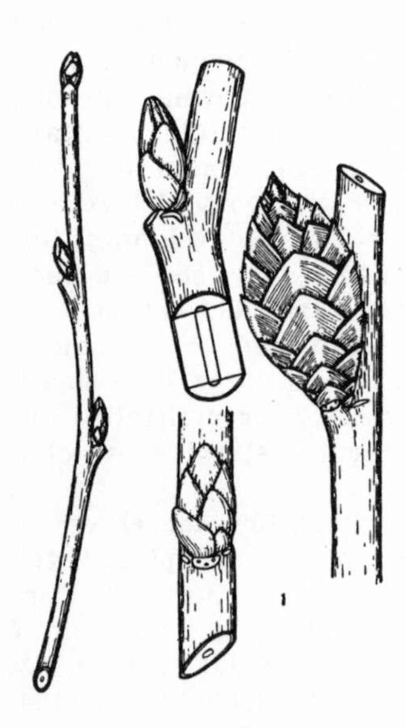

Rather round-topped and openly branched trees with sinewy-fluted trunks and smooth gray bark: deciduous. Twigs slender, zig-zag, terete: pith small, roundish or 5-sided, continuous, pale. Buds solitary or very rarely superposed, ovoid, sessile, oblique, with a dozen 4-ranked scarcely striated scales, or developing into cone-like catkin-initials, the end-bud lacking. Leaf-scars alternate, 2-ranked, raised, crescent-shaped, somewhat small: bundle-traces 3: stipule-scars subequal, elongated.

Winter-character references: — *C. Betulus*. Bösemann, 70; Fant, 16, f. 9; Schneider, f. 10, 162; Ward, 1:118, f. 59, 178, f. 88-89; Willkomm, 26, f. 29; Zuccarini, 3, pl. 2.—*C. caroliniana*. Blakeslee & Jarvis, 332, 412, pl.; Brendel, pl. 2; Otis, 82. An early paper on abscission, in which *Carpinus* figures, is by Ohlert in the journal Linnaea for 1837.

1. Buds large (fully 10 mm. long), straw-colored. C. cordata.
   Buds moderate (6-8 mm.): European. C. Betulus.
   Buds small (scarcely 5 mm.). 2.
2. Buds straw-colored. C. japonica.
   Buds brownish. 3.
3. Buds glabrous. C. Turczaninowii.
   Buds somewhat silky. 4.
4. Twigs villous. C. duinensis.
   Twigs glabrescent. (Blue beech). (1). C. caroliniana.

OSTRYA. Hop Hornbeam.
(Family Betulaceae).

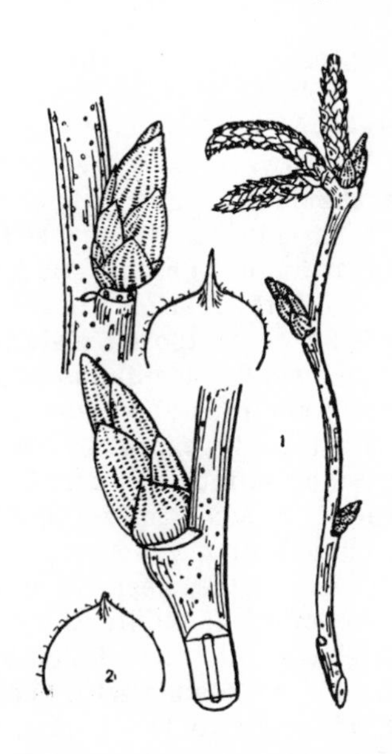

Rather deliquescent trees with scaly bark: deciduous. Twigs slender, zig-zag, terete: pith small, roundish, continuous, pale. Buds solitary, or exceptionally superposed, sessile, ovoid, oblique, with half-a-dozen spirally placed striate scales, the end-bud lacking. Leaf-scars alternate, 2-ranked, somewhat raised, crescent-shaped or half-elliptical, small: bundle-traces 3: stipule-scars unequal, elongated. Catkins often present.

Winter-character references: — *O. carpinifolia.* Bösemann, 70; Schneider, f. 163; Willkomm, 27, f. 30.—*O. virginiana.* Blakeslee & Jarvis, 332, 410, pl.; Brendel, pl. 2; Hitchcock (1), 3, (2), 18; Otis, 80; Shirasawa, 265, pl. 9.

A suggestive illustrated study of the structure of buds as revealed in their unfolding in the spring, in which *Ostrya* figures, is published by Hitchcock in volume 6 of the Transactions of the Academy of Science of St. Louis. One of many publications on buds superposed above the leaves or leaf-scars is by Damaskinos and Bourgeois in volume 5 of the Bulletin de la Société Botanique de France: in it, reference is made to *Ostrya virginiana.*

Scales of staminate catkins long-mucronate: nutlets glabrate, fusiform. (1). O. virginiana.

Scales blunt or abruptly short-pointed: nutlets pubescent above, ovoid. (European hornbeam). (2). O. carpinifolia.

BETULA. Birch.
(Family Betulaceae).

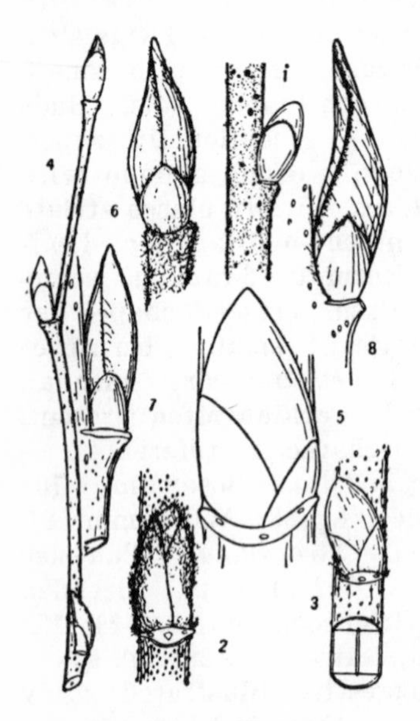

Trees or less commonly shrubs: deciduous. Twigs slender, usually zig-zag, terete, frequently developing as dwarf-shoots so as to make the lateral buds appear stalked: pith minute, compressed 3-sided, continuous, green. Buds moderate, solitary, fusiform ovoid, sessile, with 2 or 3 exposed scales, the end-bud usually deciduous except on the numerous short spurs. Leaf-scars alternate, more or less 2-ranked, half-elliptical, small: bundle-traces, 3, sometimes indistinct: stipule-scars narrow.

Though they have been much confused in botanical publications, the birches are not very difficult as a rule. In accordance with the policy of adhering to the nomenclature of the Standard Cyclopedia of Horticulture, the names here used are somewhat different from those employed in the last edition of Gray's Manual, though the latter rest on an extended critical study of the group by Fernald, published in full in The American Journal of Science for September, 1902.

An excellent character is derived from the bracts of the fruiting cones, which are sometimes available in winter; and this character has been applied successfully to the recognition of certain hybrid birches by Rosendahl in volume four of Minnesota Botanical Studies.

1. Lateral buds ellipsoid or oblong, very blunt, small. 2.
   Buds ovoid or fusiform-oblong, acute, at most ciliate. 8.
2. Buds very small (3 or exceptionally 4 mm.). 3.
   Buds moderate for the group (4 mm.): bark papery. 5.
   Buds large for the group (5 mm.): bark papery. 7.
3. Twigs not resinous-warty, softly hairy. B. pumila.
   Twigs with resinous warts. 4.
4. Twigs and buds with soft hairs. B. pumila glandulifera.
   Twigs and buds only velvety. (1). B. glandulosa.
5. Buds hairy: twigs warty: bark orange. (2). B. nigra.
   Bud-scales at most ciliate: bark creamy or white. 6.
6. Twigs very resinous-warty: glabrous. (3). B. populifolia.
   Twigs sometimes with long hairs. (4). B. papyrifera.
7. Buds glabrous: bark creamy or white. (4). B. papyrifera.
   Buds hairy: lower scales long: bark orange. (2). B. nigra.
8. Buds acutely ovoid. 9.
   Buds subfusiform, acute, with short lower scale. 12.
9. Twigs puberulent, somewhat warty. B. kenaica.
   Twigs glabrate. 10.
10. Twigs resinous-warty: buds small (3×5 mm.). B. utilis.
    Twigs little warty: buds larger ($4\text{-}5 \times 6\text{-}8$ mm.). 11.
11. Twigs and buds red-brown. (5). B. Maximowiczii.
    Twigs and buds brown. B. grossa.
12. Buds short for the group (5-6 mm.). 13.
    Buds long (7-8 mm.): twigs scarcely warty. 17.
13. Twigs softly hairy. 14.
    Twigs glabrous. 15.
14. Pubescence persistent. (6). B. pubescens.
    Pubescent only in sheltered places. (4). B. papyrifera.
15. Twigs very warty and varnished. B. occidentalis.
    Twigs sparingly if at all resinous-warty. 16.
16. Bark white: trees usually weeping. (7). B. pendula.
    Bark yellowish or silvery-gray. (Yellow birch). B. lutea.
17. Buds light brown: branches red-brown, spicy. (8). B. lenta.
    Buds glossy red-brown. B. japonica.

ALNUS. Alder.
(Family Betulaceae).

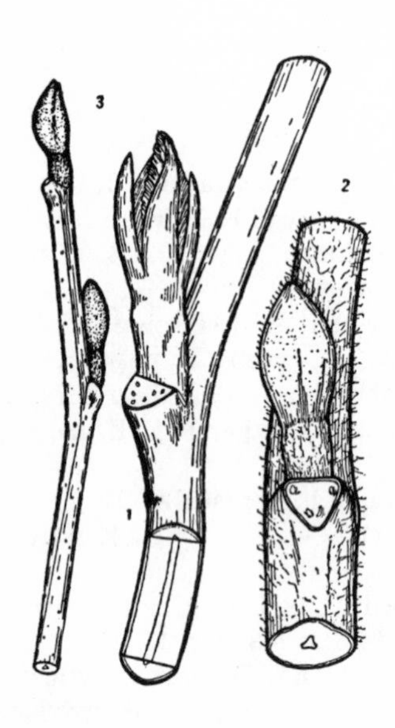

Typically shrubs: deciduous. Bark smoky or gray, smooth or fissured in rather large or scaly areas. Twigs often 3-sided: pith small, 3-sided, continuous. Buds rather large, solitary, usually stalked, with 2 or 3 often subvalvate scales. Leaf-scars alternate, half-round, somewhat raised: bundle-traces 3, or the lowest compound: stipule-scars narrow.

Alders are particularly interesting in winter through having their buds distinctly stalked. Though this character is by no means limited to them, nor do they all show it, there are few genera in which it is so readily observable. Their fruit is also persistent in the form of small cone-like bodies, which differ in shape and position in different species, and as a rule the staminate catkins for the next season are conspicuous.

1. Buds stalked. 2.
   Buds sessile: bushes. 5.
2. Very tree-like. (European alder). A. glutinosa.
   Bushy, even when large. 3.
3. Bud-scales narrow and separated. (1). A. maritima.
   Bud-scales valvate. 4.
4. Fruiting cones erect. (Smooth alder). (2). A. rugosa.
   Fruiting cones pendent. (Speckled alder). (3). A. incana.
5. Twigs glabrescent. (Mountain alder). A. crispa.
   Twigs hairy. (Downy alder). A. mollis.

Winter-character references to Betulaceae.

Alnus Alnobetula. Schneider, f. 160. *A. firma*. Shirasawa, 231, pl. 1. *A. glutinosa* (*A. vulgaris*). Blakeslee & Jarvis, 426; Bösemann, 56; Fant, 30, f. 30; Schneider, f. 17, 58, 113; Ward, 1:206, f. 106; Willkomm, 4, 21, f. 17. *A. incana*. Blakeslee & Jarvis, 426, pl.; Böseman, 56; Fant, 30; Schneider, f. 112; Willkomm, 6, 21, f. 18. *A. incana glauca*. Shirasawa, 230, pl. 1. *A. japonica*. Shirasawa, 230, pl. 1. *A rugosa* (*A. serrulata*). Blakeslee & Jarvis, 426. *A viridis*. Willkomm, 9, 11, 22, f. 19. *A. viridis sibirica*. Shirasawa, 231, pl.

Betula alpestris. Fant, 15. *B. Bhojpattra*. Shirasawa, 246, pl. 4. *B. fruticosa*. Fant, 16; Zuccarini, 18, pl. 10. *B. globispica*. Shirasawa, 246, pl. 4. *B. grossa*. Shirasawa, 251, pl. 5. *B. humilis*. Bösemann, 74; Fant, 15; Schneider, f. 161; Willkomm, 20, f. 16. *B. lenta*. Blakeslee & Jarvis, 337, 414, pl.; Otis, 86. *B. lutea*. Blakeslee & Jarvis, 337, 416, pl.; Otis, 88. *B. Maximowicziana*. Shirasawa, 252, pl. 5. *B. nana*. Bösemann, 74; Fant, 16; Schneider, f. 161. *B. nigra*. Blakeslee & Jarvis, 337, 418, pl.; Brendel, pl. 3; Hitchcock (1), 3. *B. papyrifera* (*B. alba papyrifera*). Blakeslee & Jarvis, 337, 442, pl.; Otis, 90; Shirasawa, 246, pl. 4. *B. pendula* (formerly called *B. alba; B. odorato*). Blakeslee & Jarvis, 337, 424, pl.; Bösemann, 73; Fan, 15, f. 6; Ward, 1:232, f. 119, 233, f. 120; Willkomm, 4, 20, f. 14, 15; Zuccarini, 17, pl. 10. *B. pendula verrucosa*. Schneider, f. 36, 160; Shirasawa, 246, pl. 4. *B. populifolia*. Blakeslee & Jarvis, 337, 420, pl.; Schneider, f. 161. *B. pubescens* (*B. alba*). Schneider, f. 160; Willkomm, 20, f. 15. *B. ulmifolia*. Shirasawa, 252, pl. 5.

Areschoug's Beiträge zur Biologie der Holzgewächse, a unique analysis of bud- and branch-specialization in which *Betula* figures, was published in volume 12 of Lunds Universitets Aarsskrift, in 1877, after many years of critical observation. A decade later its author made his principal conclusions more accessible in volume 9 of the Botanische Jahrbücher.

FAGUS. Beech.
(Family Fagaceae).

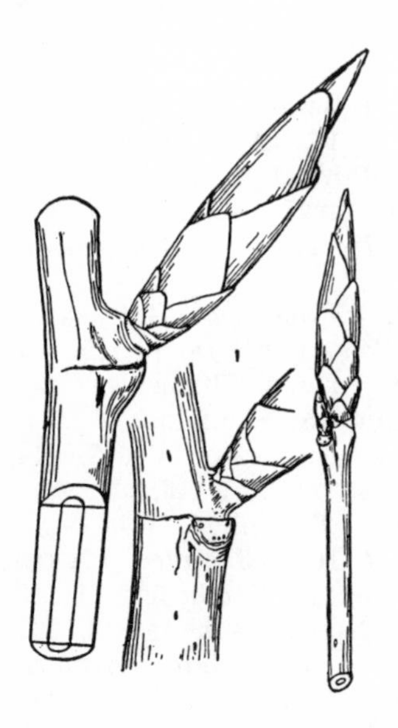

Rather ovoid or round-topped trees with cylindrical smooth gray trunk, the bark frequently with included woody nodules: deciduous or with the dead leaves persisting far into the winter. Twigs slender, zig-zag, terete: pith rather small, roundish, continuous. Buds solitary or rarely supernumerary, sessile or becoming slightly stalked, divergent and very oblique over the leaf-scars, elongated fusiform and subpungent, with some 10 or more spirally arranged scales. Leaf-scars alternate, sometimes 2-ranked, little-raised, half-round, rather small: bundle-traces 3, the lower usually compound or broken into an irregular series: stipule-scars linear, nearly meeting around the twig. Children know the "lucky-nuts" of the bark.

The beech affords an excellent illustration of buds obliquely placed over the leaf-scars,—a common occurrence when they are 2-ranked; and of buds elongated without being stalked, for the scales here begin at the very base of the bud.

The species are distinguishable with difficulty except by aid of the foliage when it is present.

1. Twigs often villous: buds puberulent. F. sylvatica.
   Twigs and lower bud-scales glabrescent. 2.
2. Buds light brown: leaves undulate. F. japonica.
   Buds more red-brown: leaves serrate. (1). F. grandifolia.

CASTANEA. Chestnut.
(Family Fagaceae).

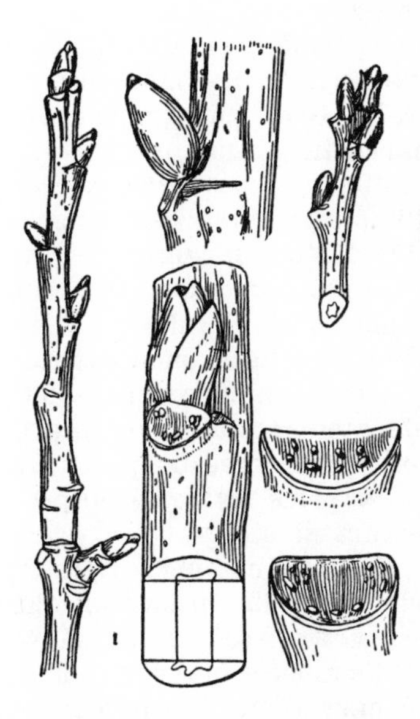

Shrubs or mostly large trees with fissured but otherwise smooth gray bark: deciduous. Twigs moderate, more or less fluted: pith moderate, star-shaped, continuous. Buds solitary, ovoid, sessile, oblique, with 2 or 3 exposed scales, the end-bud frequently lacking. Leaf-scars alternate, little raised, half-round, rather small: bundle-traces 3, often compound: stipule-scars elongated, unequal.

The deeply grooved pith of the chestnut, affording one of the most obvious means of identifying its winter twigs, attracted the attention of Malpighi who pictured it more than two centuries and a half ago among the interesting things that could be seen by the aid of a magnifying glass. In common with many other genera, *Castanea* shows a varying phyllotaxy or leaf-arrangement,—5-ranked on erect shoots, 2-ranked on those that spread horizontally,—and a correlated upward displacement of the buds on the latter. This has been attributed to a response to gravitation similar to that which directs the upward growth of stems in general; but Kny, in a short communication to the Gesellschaft naturforschender Freunde of Berlin in 1876 shows that it is rather the manifestation of an inherent tendency to bilateral symmetry.

Buds downy: shrub or small tree. (Chinquapin). C. pumila.
Buds glabrous. (American chestnut). (1). C. dentata.

QUERCUS. Oak.
(Family Fagaceae).

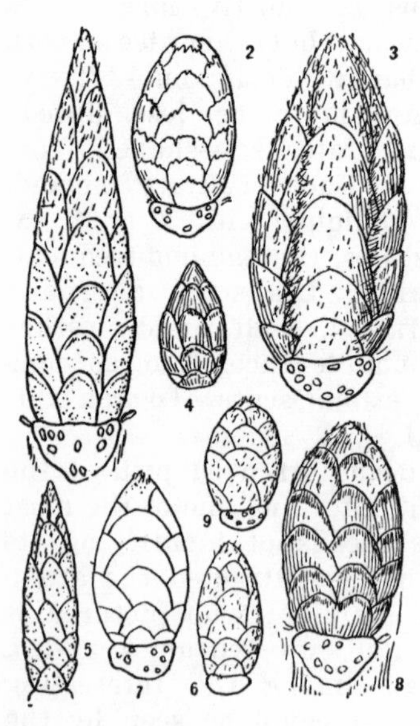

Trees or rarely shrubs: mostly deciduous, though the dried leaves often persist. Twigs moderate or slender, fluted: pith moderate, star-shaped in section, continuous. Buds solitary or sometimes collaterally multiple, sessile, globose or ovoid to conical, sometimes angled, clustered toward the tip, with numerous 5-ranked scales. Leaf-scars alternate, moderate or rather small, half-round, somewhat elevated: bundle-traces nearly a dozen, scattered or partly in a more or less evident ellipse: stipule-scars small.

The Danish botanist Oersted was very keen in discerning the differences that oak buds show, and Willkomm's differentiation of the two oaks of northern Europe that have been confused under the name *Quercus Robur* is as clean-cut when this character only is used as it is when their fruits show the distinction because of which one has been called variety *pedunculata* and the other variety *sessiliflora*. No differences between the common red oak (*Q. rubra*) and Schneck's oak (*Q. Schneckii*), or between this and the Texan oak (*Q. texana*), are more obvious to a close observer than those between their winter buds, but comparisons need to be made between developed buds on mature branches.

1. Black oaks: fruit maturing the second year. 2.
   White oaks: fruit maturing the first year. 16.

2. Buds conical-fusiform, large (8-10 mm. long). 3.
   Buds ovoid or conical-ovoid or else very thick. 4.

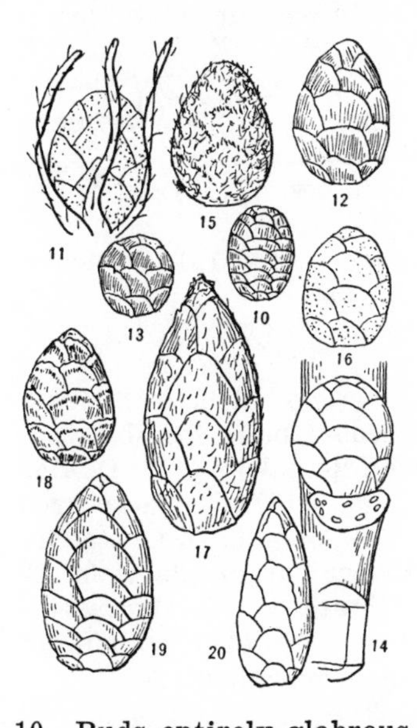

3. Twigs glabrous. (1). Q. laevis.
   Twigs puberulent.
   (Blackjack). Q. marilandica.
4. Evergreen. Q. laurifolia.
   Deciduous. 5.
5. Buds dull clay-colored, glabrous. (2). Q. Schneckii.
   Buds red or brown or silky. 6.
6. Buds large (7-10 mm.), hairy, angular. (3). Q. velutina.
   Buds moderate or small. 7.
7. Twigs tomentulose. 8.
   Twigs glabrous. 9.
8. Buds short (4 mm.): glabrous. (Bear oak). Q. ilicifolia.
   Buds long (3 × 7 mm.), silky. (5). Q. cinerea.
9. Buds small (3 mm. long), glabrate. Q. georgiana.
   Buds larger or hairy. 10.
10. Buds entirely glabrous. 11.
    Buds more or less silky, or tardily glabrescent. 13.
    Buds almost woolly, dull gray-brown. (6). Q. nigra.
11. Buds red, relatively large (3 × 5 mm.). (7). Q. rubra.
    Buds brown, smaller (2 × 3-4 mm.). 12.
12. Buds rather obtuse. (Pin oak). Q. palustris.
    Buds very acute. (Willow oak). Q. Phellos.
13. Buds almost blood-red. (Spanish oak). Q. falcata.
    Buds brown. (Shingle oak). Q. imbricaria.
    Buds brownish-red, or at first silvery-pubescent. 14.
14. Buds large (4 × 5-6 mm.). (8). Q. coccinea.
    Buds smaller (scarcely 3 × 4 mm.). 15.

15. Buds and twigs rather dark (9). Q. ellipsoidalis.
Buds and twigs bright brown: Texas. Q. texana.
16. Buds subglobose or ellipsoid, nearly or quite glabrous. 17.
Buds ovoid or conical-ovoid. 22.
Buds distinctly conical. 27.
17. Evergreen: buds small. (Live oak). (10). Q. virginiana.
Deciduous. 18.
18. Buds invested by long narrow stipules. (11). Q. Cerris.
Stipules lacking or inconspicuous. 19
19. Bark exfoliating from the branches. (12). Q. bicolor.
Bark not exfoliating. 20.
20. Buds small (scarcely 3 mm.), pale. (13). Q. Durandii.
Buds medium-size. 21.
21. Twigs buff: buds pale brown. (Overcup oak). Q. lyrata.
Twigs gray or purple, often glaucous: buds deep brown.
(White oak). (14). Q. alba.
22. Twigs and buds gray-pubescent. (15). Q. macrocarpa.
Twigs yellow-scurfy: buds dull, silky. (16). Q. stellata.
Twigs glabrous: buds brown-puberulent or glabrous. 23.
23. Buds rather glossy blood-red, glabrate. Q. Margaretta.
Buds very large, gray-pubescent. (17). Q. dentata.
Buds light brown or the scales pale-margined. 24.
Buds deep brown or red-brown. 25.
24. Shrub. (Chinquapin oak). Q. prinoides.
Tree. (Yellow oak). (18). Q. Muehlenbergii.
25. Buds terete: twigs gray or purple. Q. alba.
Buds somewhat grooved, often brown-silky. 26.
26. Twigs reddish. (English oak). (19). Q. Robur.
Twigs olive or brown. (Cow oak). Q. Prinus.
27. Buds light brown. 28.
Buds deep brown. 29.
28. Bud-scales brown- or rosy-margined. Q. grosseserrata.
Bud-scales not darker at margin. Q. crispula.
29. Buds dull: outer scales pale-margined. Q. montana.
Buds glossy: scales not pale-margined. (20). Q. sessiliflora.

Winter-character references to Fagaceae:—*Castanea dentata* (*C. americana*). Blakeslee & Jarvis, 331-333, 430, pl.; Otis, 94. *C. sativa* (*C. vesca; C. vulgaris*). Bösemann, 67; Schneider, f. 25, 26, 162; Shirasawa, 264, pl. 8; Ward, 1:188, f. 94; Wilkomm, 24, f. 24.

Fagus grandifolia (*F. ferruginea*). Blakeslee & Jarvis, 428, pl.; Brendel, pl. 2; Otis, 92; Schneider, f. 163. *F. japonica*. Shirasawa, 264, pl. 8. *F. sylvatica*. Blakeslee & Jarvis, 428; Bösemann, 70; Fant, 12, f. 2; Schneider, f. 163; Ward, 1:176, f. 87; Willkomm, 3, 4, 25, f. 25; Zuccarini, 4, pl. 2. *F. sylvatica Sieboldi*. Shirasawa, 264, pl. 8.

Quercus agrifolia. Trelease (3), pl. 13. *Q. alba*. Blakeslee & Jarvis, 338-9, 432, pl.; Brendel, pl. 2; Cobb, Proceedings of the American Philosophical Society, 54:174, pl. 4; Hitchcock (1), 5; Otis, 100; Schneider, f. 52, 154. *Q. bicolor* (*Q. platanoides*). Blakeslee & Jarvis, 338-9, 438, pl.; Brendel, pl. 2; Cobb, *l. c.* pl. 5; Otis, 104. *Q. californica*. Trelease (3), pl. 13. *Q. Cerris*. Bösemann, 71; Schneider, f. 38, 156; Ward, 1:118, f. 59; Willkomm, 6, 24, f. 23. *Q. cinerea* (*Q. brevifolia*). Trelease (3), 1, pl. 12. *Q. coccinea*. Blakeslee & Jarvis, 450, pl.; Otis, 112; Schneider, f. 154; Trelease (3), 1, pl. 11. *Q. dentata*. Shirasawa, 258, pl. 7. *Q. ellipsoidalis*. Otis, 114; Trelease (3), pl. 11. *Q. Emoryi*. Trelease (3), pl. 13. *Q. falcata* (*Q. digitata*). Trelease (3). *Q. georgiana*. Trelease (3), pl. 12. *Q. glandulifera*. Shirasawa, 257, pl. 7. *Q. grosseserrata*. Shirasawa, 258, pl. 7. *Q. hypoleuca*. Trelease (3), pl. 13. *Q. ilicifolia* (*Q. nana*). Blakeslee & Jarvis, 338-9, 454, pl.; Trelease (3), pl. 11. *Q. imbricaria*. Brendel, pl. 2; Hitchcock (1), 5; Otis, 120; Trelease (3), pl. 12. *Q. laurifolia*. Trelease (3), pl. 12. *Q. macrocarpa*. Blakeslee & Jarvis, 338-9, 436, pl.; Brendel, pl. 2; Cobb, Proc. Amer. Phil. Soc., 54:174, pl. 5; Hitchcock (1), 5, (3), 19, (4), 138, f. 106-110; Otis, 102; Schneider, f. 155. *Q. marilandica* (formerly called *Q. nigra*). Brendel, pl. 2; Hitchcock (1), 5, (3), 19; Otis, 118; Trelease (3), pl. 10. *Q. montana* (*Q. Prinus*).

Blakeslee & Jarvis, 338-9, 444, pl.; Cobb, Proc. Amer. Phil. Soc., 54:174, pl. 6; Schneider, f. 155. *Q. Muehlenbergii*. Blakeslee & Jarvis, 338-9, 440, pl.; Brendel, pl. 2; Hitchcock (3), 139, f. 111-112; Otis, 106. *Q. myrtifolia*. Trelease (3), pl. 12. *Q. nigra* (*Q. aquatica*). Trelease (3), pl. 12. *Q. palustris*. Blakeslee & Jarvis, 338-9, 448, pl.; Hitchcock (1), 5; Otis, 110; Trelease (3), pl. 12. *Q. Phellos*. Schneider, f. 157; Trelease (3), pl. 12. *Q. prinoides*. Blakeslee & Jarvis, 338-9, 442, pl.; Hitchcock (1), 5, (3), 19. *Q. prinoides rufescens*. Blakeslee & Jarvis, 442. *Q. pubescens*. Bösemann, 71; Willkomm, 4, 23, f. 22. *Q. pumila*. Trelease (3), pl. 12. *Q. Robur* (*Q. pedunculata*). Bösemann, 71; Fant, 11, f. 1; Schneider, f. 16, 157; Ward, 1:47, f. 30, 418, f. 59, 217, f. 111: The Oak, 72, f. 19; Willkomm, 7, 22, f. 20; Zuccarini 6, pl. 3. *Q. rubra*. Blakeslee & Jarvis, 338-9, 446, pl.; Brendel, pl. 2; Hitchcock (1), 5, (3), 19; Otis, 108; Schneider, f. 55, 154; Trelease (3), pl. 11. *Q. Schneckii*. Trelease (3), pl. 11. *Q. serrata* and var. *variabilis*. Shirasawa, 258, pl. 7. *Q. sessiliflora* (held by many as true *Q. Robur*). Bösemann, 71; Fant, 11; Schneider, f. 157; Willkomm, 23, f. 21. *Q. stellata*. Blakeslee & Jarvis, 338-9, 434, pl.; Cobb, Proc. Amer. Phil. Soc., 54; 174, pl. 4; Hitchcock (1), 6. *Q. texana*. Trelease (3), pl. 11. *Q. velutina* (often referred to as *Q. coccinea; Q. tinctoria*). Blakeslee & Jarvis, 338-9, 452, pl.; Brendel, pl. 2; Hitchcock (1), 5, (3), 19, (4), 138, f. 113-115; Otis, 116; Trelease (3), pl. 10. *Q. Wislizeni*. Trelease (3), pl. 13.

Oaks, like poplars, willows and some other trees, cast off many of their twigs by imperfect abscission in the autumn,—a normal and regular process each year on old trees, as Areschoug has pointed out in his Biologie der Holzgewächse. This self-pruning forms the subject of a communication in 1865 to the Botanische Zeitung by Röse. Engelmann (Botanical Works, 391) has indicated the differences in vernation shown by species of *Quercus*, and Diez published a comparative study of the subject in Flora for 1887.

MORUS. Mulberry.
(Family Moraceae).

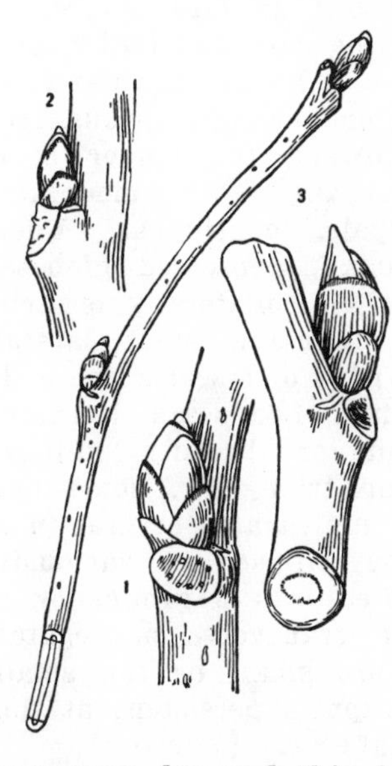

Trees with rather scanty milky sap: deciduous. Twigs moderate or rather slender, rounded: pith moderate, round, continuous. Buds sessile, solitary or collaterally multiplied, ovoid, oblique, with 3 or mostly a half-dozen 2-ranked thin scales, the end-bud lacking. Leaf-scars alternate, round or half-round or obtusely triangular somewhat raised: bundle-traces numerous and scattered or in an ellipse or more or less definitely aggregated into 3; stipule-scars narrow, the one below the bud larger.

Mulberry twigs are frequently mistaken for those of linden when carelessly observed. Apart from their browner color they differ in their milky sap and in their more numerous dry and thin bud-scales.

1. Buds triangular-ovoid, short and closely appressed. 2.
   Buds more elongated (6-8 mm.) and somewhat spreading. 4.
2. Bud-scales uniformly colored. (White m.). (1). M. alba.
   Bud-scales often brown-margined. 3.
3. Not weeping. (Tartarian m.). (2). M. alba tatarica.
   Weeping, usually grafted as a standard. M. alba pendula.
4. Bud-scales white-margined. M. acidosa.
   Bud-scales dark-margined. 5.
5. Twigs often downy above. (Red Mulberry). (3) M. rubra.
   Twigs glabrous. (Black mulberry). M. nigra.

MACLURA. Osage Orange.
(Family Moraceae).

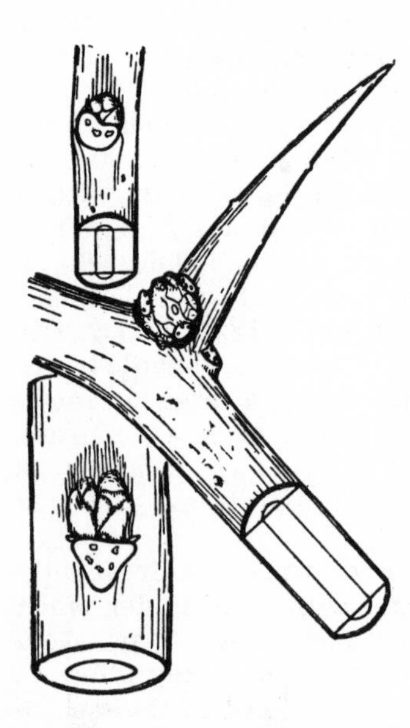

Trees with axillary spines, fibrous-flaking bark and milky sap: deciduous. Twigs moderate, rounded, or 3-sided, glabrous, frequently dwarf, the longer commonly zig-zag. Pith moderate, round, pale, continuous. Buds rather small, depressed globose, sessile, often collaterally branching or producing stout lateral spines, with 4 or 5 scales, the end-bud lacking. Leaf-scars alternate, half-round or broadly kidney-shaped or triangular, somewhat raised: bundle-traces several in a transverse ellipse or variously consolidated into 3 groups or a composite transverse aggregate: stipule-scars small or the small deltoid stipules persistent at top of the leaf-scar. (*Toxylon*).

The Osage orange, closely related to the tropical tree (*Maclura* or *Chlorophora tinctoria*) from which fustic is obtained, contains a similar dye-stuff, which has been made the subject of industrial exploitation during the scarcity of aniline dyes. One of its most marked characteristics is the orange bark that peels from its roots in papery layers. The tradition that it was a favorite bow wood with the Osage Indians gave it the name bois d'arc, which has been transformed into the redundant bow d'arc.

Twigs buff or olive, with spines. M. pomifera.
Unarmed. M. pomifera inermis.

BROUSSONETIA. Paper Mulberry.
(Family Moraceae).

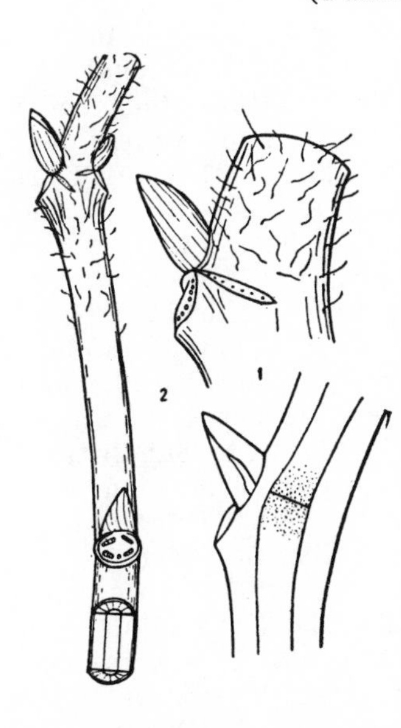

Rather small trees with soft ring-porous pale wood with tangential wood-parenchyma pattern and milky sap: deciduous. Twigs moderate, rounded, zig-zag, hispid when young: pith rather large, round, white, with a very thin green diaphragm at each node. Buds moderate, conical, solitary, sessile, with an outer striate scale. Leaf-scars typically alternate and 2-ranked, rather large, rounded, elevated: bundle-traces about 5, compound, aggregated in an ellipse: stipule-scars long and narrow.

Winter-character references to Moraceae: —*Broussonetia Kasinoki.* Shirasawa, 243-4, pl. 4.—*B. papyrifera.* Schneider, f. 112,—the *contraria* form; Shirasawa, 244, pl. 4.—*Ficus Carica.* Schneider, f. 112; Shirasawa, 240, pl. 3; Ward, 1:51, f. 33, 118, f. 59; Zuccarini, 25, pl. 14.—*Maclura pomifera.* Blakeslee & Jarvis, 330, 494; Hitchcock (3), 17; Otis, 132; Schneider, f. 144-145.—*Morus alba.* Blakeslee & Jarvis, 340, 468, pl.; Bösemann, 75, Schneider, f. 144; Willkomm, 28, f. 32.—*M. nigra.* Bösemann, 75; Schneider, f. 143. —*M. ruba.* Blakeslee & Jarvis, 340, 466, pl.; Brendel, 27, 29, pl. 4; Hitchcock (1), 3, f. 14, (3), 17, (4), 138, f. 90-94; Otis, 134.

1. Twigs slender (2-3 mm.), brown. B. Kasinoki.
   Twigs relatively stout (4 mm.), greenish gray. 2.
3. Leaf-scars alternate and 2-ranked. (1). B. papyifera.
   Scars often opposite. (2). B. papyrifera contraria.

FICUS. Fig.
(Family Moraceae).

Rather small trees (for our purpose) and deciduous: sap milky. Twigs rather stout, rounded: pith large, more or less angular, very white, with a thick firm diaphragm at each node. Buds moderate, globose, often collaterally multiple, with several exposed scales, the end-bud large, conical, with a single infolding striate scale. Leaf-scars alternate, 2-ranked, rather large, round, somewhat elevated: bundle traces several, unequal, compound or aggregated in a broken ring: stipule-scars encircling the stem.

Though there is nothing very interesting about the edible fig as ordinarily grown, it is well known that the oriental varieties of this species require fertilization for the development of their fruit through the activities of a minute gall-fly which breeds in a specialized type of gall flowers that accompany functionally active staminate and pistillate flowers in the large fleshy receptacle that we call the fruit. Similiar interrelations exist between other figs and gall insects. In tropical regions many species send roots down from the branches, these enlarging into supplementary trunks which sometimes transform a single tree into an intricate grove. Others, which start as epiphytes on other trees, send down similar but interlacing roots, of which enormous trunks are formed at length.

Glabrous: end-bud green: lateral buds brown. F. Carica.

ULMUS. Elm.
(Family Ulmaceae.)

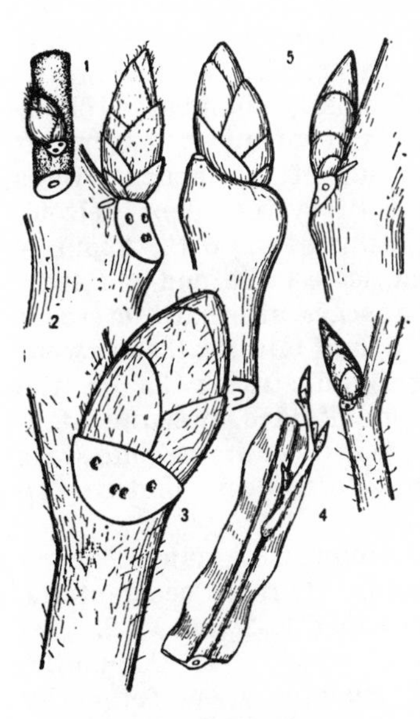

Trees, usually of large size: deciduous. Twigs rather slender, zig-zag, terete: pith small, rounded, continuous. Buds solitary or collaterally branching, variously ovoid, obliquely sessile, the terminal lacking: scales about half-a-dozen, 2-ranked. Leaf-scars alternate, 2-ranked, broadly crescent-shaped or half round, scarcely raised: bundle-traces 3 or compounded in 3 usually distinct groups: stipule-scars unequal.

References under *Aphananthe.*

1. Buds small (1.5 mm.), globose: scales. 4. (1). U. pumila.
   Buds distinctly larger or with more visible scales. 2.
2. Twigs gray-buff, rough: buds red-hairy. (2). U. fulva.
   Twigs red-brown, or gray. 3.
3. Buds blackish-red. 4.
   Buds brown. 7.
4. Buds and twigs glabrous. U. laevis.
   Buds more or less hairy. 5.
5. Twigs glabrescent: bark rough. 6.
   Twigs hispid: bark of branches smooth. (3). U. glabra.
6. Twigs not corky. U. campestris.
   Twigs often with corky ridges. U. campestris suberosa.
7. Twigs moderately slender. 8.
   Twigs very slender, often corky-winged. (4). U. alata.
8. Twigs not corky. (White elm). U. americana.
   Twigs often with corky outgrowths. (5). U. racemosa.

CELTIS. Hackberry.
(Family Ulmaceae.)

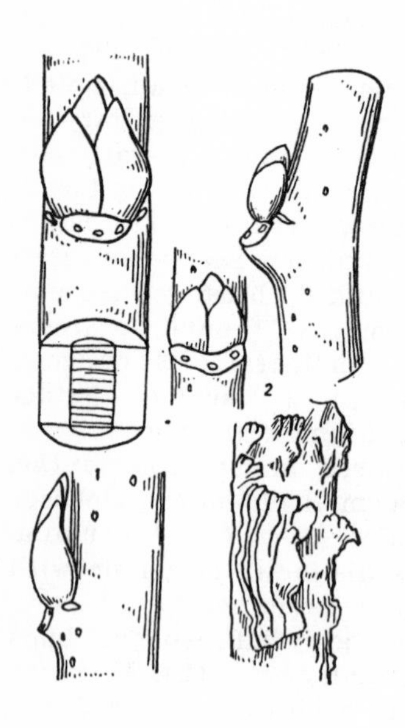

Trees, or a few shrubs: deciduous. Twigs rounded, slender, zigzag. Pith rather small, white, rounded, closely chambered, or exceptionally continuous except at some or all of the nodes. Buds sessile, solitary, ovoid or deltoid, closely appressed, with about 4 2-ranked scales, the end-bud lacking. Leaf-scars alternate, crescent shaped or half elliptical, somewhat raised: bundle-traces 3, or the middle one divided, or confluent in a C-shaped group: stipule-scars narrow. References under *Zelkova.*

1. Buds long (3-4 mm.): bark ridged. (1). C. occidentalis.
   Buds short (1-2 mm.). 2.
2. Shrub. C. pumila.
   Tree, smooth except for corky warts. (2). C. mississippiensis

PLANERA.
(Family Ulmaceae.)

Winter characters of *Ulmus*, from which the warty ovary and unwinged fruit distinguish it in early spring. Our native species, *P. aquatica*, in bud and twig somewhat resembles *U. pumila*, but its red-brown puberulent buds are sometimes somewhat elongated so as to resemble those of *U. alata*, from which it differs in the absence of corky wings on the second year's growth.

References to *Planera* in winter are given under the next genus, *Zelkova.*

ZELKOVA.
(Family Ulmaceae.)

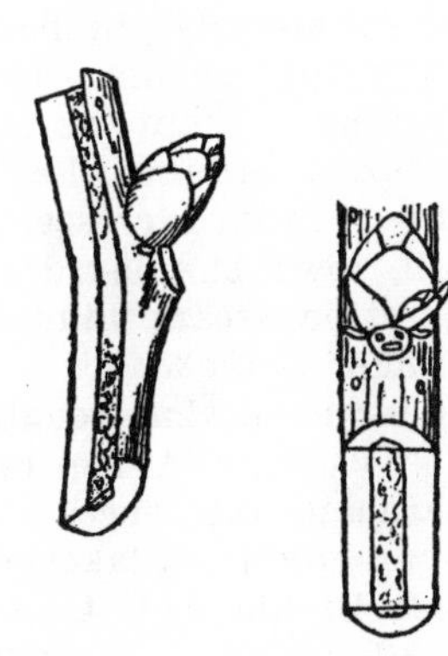

Moderate-sized trees with somewhat exfoliating bark: deciduous. Twigs slender, zig-zag, terete: pith small, roundish, spongy except at the nodes, pale. Buds solitary or collaterally branching, ovoid, sessile, somewhat oblique, with 4 or 5 pairs of 4-ranked scales, the end bud lacking. Leaf-scars alternate, 2-ranked, little raised, crescent-shaped or elliptical, small: bundle traces 3, more or less confluent: stipule-scars unequal, one elongated. (*Abelicea*).

Buds relatively large (2 × 3 mm.): glabrate. (1). Z. serrata.

Buds small (scarcely 1×1.5 mm.): pubescent. Z. crenata.

Winter-character references to Ulmaceae (except *Ulmus*):—*Aphananthe aspera*. Shirasawa, 265, pl. 8.—*Celtis australis*. Schneider, f. 166.—*C. occidentalis*. Blakeslee & Jarvis, 331, 464, pl.; Brendel, 27, 29, pl. 4; Hitchcock (1), 3; (3), 17; (4), 137, f. 88-9; Otis, 130; Schaffner, Ohio Naturlist, 2: 173; 3:328; Schneider, f. 136, 166—*C. sinensis*. Shirasawa, 263, pl. 8.—*Planera aquatica*. Schneider, f. 135.—*Zelkova serrata* (under various names).—Schneider, f. 2, 53, 166; Shirasawa, 267, pl. 9.

Zelkova has been much confused with other genera. For our purposes it differs in its 4- and not 2-ranked bud-scales from other Ulmaceae,—a family merged in the Urticaceae, with the Moraceae, by many botanists.

APHANANTHE.
(Family Ulmaceae.)

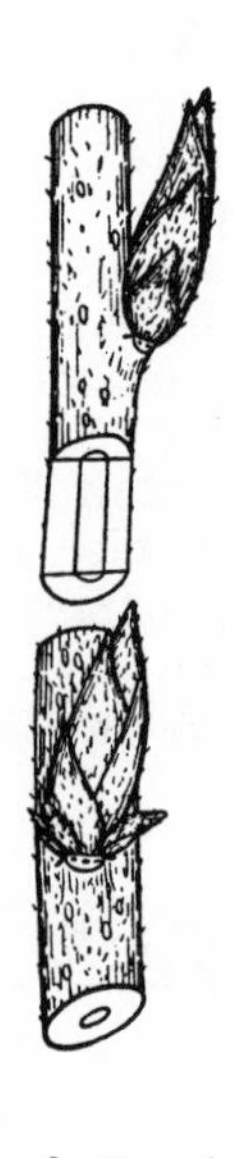

Trees: deciduous. Twigs slender, somewhat zig-zag, terete; pith small, rounded, continuous. Buds solitary or collaterally branching, ovoid-conical, sessile, the terminal lacking; their scales about half-a-dozen, 2-ranked. Leaf-scars alternate, 2-ranked, crescent-shaped, small, low: bundle-traces 3, indistinct: stipule-scars minute. References under *Zelkova.*

Twigs and buds somewhat rough-hairy. A. aspera.

Winter-character references to *Ulmus*: *Ulmus alata.* Blakeslee & Jarvis, 462; Brendel, pl. 4. *U. americana.* Blakeslee & Jarvis, 340, 460, pl.; Brendel, pl. 4; Otis, 126; Hitchcock (1), 3; (3), 17; (4), 137, f. 86-7; Smith, Ohio Naturalist, 5:315. *U. campestris.* Blakeslee & Jarvis, 340, 458, pl.; Bösemann, 69; Fant, 14, f. 5; Shirasawa, 265, pl. 9; Smith, Ohio Naturalist, 5:315; Ward, 1:181, f. 90; Willkomm, 4, 28, f. 33; Zuccarini, 19, pl. 11.—*U. fulva.* Blakeslee & Jarvis, 340, 456, pl.; Brendel, pl. 4; Hitchcock (1), 3; (3), 17; (4), 137, f. 83-5; Otis, 124; Smith, Ohio Naturalist, 5:315.—*U. glabra.* Bösemann, 69; Schneider, f. 153; Ward, 1:182, f. 91.—*U. laciniata.* Shirasawa, 266, pl. 9.—*U. laevis.* Bösemann, 69; Fant, 14; Schneider, f. 120, 153; Shirasawa, 266, pl. 9; Willkomm, 29, f. 35; Zuccarini, 20, pl. 11.—*U. parvifolia.* Shirasawa, 266.—*U. racemosa.* Blakeslee & Jarvis, 340, 462, pl.; Otis, 128; Smith, Ohio Nat., 5:315.—*U. suberosa.* Bösemann, 69; Fant, 14; Willkomm, 4, 29, f. 34.

GREVILLEA. Silk Oak.

(Family Proteaceae).

Tender rapid-growing trees. Twigs moderately stout, for a time rather irregularly fluted from the nodes: pith rather large, angled, continuous. Buds moderate, solitary, sessile or developing promptly at least into dwarf-branches, oblong, naked, very hairy. Leaf-scars alternate, round to transversely elliptical, deeply 3-lobed, somewhat raised at the lower margin: bundle-traces 3 compound groups: stipule-scars lacking.

Grevillea robusta, which is now one of the most commonly grown potted plants of the florist because of its ready cultivation and attractive fern-like foliage, has been much planted in dry tropical countries where it makes a modrately large open-topped shade- or avenue-tree. During the flowering season its large clusters of orange flowers are much frequented by certain birds which feed on the abundant nectar and the insects attracted by this. Its most obvious disqualification as a shade tree lies in the tenacity with which its foliage holds dust, so that except in the rainy season it is dingily gray rather than attractively green. In parts of Guatemala the silk oak has found favor as a cover-tree for coffee plantations which it shades adequately without depriving the crop of properly distributed direct sunshine.

Twigs and buds at first very red-hairy. G. robusta.

BUCKLEYA.

(Family Santalaceae).

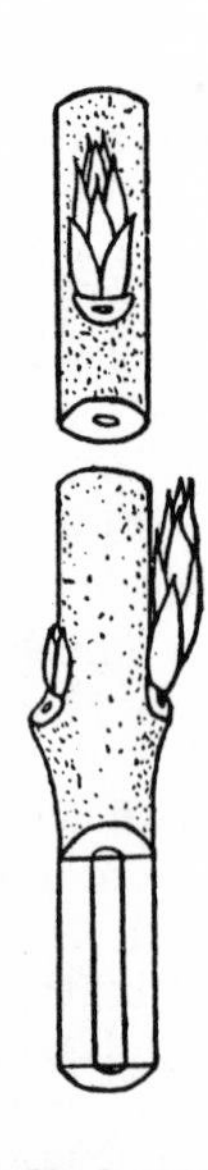

Shrubs, parasitic on *Tsuga*: deciduous. Twigs slender, forking, terete or obscurely 6-sided: pith rather small, somewhat angular, continuous, white. Buds solitary, moderate, sessile, oblong, appressed, with some 3 pairs of acute loose scales, the end-bud lacking. Leaf-scars opposite but by torsion standing nearly in 2 ranks instead of decussately in 4 ranks, small, half-round or broadly crescent-shaped, slightly raised: bundle-trace 1: stipule-scars lacking.

Buckleya affords one of the comparatively few illustrations of successful garden cultivation of a parasitic plant of large size. Like its close relative *Commandra*, though possessing foliage abundantly supplied with the mechanism for manufacturing carbohydrates through photosynthesis, as green plants ordinarily do, *Buckleya* appears to be incapable of existing without deriving mineral nutrients and perhaps some proteins from other plants. In this respect it is partially comparable with the mistletoes—belonging to the closely related family Loranthaceae, and other green parasites. It has long been grown successfully in the botanical garden of Harvard University under an old hemlock, to the roots of which it had attached itself.

Puberulent: buds straw-colored, glabrous. B. distichophylla.

PYRULARIA. Oil Nut.
(Family Santalaceae).

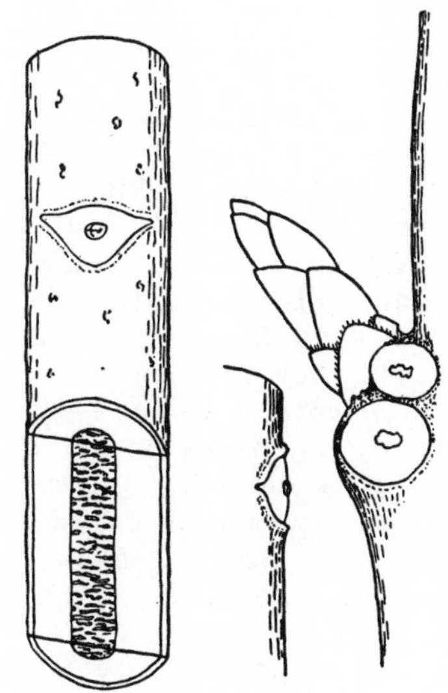

A shrub of the Appalachian mountains (other species Asiatic trees); deciduous. Twigs moderate, terete; pith moderate, white, transversely spongy. Buds not evident on the young growth, irregularly multiple in the old axils, sessile, conical-oblong, spreading, with half-a-dozen short ciliate scales at base and as many elongated green scales above, the end-bud lacking. Leaf-scars alternate, shield-shaped, little elevated; bundle-trace 1, round; stipule-scars lacking.

Like *Buckleya*, *Pyrularia* grows parasitically attached to hemlock roots. The large oily seeds are said to be poisonous to stock. Its anatomy is discussed by Behm in vol. 62 of the Botanisches Centralblatt.

Twigs olive-brown. (1). P. pubera.

ARISTOLOCHIA. Dutchman's Pipe.
(Family Aristolochiaceae).

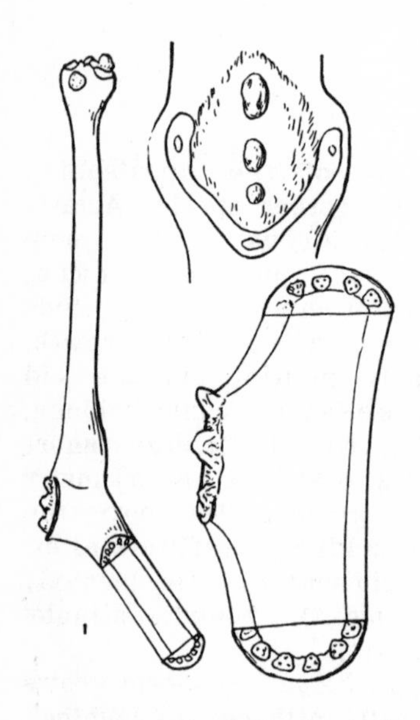

Soft-wooded twiners: deciduous. Stems terete, green, swollen at the nodes: wood with large diffused ducts and broad medullary rays: pith large, rounded, continuous, pale. Buds small, sessile, rounded, superposed on a silky area in arch of the leaf-scar, with 1 silky scale, the end-bud lacking. Leaf-scars alternate, U-shaped, somewhat raised: bundle-traces 3: stipule-scars lacking.

The Dutchman's Pipe is one of many plants in which axillary buds are not to be seen until after the leaves have fallen. This is not because they are absent or sunken in or covered by the bark, but because, like those of *Platanus*, *Cladrastis* and other genera, they are enclosed in a cup-like enlargement of the petiole base. When the leaf is removed, or after it has fallen, this is quite evident, though the *Aristolochia* buds are small and less easily seen than those of *Platanus* or *Cladrastis*. Like those of the latter, they are not solitary in the axil, but in a series of several superposed one above the other. In a paper on such serial buds published in 1884, Velenovsky showed that this multiplicity of buds produced above ground is not shared by subterranean buds, which are solitary, in *Aristolochia*.

Stem glabrous. (1). A. macrophylla.
Stem puberulent. A. tomentosa.

COCCOLOBA. Sea Grape.
(Family Polygonaceae).

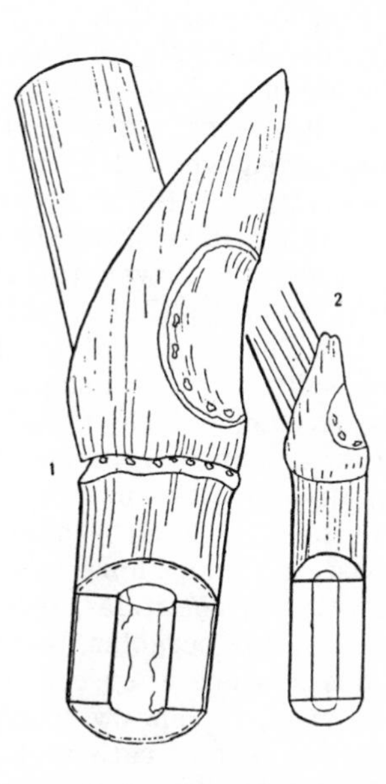

Tender trees: evergreen. Twigs moderate, more or less grooved or nearly terete: pith round, in some species continuous, in others spongily excavated between the nodes. Buds solitary, sessile, concealed by the leaf-base, naked. Leaf-scars alternate, large and nearly round, with 3 or 5 bundle-traces: not on the stem, but on a persistent sheath (ochrea) that encircles the stem and finally falls from an annular scar, corresponding to the usual stipular scars. Leaves simple, entire. (*Coccolobis*).

Like *Ficus*, *Magnolia* and *Platanus*, *Coccoloba* shows on the older twigs a series of scars which run entirely around or encircle the stem, but it differs from these and all other genera considered in this book in that these do not appear immediately after the leaves have fallen, but later. The thick base of the petiole here disarticulates from the sheathing stipules—or ochreae as they have been called in this family—by a clean-cut abscission, and it is only much later that the ochrea itself separates with an equally clean-cut scar, remaining for a time loosely about the twig before finally disappearing.

Twigs rather stout: pith excavated. (Seaside grape).
(1). C. uvifera.

Twigs rather slender: pith continuous. (Pigeon plum).
(2). C. floridana.

BOUGAINVILLEA.
(Family Nyctaginaceae).

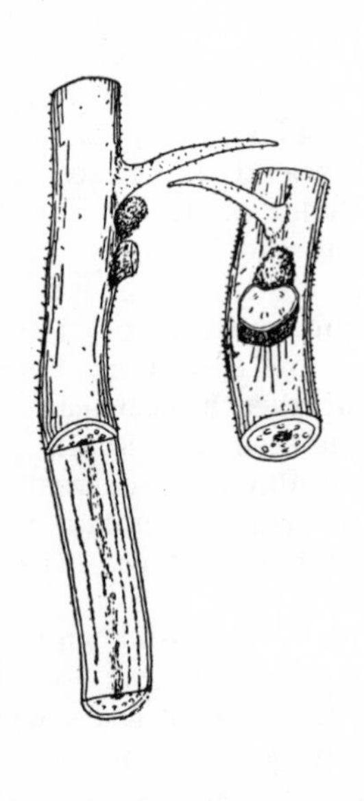

Scrambling shrubs, often climbing to considerable heights where hardy: deciduous. Shoots moderate, terete becoming irregularly angular or ridged when dry: pith minute, indistinct. Buds superposed, the upper developing into a curved spine, the lower rather small, ovoid or oblong, hairy, with 2 exposed scales. Leaf-scars alternate, broadly crescent-shaped to nearly round, much raised: bundle-traces about 5, very indistinct: stipule-scars lacking.

Bougainvilleas, which produce thick almost tree-like short basal trunks in tropical countries, form brilliant covers for pergolas, walls or even houses where they can be used in the open, the showy bracts that surround their rather inconspicuous flowers ranging from magenta to terra-cotta.

In common with other woody members of their family, they produce several zones of woody bundles between the pith and cortex of the stem, these occurring in a mass of conjunctive tissue as it has been called. The result is an appearance somewhat like that of a monocotyledonous or "endogenous" stem, in cross section. The literature of this, and of comparable anatomical facts of other families, has been assembled in Solereder's compendious Systematic Anatomy of the Dicotyledons.

Very hairy, scrambling. B. spectabilis.
Glabrate, more bushy. (1). B. glabra.

EUPTELEA.

(Family Trochodendraceae).

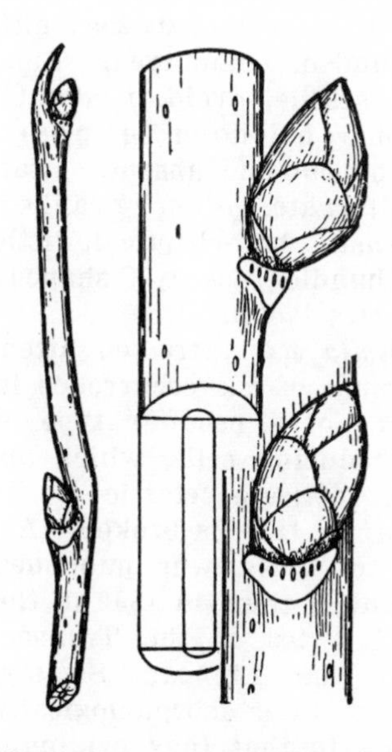

Shrubs or small trees: deciduous. Twigs moderate or rather slender, terete, somewhat zig-zag: pith rather small, firm, continuous, greenish. Buds solitary, sessile, ovoid, moderate, with half-a-dozen blunt glossy scales, sparingly hairy at base: end-bud lacking. Leaf-scars alternate, 2-ranked, moderate, broadly crescent-shaped, little raised: bundle-traces 7, relatively small: stipule-scars lacking.

Euptelea, like *Cercidiphyllum* and *Eucommia*, is an anomalous genus. evidently related to the Magnoliaceae but not fitting into that family without doing violence to its usual association of characters. Unlike the genera usually taken to represent the Magnoliaceae, this does not produce stipules, so that its twigs lack the narrow scars that characterize the nodes of *Magnolia*, *Michelia* and *Liriodendron*, and the horizontal series of bundle-traces in its leaf-scar suggests rather a broken composite group than either of the usual magnoliaceous types. The winter-characters of *E. polyandra* are described and figured by Shirasawa, p. 257, pl. 7.

Though of rather recent introduction and rarely seen, *Euptelea* is proving fairly hardy and is likely to find extended use where open round-topped trees are desired.

Glabrate: buds glossy chestnut. E. polyandra.

EUCOMMIA.
(Family Eucommiaceae).

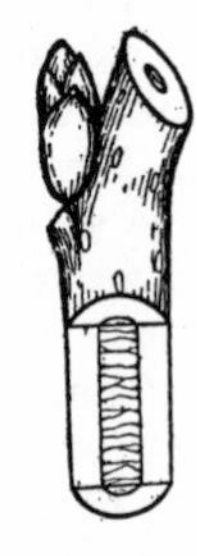

Tree: deciduous. Twigs moderate, terete, somewhat zig-zag: pith pale, rounded, chambered. Buds solitary, sessile, ovoid, moderate, with some half-dozen exposed scales, the end-bud absent. Leaf-scars alternate, often 2-ranked, rather small, half-elliptical, little raised: bundle-trace 1, C-shaped: stipule-scars lacking.

Eucommia has attracted attention because of the occurrence in its organs of a peculiar type of rubber-producing cells, which appear as delicate elastic cords when leaf or twig is broken. According to Weiss, who published an account of them in 1892 in the botanical series of the Transactions of the Linnean Society, these cells differ morphologically from the latex tissue of other plants in that they originate here from new initials in the developing organs, while in other cases their development is progressive and continuous from a few initial cells formed in the embryo.

The name *ulmoides* is given because of the elm-like habit of growth of the tree, which is of recent introduction but is proving hardy and so is likely to find an extended use. Though no industrial application may be made of it, the fact that *Eucommia* contains rubber is not to be overlooked at a time when every possible source of that essential substance is being investigated.

Glabrous: twigs red-brown, with pale lenticels. E. ulmoides.

CERCIDIPHYLLUM.

(Family Cercidiphyllaceae).

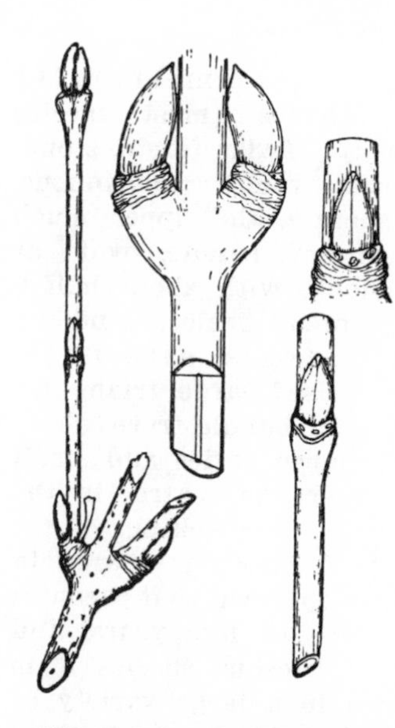

Rather small finely branched trees: deciduous. Twigs terete, slender, swollen at the nodes: pith small, creamy, somewhat angular, continuous. Buds moderate, solitary, often developing into short spurs, oblong, pointed, appressed, with 1 exposed scale standing next the stem, the end-bud lacking. Leaf-scars opposite, or 4 ranked if separate, crescent shaped, raised, deciduous at end of the first winter: bundle-traces 3: stipule-scars lacking.—Sometimes placed in the family Trochodendraceae.

One of the most dainty fine-twigged trees of relatively recent introduction, this shares with the two preceding genera a combination of characters which have subjected its systematic position to great and fluctuating uncertainty. Unlike the first, which remains in the Trochodendraceae, this genus possesses a suggestion of affinity to the Hamamelidaceae; the prevailing disposition has been to erect for it a distinct family, and to leave it in juxtaposition to the Trochodendraceae. As in the two genera here considered, and unlike the other genera referred to that family, its wood consists in part of true ducts. Its winter-characters are described and figured by Schneider, f. 92, 135; and Shirasawa, 275, pl. 11.

Glabrous: buds red. C. japonicum.

PAEONIA. Paeony.

(Family Ranunculaceae).

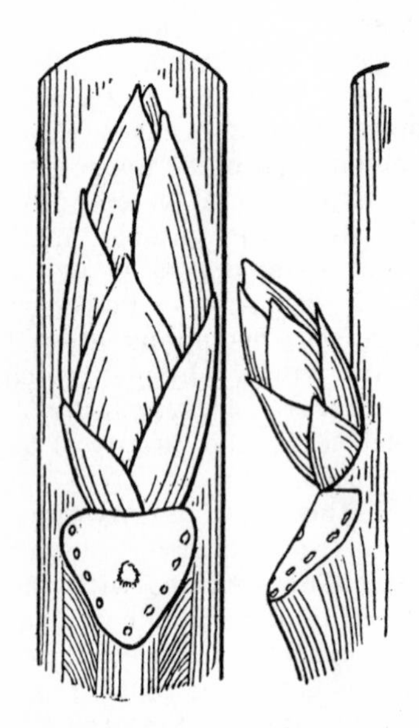

Small unsymmetrically branched shrubs (most species herbaceous). Twigs terete, stout: pith large, round, continuous. Buds moderate, the upper much larger, solitary, sessile, ovoid or rather oblong, with about half-a-dozen pointed scales, end-bud lacking. Leaf-scars alternate, somewhat raised, large, triangular or half-round: bundle traces about 7 in a U-shaped series and small with a larger one central in the scar: stipule-scars lacking.

The tree paeony has shared in the popular approval that paeonies have received of late years, and like the herbaceous species it is now grown in a large variety of forms which differ greatly in their flowers.

Paeonia differs from other Ranunculaceae in having the septa between the ends of the cells that forms its ducts perforated by a series of transverse slits (scalariform perforations), the cross-wall disappearing entirely in other genera. Its winter-characters are figured by Schneider, p. 119, f. 121.

Buds more or less rosy: glabrous. (Tree paeony).
P. suffruticosa.

ZANTHORHIZA. Yellowroot.

(Family Ranunculaceae).

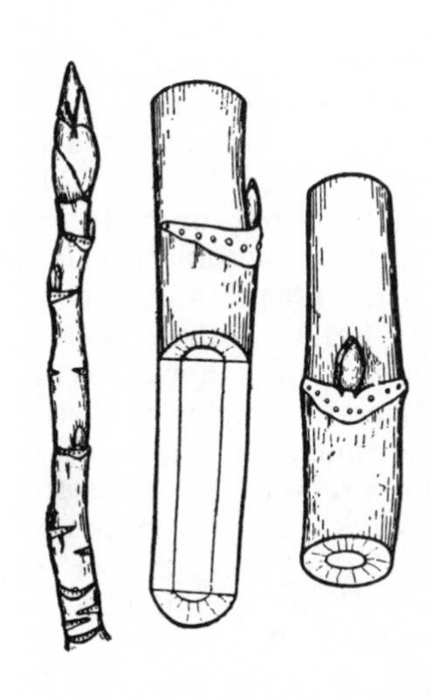

Small little-branched shrubs, lemon-yellow when cut. Wood tangentially diffused-porous: medullary rays coarse. Twigs terete, moderate, very smooth: pith relatively large, rounded, continuous. Buds very unequal: the lateral solitary, sessile, ovoid-oblong, much compressed and flattened against the stem, with about 3 exposed blunt scales; the terminal much larger, fusiform, terete, with about 5 retuse mucronate scales. Leaf-scars alternate, low, shallowly U-shaped, more than half-encircling the twig: bundle-traces about 11; stipule-scars lacking.

The enlargement of the leaf-base so as to embrace a large part of the circumference of the stem, as in *Aralia*, *Nandina*, etc., and the yellow coloration of the cut tissues, form ready aids to the determination of yellow-root. Though low and lacking the graceful branching of many plants, its foliage is pleasing, and it merits more general planting than it receives. Its winter-characters are described and figured by Schneider, p. 119, f. 121.

Glabrous: twigs gray: buds red-brown. Z. apiifolia.

CLEMATIS. Virgin's Bower.
(Family Ranunculaceae).

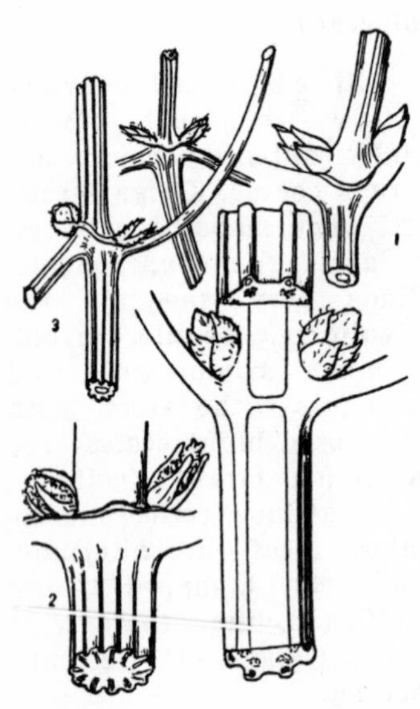

Soft-wooded climbers. Shoots 6- or 12-angled over the vascular bundles, with cavities in the cortex under the ridges, straw-colored or brown: pith angled or star-shaped, white, continuous with thin firmer diaphragms at the nodes, or said to be excavated between them in *C. Vitalba.* Buds rather small, ovoid or flattened, sessile, solitary, or superposed in *C. recta*, with 1-3 pairs of exposed somewhat hairy scales. Leaves not disarticulating, though dying, with prehensile petioles or petiolules: no stipules or stipule-scars.

Winter-character references:—*C. japonica.* Shirasawa, 281, pl. 12. *C. recta.* Velenovsky (paper on superposed buds published at Prag in 1884) Botanisches Centralblatt, 26:10.—*C. vitalba.* Bösemann, 40; Schneider, f. 121; Willkomm, 7.—*C. viticella.* Bösemann, 40.

1. Stem glaucous and glabrous. 2.
   Stem not glaucous. 3.
2. Stem 6-sided, brown. (1). C. verticillaris.
   Stem 6-ridged, gray. C. texensis.
3. Stem straw-colored, 12-or 18-ridged. (2). C. paniculata.
   Stem brown, the 6 primary ridges stronger. 4.
4. Stem glabrate. (3). × C. Jackmanni.
   Stem more or less hairy. 5.
5. Finely pubescent. (4). C. virginiana.
   Rather woolly at the nodes. C. Pitcheri.

DECAISNEA.
(Family Lardizabalaceae).

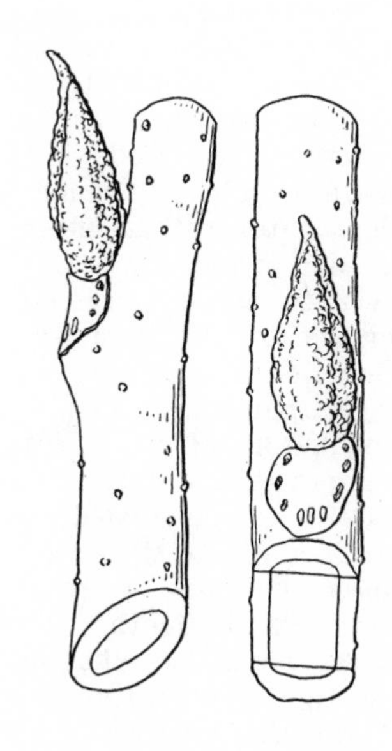

Loosely branched large glabrous shrubs: deciduous. Twigs coarse, terete: pith large, homogeneous, roundish, pale. Buds solitary, sessile, large, ovoid-acuminate, suberect or appressed, obtusely somewhat 2-edged, with 2 scales, the end-bud lacking. Leaf-scars alternate, low, shield-shaped, very large, with 7-9 bundle-traces: stipule-scars lacking

Decaisnea and the two following genera, with four others, are now admitted to constitute a natural family, named after the genus *Lardizabala.* The affinities of the plants are such, however, that those now placed in the Lardizabalaceae have found earlier classification in the related families Berberidaceae and Menispermaceae.

Twigs buff: buds glaucous, coarsely wrinkled. D. Fargesii.

STAUNTONIA.
(Family Lardizabalaceae).

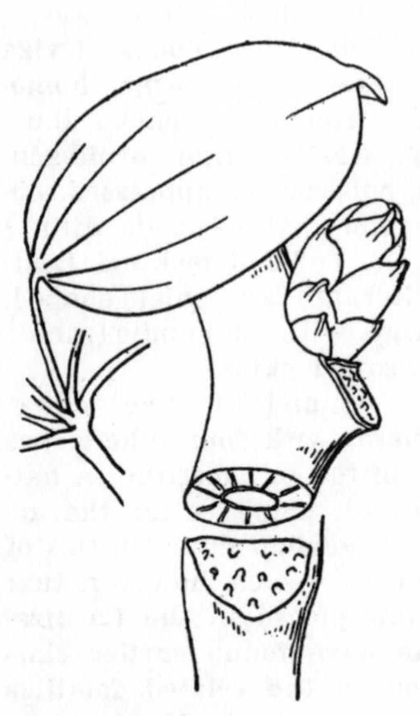

Strong woody twiners, some times cut back and grown in bush form: evergreen. Stems terete, moderate: pith moderate, continuous, at first white. Buds moderate, sessile, ovoid, with some 8 ovate mucronate rather fleshy scales, the end-bud lacking. Leaf-scars alternate, deeply crescent-shaped or half-round, somewhat raised: bundle-traces numerous, scattered: stipule-scars lacking. Leaves long-petioled, digitate, with about 6 long-stalked elliptical entire leaflets with channeled abruptly short-acuminate tip.

Stauntonia becomes a high-climbing vine in the South. It is grown as far north as Washington, where, in the Botanical Garden, its branches are cut back though the trunk is not killed. In foliage it is quite unlike any other shrub hardy in the same latitude.

Stems green, glabrous: leaves paler beneath. S. hexaphylla.

AKEBIA.
(Family Lardizabalaceae).

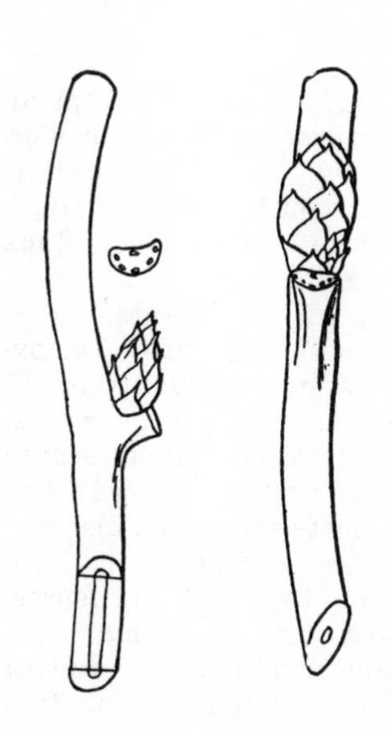

Woody twiners: deciduous in the North. Stems terete, slender: pith small, continuous and homogeneous, pale. Buds rather small, sometimes branching from the axils of their lower scales, sessile, ovoid, subacute, with a dozen or more ovate mucronate scales. Leaf-scars alternate, half elliptic, much-raised: bundle-traces half-a-dozen in a broken ellipse (reduced to 3 at level of the stem): stipule-scars lacking.

Winter-character references to *Akebia* are to be found in Schneider, f. 148 (*A. quinata*); and Shi rasawa, p. 261, pl. 7 (*A. quinata* and *A. lobata*).

Stems green becoming brown, glabrous. A. quinata.

MENISPERMACEAE.

Winter-character references to Menispermaceae:—*Cocculus carolinus* (*C. virginica*). Schneider, f. 65. *C. Thunbergii.* Shirasawa, 259, pl. 7. *Menispermum canadense.* Bösemann, 43; Hitchcock (3), 8, (4), 134, f. 4-9; Schaffner, Ohio Naturalist, 6:506; Schneider, f. 65. *M. davuricum.* Shirasawa, 259, pl. 7.

NANDINA.
(Family Berberidaceae).

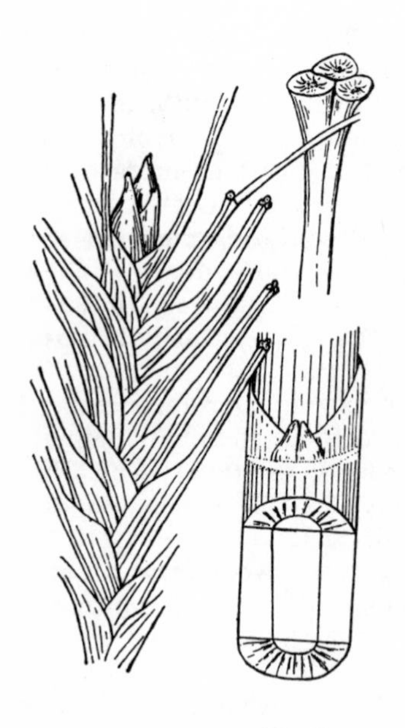

Shrubs, rather simple except at base: evergreen. Twigs moderate, rounded, the bark yellow when cut: pith rather large, round, white, continuous. Buds solitary, sessile, the lateral small, triangular, with 2 valvate scales, and to be seen only after removing the leaf-bases; the terminal larger, ovoid, with 3 or 4 scales. Leaf-scars lacking, the alternate dilated imbricated nerved amplexicaul leaf-bases not disarticulating, the persistent petioles enlarged at top with 3 depressions, each corresponding to a fallen leaflet and with a central bundle-trace: stipules lacking. Leaves ternate, each primary division odd-pinnate with several lanceolate acute entire leaflets, or again ternately parted.

Glabrous: leaflets acute at both ends, arcuately 3-nerved.
N. domestica.

BERBERIS. Barberry.
(Family Berberidaceae).

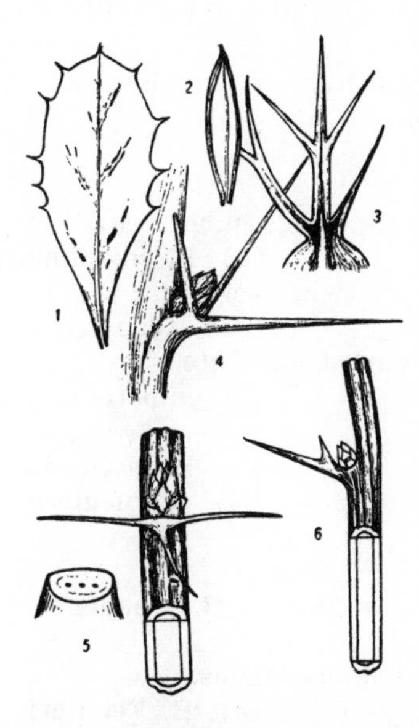

Shrubs, mostly with branched leaf-spines subtending short spurs on which the foliage-leaves are fascicled. Wood and pith often greenish or bright yellow. Twigs mostly sulcate, rather slender: pith relatively large, round, continuous. Buds rather small, solitary, sessile, ovoid, with about half-a-dozen pointed scales and, on spurs, the dilated bases of several leaves of the season; alternate, like the spines. Leaf-scars small, at top of the broad persistent leaf-bases, half-round: bundle-traces 3, minute, often indistinct: stipule-scars lacking.

The barberries, long represented in gardens by the single European species *Berberis vulgaris*, have come into popularity of recent years through the introduction of numerous Asiatic species of which the compact-gowing *B. Thunbergii* is now al most universally planted for low hedges and masses. Fortunately, this species does not serve as an alternate host for the black- or stem-rust of wheat, as *B. vulgaris* does, so that in the prevalent crusade against the latter it may be spared safely; and it may be added that the common barberry possesses no properties which particularly justify its retention as a cultivated plant.

It is to be noted that the evergreen Mahonias, sometimes referred to the genus *Berberis*, share with the common barberry susceptibility to the black-rust (*Puccinia graminis*).

Winter-characters of *Berberis Thunbergii* or *B. vulgaris* are given by Bösemann, 48; Fant, 26, f. 24; Schneider, f. 80; Shirasawa, 49, pl. 5; Ward, 1:200, f. 101; and Willkomm, 45, f. 76.

1. More or less evergreen: twigs brownish or purplish. 2.
   Foliage promptly deciduous. 6.
2. Twigs pubescent. 3.
   Twigs glabrous. 4.
3. Leaves broad (10-20 mm.), toothed: twigs puberulent. (1). B. concinna.
   Leaves narrow (2-4 mm.), entire: twigs velvety. (2). B. stenophylla.
4. Leaves very narrow (2 mm.), entire, revolute. B. empetrifolia.
   Leaves broader. 5.
5. Twigs angled, not roughened. B. buxifolia.
   Twigs not angled, granular. B. verruculosa.
6. Twigs glabrous. 7.
   Twigs pubescent. 13.
7. Twigs finely very warty, slightly angled. B. canadensis.
   Twigs not or scarcely roughened. 8.
8. Spine-branches mostly 5-7, often dichotomous. (3). B. Fendleri.
   Spine-branches 1 or mostly 3, simple. 9.
9. Spines long (20-40 mm.), terete. (4). B. Julianae.
   Spines shorter (15 mm.), grooved or dilated. 10.
10. Twigs gray or buff. (Barberry). (5). B. vulgaris.
    Twigs red or orange, or brown or purple. 11.
11. Twigs somewhat glaucous. B. koreana.
    Twigs not glaucous. 12.
12. Compact and low-spreading. (6). B. Thunbergii.
    Bushy and rather tall. B. Sieboldii.
13. Twigs reddish, very minutely puberulent. B. aggregata.
    Twigs buff or gray, dingy-velvety. B. brachypoda.

MAHONIA. Evergreen Barberry.
(Family Berberidaceae).

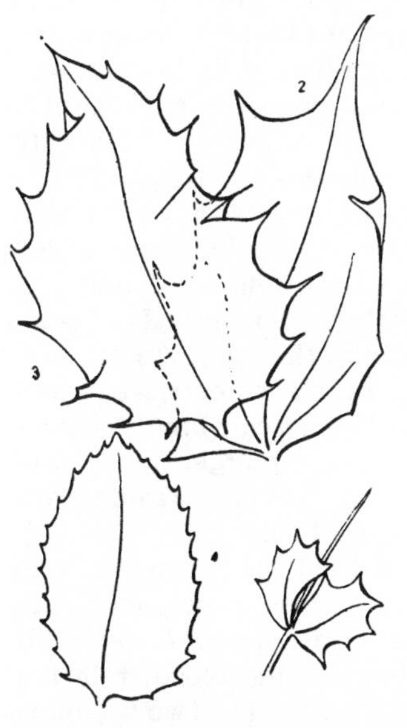

Mostly low and sparingly branched shrubs: evergreen. Twigs roundish, relatively stout: pith comparatively large, pale, continuous. Buds alternate, rather small except for the terminal one which is ovoid with half-a-dozen exposed scales. Leaf-scars narrow, low, half-encircling the stem: bundle-traces about 9. Leaves alternate, pinnately compound, pungently toothed: stipules and stipule-scars lacking. (*Odostemon; Berberis*).

Though less hardy than the true barberries, the Mahonias are cultivated to a considerable extent. Sometimes their leaves are affected by cluster-cup fungi, and when this is the case they are serving as alternate host for the black-rust of wheat (*Puccinia graminis*).

1. Leaves hard and coriaceous. 2.
   Leaves rather thin and membranaceous. 5.
2. Leaflets 3-or 5-nerved at base. 4.
   Leaflets 1-nerved. 3.
3. Leaflets small. (1). M. Fendleri.
   Leaflets large, netted-veined beneath. M. dictyota.
4. With long persistent bud-scales at base. M. nervosa.
   Without conspicuous scales at base. (2). M. japonica.
5. Leaflets large: habit erect. (3). M. Aquifolium.
   Leaflets moderate: low. (4). M. repens.

MAHOBERBERIS. Hybrid Barberry. (Family Berberidaceae).

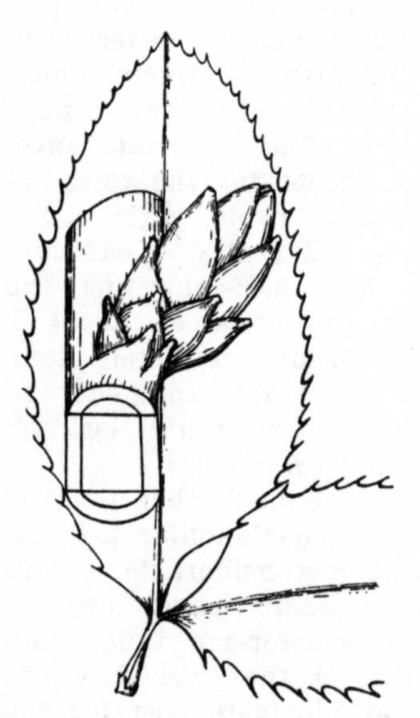

Rather low and sparingly branched shrubs: subevergreen. Twigs roundish, relatively stout: pith relatively large, pale, continuous. Buds alternate, moderate, solitary, sessile, with half-a-dozen or so loose gray scales, usually developing into short spurs covered by the long-persistent basally dilated petioles. Leaf-scars terminating the persistent petioles, half-round, sometimes paired, with indistinct bundle-traces. Leaves papery, pungently serrate, mostly of 1 leaflet: stipules and stipule-scars lacking.

This hybrid between a true barberry (*Berberis vulgaris*) and a *Mahonia* (*M. Aquifolium*) indicates clearly the close relationship between the two groups, which on technical characters are combined in the genus *Berberis* by many conservative botanists. Such botanists write its name × *Berberis Neuberti.* When species belonging to different genera hybridize, as here, it will be found that the genera commonly differ by relatively small or instable technical characters. If, however, they are maintained as distinct, their hybrid progeny pertains to neither in fact. For this reason, as in the present case, a bigeneric hybrid is given a generic name different from that of either parent, by those who believe in the generic separability of the parents.

Glabrous: leaves exceeding the petioles. × M. Neuberti.

MENISPERMUM. Moonseed.
(Family Menispermaceae).

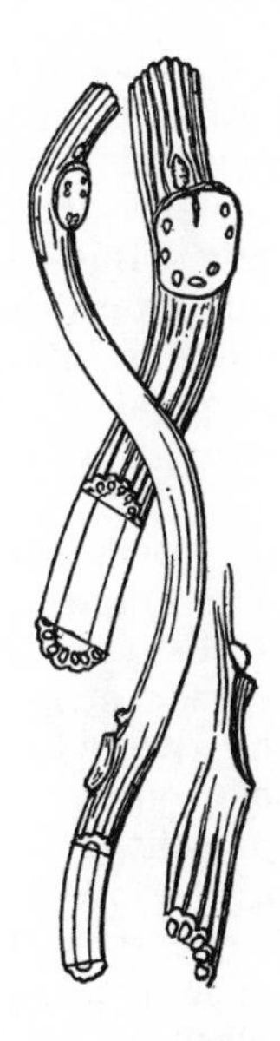

Woody twiners: deciduous. Twigs terete, fluted, rather slender: pith relatively large, continuous and homogeneous, white. Buds small, hairy, superposed with the uppermost quickly developing into an inflorescence and the others covered by the leaf-scar, with about 3 scarcely distinguishable scales. Leaf-scars alternate, elliptical, raised and concave: bundle-traces 3 or divided into about 7: stipule-scars lacking. Fruit, when present, with a ring-like or crescent-shaped stone keeled on the back.

Winter characters to the family are given under *Akebia*.

Twigs green becoming buff, glabrescent. M. canadense.

COCCULUS. Carolina Moonseed.
(Family Menispermaceae).

Winter-characters of *Menispermum*, but the fruit, when present, with the crescent-shaped stone with cross-ridges.

Twigs, like the buds, loosely hairy. C. carolinus.

CALYCOCARPUM. Cupseed.
(Family Menispermaceae).

Winter-characters of *Menispermum*, but the fruit, when present, with deep cup-like stone.

Twigs, like the buds, loosely hairy. C. carolinus.

LIRIODENDRON. Tulip Tree. "Poplar." (Family Magnoliaceae).

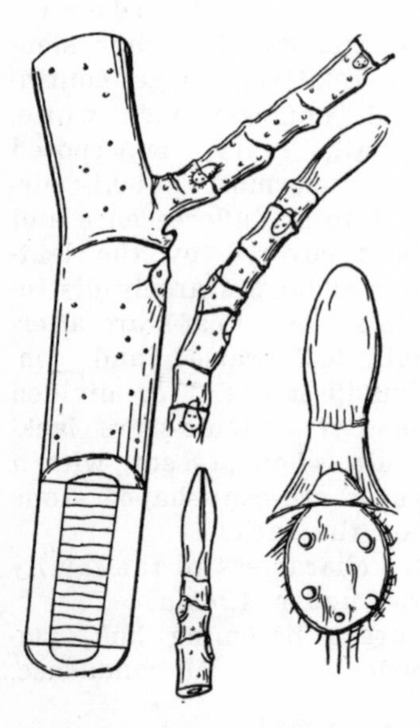

Large trees: deciduous. Twigs aromatic, moderate, terete: wood green: pith rounded, pale, continuous, with firmer diaphragms at short intervals. Buds solitary or superposed, the lateral or lower small, rounded and sessile or indistinct, the terminal larger, oblong and somewhat stalked, compressed or 2-edged, with 2 valvate scales. Leaf-scars alternate, rather large, round, low: bundle-traces a dozen or more in an irregular ellipse or scattered: stipule-scars linear, encircling the twig. Fruit, in the form of cone-like aggregates, is often present in winter.

The bark of *Liriodendron* is strikingly different from that of any other common tree in being longitudinally fissured with connecting cross-strands, so as to suggest a series of parallel mountain ridges with deep gullies in their sides. The flattened winter buds are favorite objects for easy dissection. Each is enclosed by a pair of scales representing the stipules of the lowermost leaf of the next year: these separate easily at their edges and when removed reveal the leaf. The process may be continued several times. At the center, if the bud be a flower-bud, rudiments of this organ are to be seen in a fair stage of development.—References under *Schizandra.*

Glabrous: twigs and buds glossy red- or purplish-brown.
L. Tulipifera.

MAGNOLIA.
(Family Magnoliaceae).

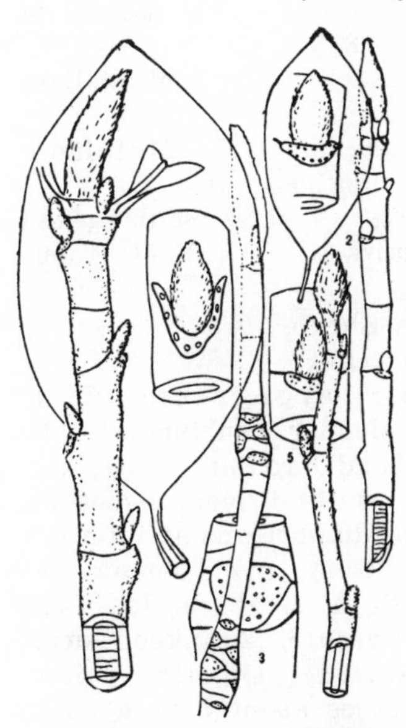

Trees or shrubs: deciduous or evergreen. Twigs somewhat aromatic, moderate or stout, or less commonly slender, subterete: pith rather large, continuous, round, sometimes with firmer diaphragms. Buds solitary, ovoid or fusiform, sessile, the terminal sometimes enlarged or the lateral greatly reduced, with a single scale keeled and with a scar on its back. Leaf-scars alternate, commonly 2-ranked, moderate or small, round to U-shaped, low: bundle-traces numerous and scattered: stipule-scars linear, encircling the twig. Leaves, when persistent, simple and entire.

Winter-character references to *Liriodendron* and *Magnolia* under *Schizandra*.

1. Essentially evergreen: firm plates of pith evident. 2.
   Deciduous: pith diaphragms often sparse. 3.
2. Leaves thick: twigs rusty-pubescent (1). M. grandiflora.
   Leaves thin or falling: twigs silvery. (2). M. glauca.
3. Leaf-scars clustered on annual swellings. 4.
   Leaf-scars not clustered: lateral buds evident. 6.
4. Glabrous and glaucous: twigs often slender. (3). M. Fraseri.
   Puberulent, or twigs stouter. 5.
5. Glabrous except near the end-bud.
   (Umbrella magnolia). M. tripetala
   Downy: twigs very stout.
   (Great-leaved magnolia). M. macrophylla.

6. Leaf-scars U-shaped. (4). M. acuminata.
   Leaf-scars broadly crescent-shaped. 7.
7. End-bud slender: glabrous. M. salicifolia.
   End-bud mostly enlarged: hairy. 8.
8. Low shrub: twigs slender, brown. M. stellata.
   Large shrubs or small trees. 9.
9. Twigs green, slender. (Purple magnolia). M. liliflora.
   Twigs brown, dotted with white lenticels. 10.
10. Pubescence of buds rather short. × M. Soulangeana.
    Flower-buds with long coarse hairs. (5). M. Kobus.

MICHELIA. Banana Shrub.
(Family Magnoliaceae).

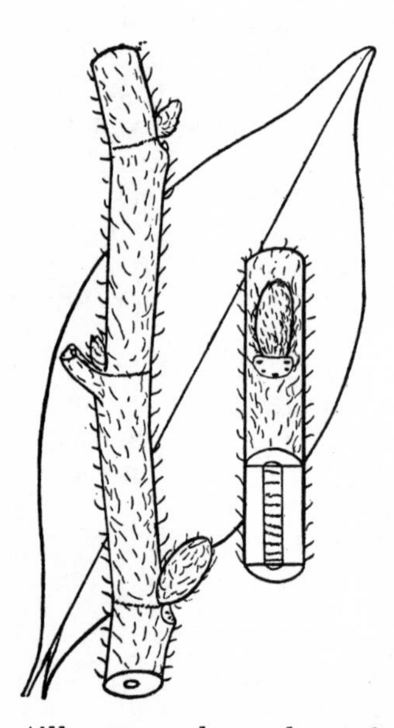

Shrubs: evergreen. Twigs rather slender, subterete: pith rather small, round, white, continuous, with firmer sometimes brownish diaphragms at intervals. Buds, solitary, ovoid-oblong, sessile, with a single scale. Leaf-scars alternate, 2-ranked, small, half-round, slightly raised: bundle-traces about 5 in a single series, or less definitely fixed if more numerous: stipule-scars linear, encircling the twig, but usually concealed by pubescence. Leaves oblanceolate-obovate, bluntly mucronate, entire, veiny beneath.

Though now considered to be a distinct genus, *Michelia* has been placed in *Magnolia* by many writers, and the banana shrub is still commonly spoken of as a species of *Magnolia*.

Twigs and buds very golden-rusty. M. fuscata.

SCHIZANDRA.
(Family Magnoliaceae).

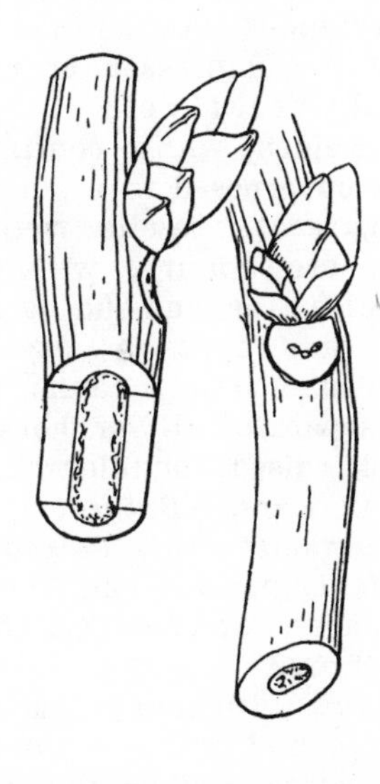

Woody twiners: deciduous. Stems moderate, terete, aromatic: pith moderate, browning and becoming spongily excavated. Buds moderate, collaterally multiole in the axils of their lower scales, sessile, elongated-ovoid, acute, with some 6 or 8 ciliolate scales. Leaf-scars alternate half-round, scarcely raised: bundle-traces 3, clustered: stipule-scars lacking.

Schizandra differs from the preceding Magnoliaceae in the conspicuous characters of being a climbing shrub and of lacking the annular stipule-scars that so distinctly mark *Magnolia, Michelia* and *Liriodendron*; and on technical characters it is placed in a different section of the family.

The winter-characters of *S. chinensis* have been studied by Schneider, f. 92; and Shirasawa, 261, pl. 7. Other winter-character references:—*Liriodendron Tulipifera.* Blakeslee & Jarvis, 330, 474, pl.; Bösemann, 61; Brendel, 30, pl. 3; Otis, 136; Schneider, f. 108. *Magnolia acu minata.* Blakeslee & Jarvis, 340, 470, pl.; Schneider, f. 42, 108 *M. denudata* (*M. conspicua; M. Yulan*). Blakeslee & Jarvis, 470. *M. glauca* (*M. virginica*). Blakeslee & Jarvis, 340, 470. *M. hypoleuca.* Shirasawa, 242, pl. 3. *M. Kobus.* Shirasawa, 241, pl. 3. *M. macrophylla.* Blakeslee & Jarvis, 340, 470; Schneider, f. 3, 54. *M. liliflora* (*M. obovata; M. purpurea*). Schneider, f. 108; Shirasawa, 241, pl. 3. *M. tripetala* (*M Umbrella*). Blakeslee & Jarvis, 340, 472, pl.

Stems brown, glabrous. S. chinensis

CALYCANTHUS. Strawberry Shrub.
(Family Calycanthaceae).

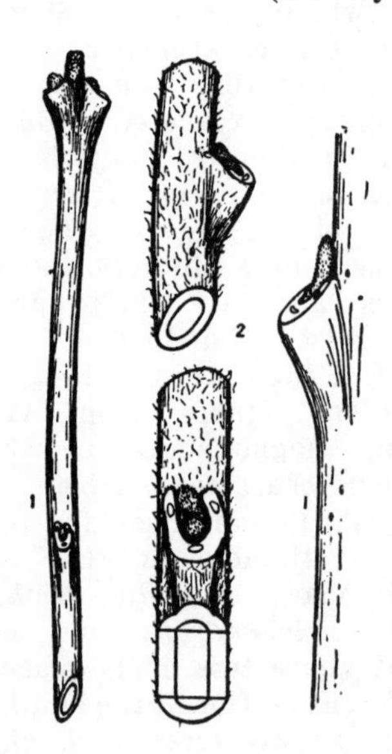

Sparingly branched aromatic shrubs: deciduous. Twigs moderately slender, compressed at the nodes: pith relatively large, somewhat 6-sided, white, continuous. Buds superposed in a single bud-like aggregate, sessile, round or oblong, brown-hairy, without evident scales, the end-bud lacking. Leaf-scars opposite, exceptionally twisted into 2 ranks or the pairs separated, U- or horseshoe-shaped, raised: bundle-traces 3: no stipule-scars. (*Butneria*).

Winter-characters of *Calycanthus fertilis*, *C. floridus* and *C. occidentalis* are contrasted by Schneider, f. 222.

Calycanthus, with many bracts, sepals, petals and stamens intergrading so as to confirm the impression that all are modified leaves, and lacking the definite arrangement in whorls that marks many flowers, in these respects presents a primitive floral type. On the other hand, as in a rose, the receptacle or end of the stem is produced into a deep cup on which these parts originate. Such cases furnish an argument against an opinion that the Dicotyledones are primarily divisible into axifloral and calycifloral groups.

1. Buds rounded. 2.
   Buds conical-oblong. (1). C. occidentalis.
2. Twigs more or less persistently villous. (2). C. floridus.
   Twigs glabrescent or puberulous. C. fertilis.

MERATIA.
(Family Calycanthaceae).

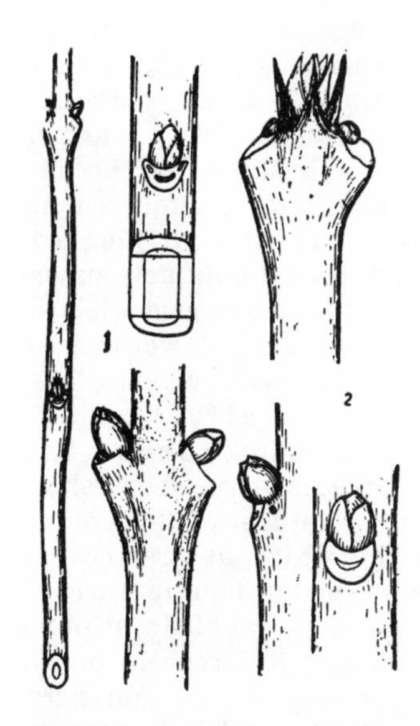

Aromatic shrubs: deciduous or partly evergreen. Twigs rather slender, somewhat 4-sided or 4-angled or roundish: pith moderate, somewhat 4- or 6-sided, white, continuous. Buds solitary or 2 superposed, sessile, subglobose, with about 2 pairs of evident scales, the end-bud lacking or loosely scaly. Leaf-scars opposite, half-round or broadly crescent-shaped, somewhat raised: bundle-trace 1, crescent-shaped, sometimes with a minute additional trace at each end: stipule-scars lacking. Frequently united with the genus *Calycanthus* or called *Chimonanthus*.

A structural anomaly in the Calycanthaceae is found in the occurrence of a series of four vascular bundles outside of the normal zone. *Meratia* differs from *Calycanthus* in its 4-sided inner zone, which is cylindrical in *Calycanthus*—a genus which has been compared in its cortical structure with the very distantly placed family Myrtaceae. Winter-characters of *Meratia praecox* are considered by Schneider, f. 222; and Shirasawa, 278, pl. 12.

Twigs and buds gray-buff. (1). M. praecox.
Twigs and buds brown. (2). M. retusa.

Winter-character references to *Asimina triloba*:—Brendel, 27, 30, pl. 4; Hitchcock (1), 4, f. 1, (3), 8, (4), 134, f. 1-3; Schneider, f. 92, 100. Wiesner shows that some Annonaceae afford illustrations of epitrophy.

ASIMINA. Papaw.
(Family Annonaceae).

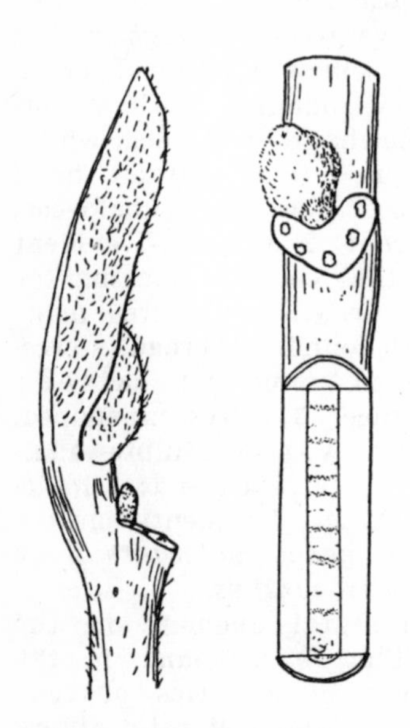

Small trees or arborescent shrubs: deciduous. Twigs rounded, moderate. Pith roundish, white, continuous with firmer greenish diaphragms, or becoming brownish and chambered in age. Terminal bud clearly naked, larger; the lateral obliquely superposed with the uppermost globose and stalked when a flower-bud or oblong and subsessile when a leaf-bud. Leaf-scars alternate, 2-ranked, half-round becoming broadly crescent- or horseshoe-shaped by rupture of the membranous top which at first covers the smaller buds: bundle-traces 5 or 7, sometimes doubled: stipule-scars lacking. References, p. 69.

The "papaw" of the northern States and the related custard apples, sweet-sops, sour-sops, cherimoyas, etc., of the tropics, which belong to the related genus *Annona*, illustrate a type of pith which recurs here and there (*e. g.* in *Magnolia* and *Nyssa*), in which cross-bands of firmer cells are found at intervals. In the present treatment continuous pith of this kind is spoken of as diaphragmed, in contrast with the chambered pith of *Juglans*, etc., where the cross-bands remain but the softer parts of the pith have disappeared. *Asimina* is somewhat puzzling in this respect, for the firm diaphragms are not always readily seen when a young twig is split.

Twigs and especially buds red-hairy. A. triloba.

CINNAMOMUM.
(Family Lauraceae).

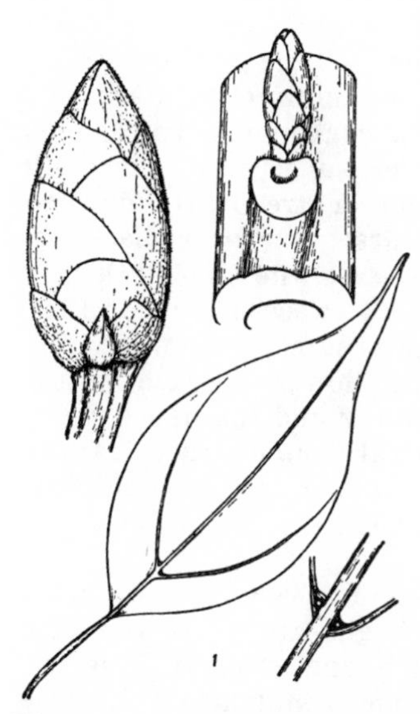

Small aromatic trees: evergreen. Twigs terete, or compressed at base, moderately stout or those developed from buds of the season slender: pith rather large, continuous, white. Buds solitary, ovoid, sessile or promptly developing so as to be stalked for a time, small and either naked or scaly, the terminal enlarged and with more numerous scales. Leaf-scars opposite or alternate in 4 ranks, half-round somewhat raised: bundle-scar 1, C-shaped: stipule-scars lacking. Leaves simple, entire, stalked.

The camphor tree has become frequent as a street tree in southern cities, where it thrives. The true Malayan cinnamon appears to be scarcely hardy in the United States, but the Chinese cassia-bark tree (*C. Cassia*) is said to stand frost and to be grown as a shade tree, and also for its cinnamon-flavored bark, etc., in Florida, where, as in southern California, several other species of the genus are planted.

Like many other genera which are confined to the tropics today, *Cinnamomum* was widespread in northern latitudes when circumpolar cold was less pronounced than it is now.

Buds scaly: leaves alternate: camphor-scented.
(Camphor). (1). C. Camphora.
Buds naked: leaves opposite: cinnamon-scented.
(Cinnamon). C. zeylanicum.

PERSEA.

(Family Lauraceae)

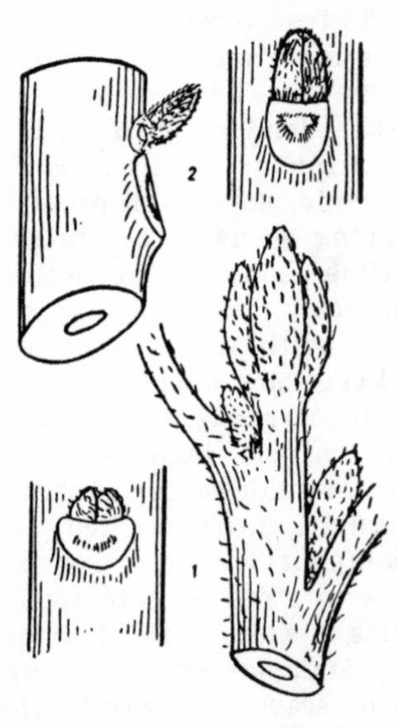

Shrubs or small or moderate-sized trees with aromatic bark: evergreen. Twigs moderate, 3-angled and minutely fluted: pith roundish, continuous, pale. Buds solitary or superposed, subsessile and ovoid or frequently developing the first year or replaced by peduncle-scars, the end-bud larger, with 3 or 4 exposed scales. Leaf-scars alternate, somewhat elevated, the lower of each season nearly linear and the upper round or elliptical: bundle-trace 1, transverse, compound: stipule-scars lacking. Leaves lanceolate, entire.

Of recent years the alligator pear, or aguacate as it is called in Mexico and Central America, has become a standard fruit tree of Florida and southern California. In our eastern markets, where the fruits have been sold from the West Indies for many years, they are familiar as large and pear-shaped, with smooth thin green skin. As offered at railroad stations in Mexico, they are much smaller and rather purple. In Guatemala they are very large, round and with thick skin.

1. Leaves golden-satiny beneath: small shrub. P. humilis.
   Leaves glabrate or loosely hairy: larger. 2.
2. Leaves honeycomb-pitted beneath. P. littoralis.
   Leaves not pitted. 3.
3. Leaves whitened beneath, not veiny. (1). P. borbonica.
   Leaves green, veiny. (Alligator pear). (2). P. gratissima.

SASSAFRAS. Sassafras.
(Family Lauraceae).

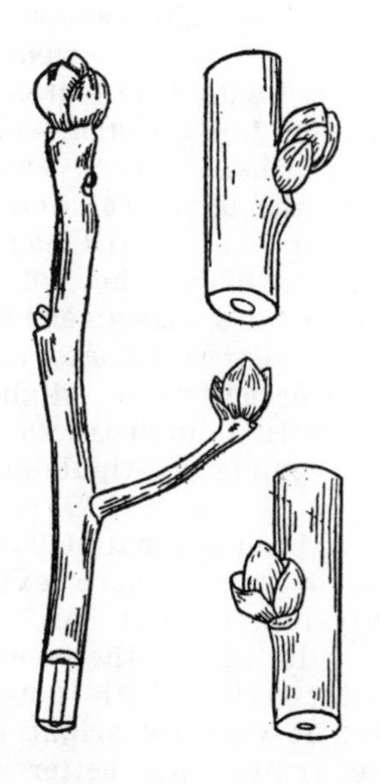

Aromatic tree or often forming dense masses of shrubbery: deciduous. Twigs green, glabrescent, rounded, moderate, often branching the first year. Pith moderate, somewhat 5-sided, white, continuous. Buds usually solitary, ovoid, sessile, subglobose; scales about 4, fleshy, rather keeled; the endbud somewhat larger. Leaf-scars small, half-round or crescent-shaped, somewhat raised: bundle-trace a transverse line more or less broken into 3: stipule-scars lacking.

The sassafras is one of the most easily recognized native trees in winter. Its rough bark, once known, is not easily forgotten. and its green mucilaginous spicy twigs are often corymbosely branched above the situation of the uppermost juncture or winter-node—marked by scars corresponding to the scales of the last winter bud. Its winter-characters are discussed by Blakeslee & Jarvis, 333, 476, pl.; Brendel, 30-32, pl. 3; Hitchcock (1); 5; Otis, 138; Schneider, f. 143.

Though only one *Sassafras* is known at present, 25 North American fossil species of the genus are included in Knowlton's catalogue of Cretaceous and Tertiary fossils published as Bulletin 152 of the United States Geological Survey. Lesquereux, however, in his Teritary Flora questions all but two.

Twigs not glaucous. S. variifolium.
Twigs glaucous. S. variifolium albidum.

BENZOIN. Spice Bush.
(Family Lauraceae).

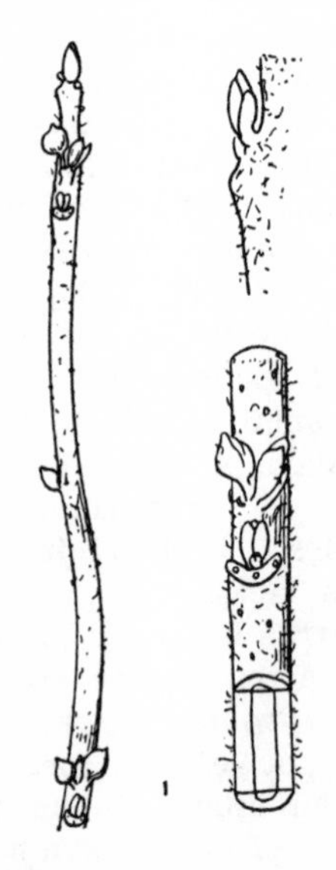

Spicily aromatic shrubs: deciduous. Twigs rounded, slender, green or olive with pale lenticels: pith relatively large, round, white, continuous. Buds rather small, superposed, the upper collaterally producing green ovoid again stalked flower-buds, the foliage buds with about 3 scales: end-bud lacking. Leaf-scars alternate, crescent-shaped or half-round, slightly raised, small: bundle-traces 3, sometimes confluent: stipule-scars lacking.

The spice bush is a native shrub deserving of much more extensive cultivation than it has been accorded. It opens the season with its interesting little flowers and closes it with its bright red berry-like fruits. No better examples of "dehiscence by uplifted valves" can be found than are afforded by its anthers, which offer themselves to observation when few other hand-lens attractions, except opening buds, are in evidence. The winter-characters of *B. aestivale* (or *Lindera Benjoin* as it is still sometimes called) are figured by Brendel, pl. 3; and Schneider, f. 117.

Twigs and buds glabrous: flower-buds globose. B. aestivale.
Loosely hairy: flower-buds pointed. (1). B. melissaefolium.

Winter-characters of the related *Lindera* are given by Shirasawa. *L. glauca*, 253, pl. 6; *L. hypoleuca*, 243, pl. 6; *L. obtusiloba*, 255, pl. 6; *L. praecox*, 255 pl. 6; *L. triloba*, 254, pl. 6; and *L. umbellata*, 253, pl. 6.

LAURUS. Laurel.
(Family Lauraceae).

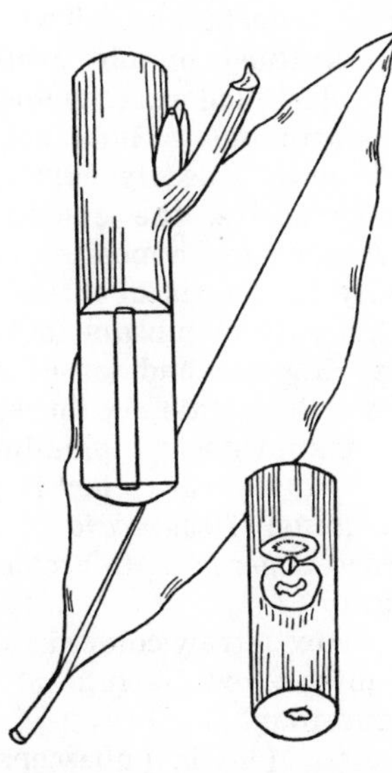

Small aromatic tender trees: evergreen. Twigs moderate, round: pith rather small, pale, continuous. Buds solitary or frequently superposed with the upper developing promptly and the lower minute, with 2 nearly or quite valvate outer scales. Leaf-scars alternate, roundish or cordate, raised: bundle-trace 1: stipule-scars lacking. Leaves simple.

Though true laurel is often replaced by *Ficus nitida* and other trees having more or less similaı foliage, it is not infrequent even in the northern States in tubbed specimens of globose or conical outline that are placed out-of-doors for formal effects through the open season, as they are planted out where they endure the winter Its buds were described (p. 202) in a treatise by Loefling on "Gemmaė Arborum" printed in 1749,—the earliest comprehensive publication of its kind.

The Roman use of wreaths of laurel has given origin to the word laureate, and, when berries or baccae were attached, to the academic expression baccalaureate and the more familiar word bachelor.

Glabrous: twigs brown: leaves crisped. (Sweet Bay).
L. nobilis.

Winter-characters of *Vella spinosa*, one of the Cruciferae, are given by Schneider, f. 102; as well as of *Capparis spinosa*, of the Capparidaceae, f. 84.

PHILADELPHUS. "Syringa." Mock Orange.
(Family Saxifragaceae).

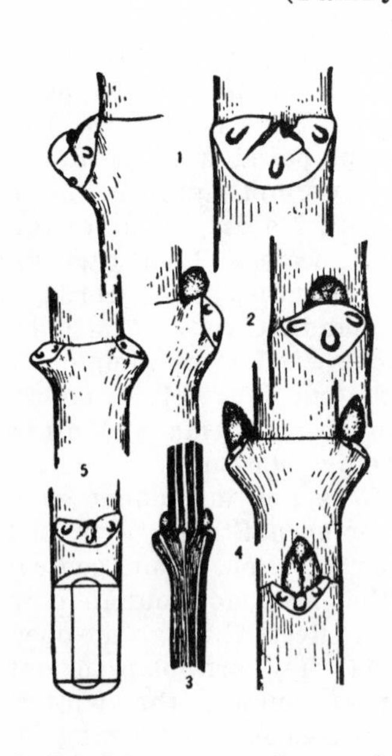

Shrubs, mostly with exfoliating outer cortex: deciduous. Twigs more or less lined or obscurely hexagonal: pith moderate, rounded, pale, continuous. Buds solitary, sessile with 2 nearly valvate mostly hairy scales, the end-bud lacking. Leaf-scars opposite or exceptionally in whorls of 3, half-round with a thin membrane more or less covering the bud, or crescent-shaped when this is burst, connected transversely: bundle-traces 3: stipule-scars lacking. References under *Decumaria*.

1. Outer cortex persistent, becoming gray. 2.
   Outer cortex straw-colored or red, quickly exfoliating. 3.
2. Membrane tough. (1). P. pubescens.
   Membrane thin. (2). P. Lewisii.
3. Leaf-scar scarcely reaching the end of bud. 4.
   Leaf-scar broad, covering the bud until burst. 7.
4. Leaf-scar narrow: twigs slender. 5.
   Leaf-scar broad: twigs moderate. P. californicus.
5. Twigs glabrous. (3). P. microphyllus.
   Twigs more or less villous or canescent. 6.
6. Pubescence scanty: buds half-covered. × P. Lemoinei.
   Pubescence abundant: buds fully exposed. (4). P. hirsutus.
7. Twigs more or less villous: fruit racemed. P. coronarius.
   Twigs glabrous: fruit nearly solitary. (5). P. inodorus.

JAMESIA.

(Family Saxifragaceae).

Shrubs: deciduous. Twigs rounded or slightly 4-sided, with quickly exfoliating bark: pith moderate, rounded, pale brown, continuous. Buds solitary, sessile, with 1 pair of white-hairy scales; the terminal rather large, the lateral small or suppressed. Leaf-scars opposite, narrowly U-shaped, white-ciliate, low, meeting: bundle-traces 3, small: stipule-scars lacking. (*Edwinia*).

Winter-studies of *Jamesia americana* are given by Schneider, f. 190.

The woody genera which are assembled here as representing the family Saxifragaceae in accordance with the views of excellent botanists, are considered by others to differ too greatly for this union with the herbs, to which they would restrict the name Saxifragaceae. These authors employ the family name Iteaceae for the genus *Itea*, Grossulariaceae for *Ribes*, and Hydrangeaceae for the remainder.

Both *Jamesia* and *Edwinia* commemorate Edwin P. James, the discoverer of the plant. The first had been used earlier for what is not considered a tenable genus: the second was given under the principle that a name once used pertains always and exclusively in its first meaning.

Twigs at first light brown and hairy. J. americana.

FENDLERA.
(Family Saxifragaceae).

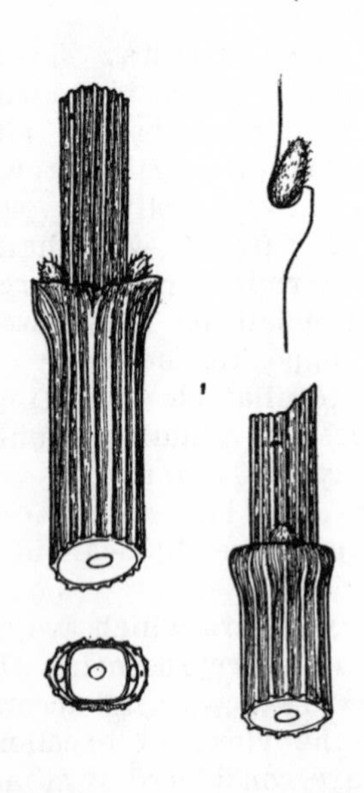

Shrubs, intricately branched: deciduous. Twigs squarish or round, soon fluted or ribbed, sometimes almost spine-tipped, rather slender, at first gray-puberulent: pith small, rounded, white, continuous. Buds rather small, solitary, sessile, with 1 or 2 pairs of white-hairy scales, partly or quite concealed by the much-raised leaf scar. Leaf-scars opposite, truncately linear: bundle-traces 3, minute: stipule-scars lacking, but the leaf-scars connected by a transverse lines.

The winter-characters of *Fendlera rupicola* are pictured by Schneider, f. 190.

The persistent base of the petiole with the narrow leaf-scar running across its top, in *Fendlera*, finds an extended parallel in *Philadelphus*, where the leaf-scar is broad. In these cases it is to be seen that the leaf-scar really has been formed by a similar but more extended oblique abscission through the enlarged base of the petiole. Among many comparative publications on such articular membranes or articular tegments is an excellent paper by Hildebrand, in volume 13 of the Botanisches Centralblatt. Other good examples of articular membranes are afforded by such Leguminosae as *Robinia* and *Sophora*.

Twigs gray or buff, stiff. (1). F. rupicola.
Twigs red-brown, flexible. F. tomentella.

DEUTZIA.
(Family Saxifragaceae).

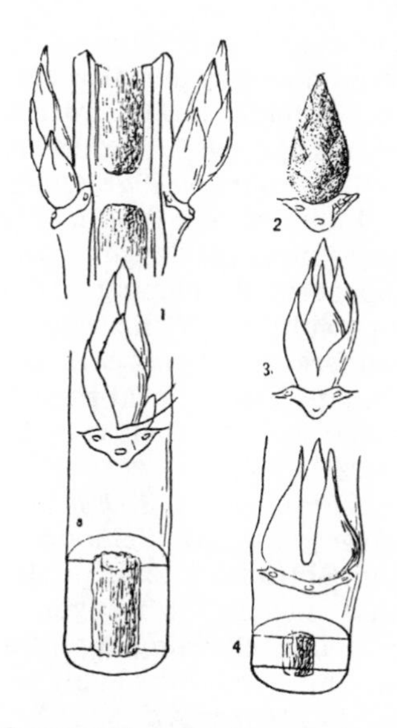

Usually small and slender-branched shrubs with exfoliating bark: deciduous as to our species. Twigs round, often stellate-pubescent, usually floriferous or dying back at the end: pith moderate, round, pale and spongy or brown and excavated between the nodes. Buds solitary or collaterally branching, nearly sessile, compressed-ovoid or triangular-oblong, with 2-6 pairs of exposed scales. Leaf-scars opposite or exceptionally whorled, triangular or transversely elongated, slightly raised, connected by transverse ridges: bundle-traces 3: stipule-scars lacking. References, p. 80.

Though the deutzias are somewhat difficult to name by ordinary characters except when in flower, the species most commonly seen differ rather markedly in pith and bud, so that they are quite as readily known in winter as at other seasons.—References under *Schizophragma*.

1. Pith brown, excavated. (1). D. scabra.
   Pith white, spongy, 2.
2. Buds canescent, ovoid: scales acute. (2). D. parviflora
   Buds glabrate, brown or straw-colored: scales attenuate. 3.
3. Buds ovoid, longer than their lowest scales. (3). × D. Lemoinei.
   Buds triangular-oblong, with long scales. 4.
4. Leaf-scars triangular. D. rosea.
   Leaf-scars linear. (4). D. gracilis

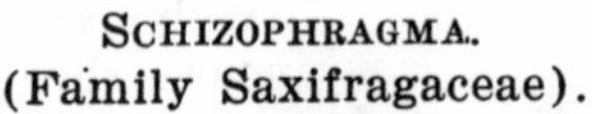

SCHIZOPHRAGMA.
(Family Saxifragaceae).

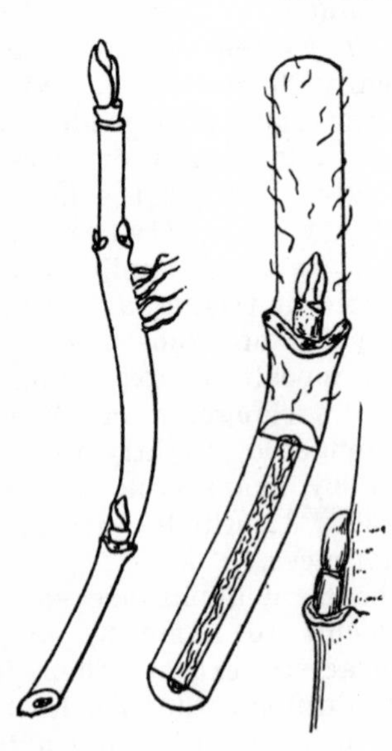

Shrubs, climbing by aerial roots: deciduous. Stems terete, rather slender, finally with splitting cortex: pith rounded, greenish, spongy. Buds rather small, the terminal somewhat larger, the lateral mostly developing into short spurs, solitary, with a couple of exposed scales. Leaf-scars opposite, U-shaped, somewhat raised, nearly meeting: bundle-traces 5: stipule-scars lacking.

Winter-characters of *S. hydrangeoides* are given by Schneider, f. 223; and Shirasawa, 282, pl. 12.

This and the following genus are often called climbing hydrangeas, but the climbing habit is found also in *Hydrangea*.

Winter-character references:—*Deutzia crenata*. Bösemann, 64; Schneider, f. 208; Shirasawa, 279, pl. 12.—*D. gracilis*. Schneider, f. 208; Shirasawa, 279, pl. 12.—*D. parviflora*. Schneider, f. 208.

Hydrangea (or *Hydatica*) *petiolaris* closely resembles *Schizophragma*, and often is cultivated for it. Its cortex is more exfoliating.

Twigs red-brown, sometimes loosely hairy. S. hydrangeoides.

DECUMARIA.
(Family Saxifragaceae).

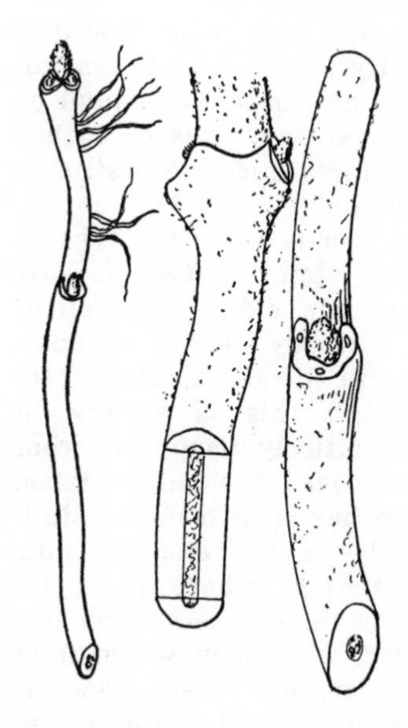

Shrubs, climbing by aerial roots: deciduous. Stems terete, rather slender, the cortex finally exfoliating: pith rounded, greenish, spongy. Buds small, solitary, sessile, with indistinct scales. Leaf-scars opposite, horseshoe-shaped, raised, with concave surface, transversely connected: bundle-traces 3: stipule-scars lacking.

Winter-character references: Schneider, f. 190.

Twigs puberulent: buds very red-hairy. D. barbara.

In addition to those given under the genera to which they pertain, the following winter-character references may be noted:—*Philadelphus coronarius*. Bösemann, 54; Schneider, f. 189; Willkomm, 2, 3, 9, 51, f. 93; Zuccarini, 13, pl. 7. *P. coronarius Satsumi*. Shirasawa, 268, pl. 10.—*P. hirsutus*. Schneider, f. 189.—*P. pubescens*. Bösemann, 54; Schneider f. 189.

ITEA.

(Family Saxifragaceae).

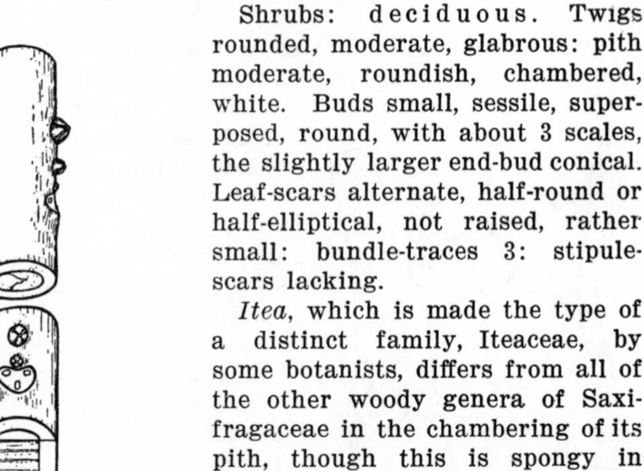

Shrubs: deciduous. Twigs rounded, moderate, glabrous: pith moderate, roundish, chambered, white. Buds small, sessile, superposed, round, with about 3 scales, the slightly larger end-bud conical. Leaf-scars alternate, half-round or half-elliptical, not raised, rather small: bundle-traces 3: stipule-scars lacking.

Itea, which is made the type of a distinct family, Iteaceae, by some botanists, differs from all of the other woody genera of Saxifragaceae in the chambering of its pith, though this is spongy in *Ribes* and entirely disappears from the internodes of some deutzias. Reference has been made to similar chambered or "discoid" pith under *Asimina*, where it is inconstant. In *Itea*, as in *Juglans* and numerous other genera, it is to be seen readily and constantly. *Celtis*, in which it is found sometimes with great uniformity, presents a case in which at other times the chambering is confined to the nodes, from some of which, even, it may be absent.

Winter-studies of *Itea japonica* have been published by Shirasawa, 242, 246, pl. 3; and of *I. virginica* by Schneider, f. 223.

Twigs green, buds more or less puberulent. I. virginica.

HYDRANGEA.
(Family Saxifragaceae).

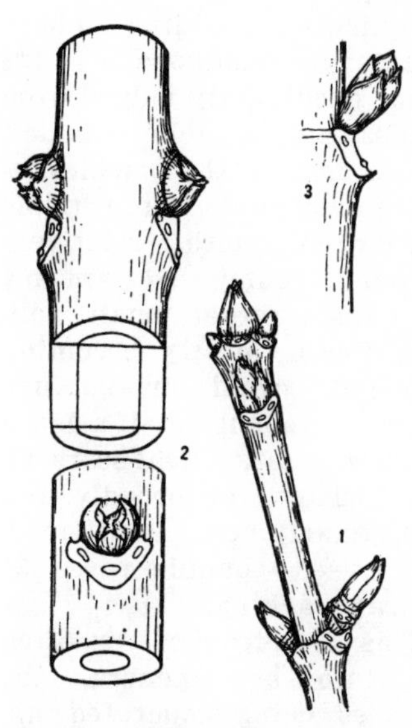

Small or moderate-sized sparingly branched soft-wooded shrubs, or exceptionally root-climbers: deciduous. Twigs round, moderate or relatively coarse; pith rather large, roundish, mostly continuous, pale. Buds moderate, solitary, sessile or very short-stalked, globose-conical to oblong, with some 4 to 6 exposed scales. Leaf-scars opposite, crescent-shaped or 3- or 5-angled, rather large, little raised, frequently in whorls of 3, or with connecting crossline: bundle-traces 3 or exceptionally 5 or 7: stipule-scars lacking.

In the main, the winter distinctions between different hydrangeas are fairly clean-cut.

The following references may be given: *H. involucrata.* Schneider, f. 206.—*H. opuloides.* Shirasawa, 276, pl. 11—*H. paniculata.* Schneider, f. 207; Shirasawa, 280, pl. 11—*H. petiolaris.* Schneider, f. 206.—*H. petiolaris cordifolia.* Shirasawa, 282, pl. 12.—*H. quercifolia.* Schneider, f. 206.—*H. Thunbergii.* Shirasawa, 276.

1. Climbing: pith spongy. (1). H. petiolaris.
   Bushy: pith continuous. 2.
2. Red-tomentose: bark extremely flaking. H. quercifolia
   Glabrate. 3.
3. Buds round-conical, horizontal. (2). H. paniculata.
   Buds oblong. 4.
4. Buds spreading: hardy. (3). H. arborescens.
   Buds appressed: tender. (Hortensia). H. opuloides

RIBES. Currant. Gooseberry.
(Family Saxifragaceae).

Loosely branching shrubs with rather quickly shredding epidermis: chiefly deciduous. Twigs terete but decurrently ridged from the nodes, moderately slender, sometimes prickly, the prickles beneath the leaf-scars often triple and enlarged: pith relatively large, pale, round, becoming spongy. Buds rather small, solitary, sessile or mostly becoming short-stalked, ovoid or subfusiform, with about half-a-dozen rather loose scales. Leaf-scars alternate, U-shaped or broadly and often angularly crescent-shaped, slightly raised: bundle-traces 3: stipule-scars lacking.

Ribes, as accepted here, is often divided into two genera, the gooseberries being separated under the name *Grossularia*. Apart from their frequent production of prickles, gooseberries are usually distinguished from currants in winter by their narrower leaf-scars.

Ribes alpinum, which is planted frequently in shrubbery masses and resembles a dwarf ninebark, may be distinguished from *Physocarpus* very readily by its narrow leaf-scars, distinctly stalked buds, and spongy pith.

Winter-character references:—*Ribes alpinum*. Bösemann, 48; Fant, f. 13; Schneider, f. 180; Willkomm, 30, f. 38.—*R. americanum*. Brendel, pl. 3.—*R. aureum*. Schneider, f. 180.—*R. fasciculatum*. Shirasawa, 231, pl. 1.—*R. Gordonianum*. Schneider, f. 181.—*R. gracile*. Hitchcock (3), 15, (4), 137, f.

74.—*R Grossularia.* Bösemann, 47; Fant, 20; Schneider, f. 180; Shirasawa, 249; Ward, 1:198, f. 100.—*R. nigrum.* Bösemann, 48; Fant, 19, f. 14; Schneider, f. 181; Ward, 1:206, f. 107; Willkomm, 31, f. 40.—*R. petraeum.* Schneider, f. 182; Willkomm, 9, 31, f. 39.—"*R. rotundifolium*" [*oxyacanthoides?*]. Brendel, pl. 3.—*R. rubrum.* Bösemann, 48; Fant, 19; Schneider, f. 181.—*R. sanguineum.* Bösemann, 48; Schneider, f 182.

1. Evergreen: stems prickly. R. speciosum.
   Deciduous. 2.
2. Buds ovoid, glandular or puberulent: leaf-scars rather broad. 3.
   Buds elongated subfusiform: leaf-scars very narrow. 7.
3. Bud-scales and twigs with some sessile resin-glands, glabrate. 4.
   Without sessile resin-glands: buds gray-puberulent. 5.
4. Resin-glands: wood fetid. R. nigrum.
   Glands large and conspicuous. R. americanum
5. Twigs quickly glabrate. 6.
   Twigs rather persistently gray-puberulent. R. odoratum.
6. Spreading and stoloniferous. R. triste.
   Bushy: commonly planted. (Red currant). (1). R. vulgare.
7. With frequent prickles. 8.
   Unarmed. 14.
8. Infra-axillary prickles often large (2 × 10 mm. or more): buds glossy straw-colored. (2). R. missouriense.
   Prickles smaller: buds dull brown. 9.
9. Buds short (3 mm.), downy. R. rotundifolium.
   Buds rather long (5 or 6 mm.). 10.
10. Infra-axillary prickles scarcely larger than the abundant others: twigs and buds glossy straw-colored. R. lacustre.
11. Infra-axillary prickles longer, if accompanied by others. 11.
    Twigs quickly nearly white, with exfoliating epidermis. 12.
    Epidermis more persistent. 13.

12. Low, spreading, often with prickles. R. oxyacanthoides.
    Larger, usually unarmed. R. hirtellum.
13. Bud-scales keeled, more or less silky. R. Cynosbati.
    Scales not keeled, glabrescent. (European gooseberry). R. Grossularia.
14. Stems with nearly white exfoliating epidermis. R. oxyacanthoides.
    Twigs buff. (3). R. alpinum.

PITTOSPORUM. Incense.
(Family Pittosporaceae).

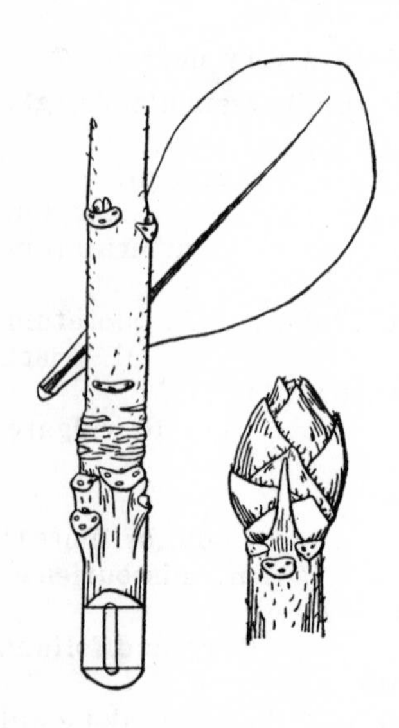

Large shrubs: evergreen. Twigs moderate, at first hairy, terete, short, often enlarged at the end of the season's growth: pith small, white, round, continuous. Buds solitary, sessile, the lateral minute and subglobose with about 3 exposed scales, the terminai larger, ovoid, with some half-dozen ciliate scales. Leaf-scars alternate, clustered toward the end of the season's growth, broadly crescent-shaped, somewhat raised: bundle-traces 3: stipule-scàrs lacking. Leaves simple, entire, spatulate-obovate in the following.

An odoriferous resin, produced in passages that are characteristically distributed in the tissues and which is especially abundant in the fruit, renders this a favorite source of incense for church purposes in the Azores.

Leaves unvariegated. P. Tobira.
Leaves variegated. P. Tobira variegatum.

LIQUIDAMBAR. Sweet Gum.
(Family Hamamelidaceae).

More or less percurrent and conical trees: deciduous. Twigs moderate, roundish and smooth or with variously developed corky ridges or thick wings: pith angled or somewhat star-shaped, subcontinuous, brownish. Buds solitary, sessile or sometimes developing into spurs the first season, ovoid, the lateral often reduced and flattened against the twig; when well developed, with half-a-dozen exposed scales. Leaf-scars alternate, half-elliptical or triangular, somewhat raised: bundle-traces 3, large: stipule-scars lacking.

Winter-character references:— *L. Maximowiczii.* Shirasawa, 254, pl. 6. *L. orientale.* Schneider, f. 107. *L. Styraciflua.* Blakeslee & Jarvis, 332, 334, 480, pl.; Brendel, pl. 2; Schneider, f. 11, 23.

Twigs glabrescent: bud-scales ciliate. L. Styraciflua.

Like *Betula* and some other trees, *Liquidambar* is very apt to show a short basal elongation of many buds before the first winter.

The sweet gum, like bur oak, rock elm and some other trees, is sometimes found with round thin-barked twigs, and sometimes has its twigs furnished with thick corky ridges, especially on the upper side. Cases of this kind have been made the subject of an extensive paper published by Miss Gregory in the Botanical Gazette for 1888 and 1889.

PARROTIA
(Family Hamamelidaceae).

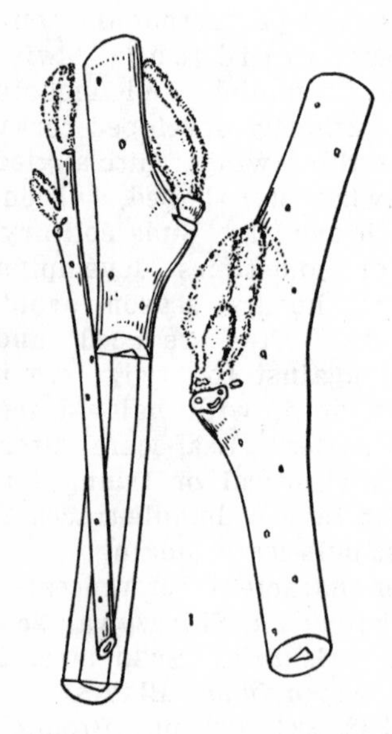

Small tree, with the bark flaking as in *Platanus*: deciduous. Twigs rounded, somewhat zig-zag, from somewhat dingy stellate-tomentose becoming glabrate: pith rather small, 3-sided, continuous, greenish. Buds moderate, solitary, stalked, oblique, ovoid-oblong, with 2 scales, the end-bud somewhat larger. Leaf-scars alternate, 2-ranked, half-round or triangular, slightly raised, small: bundle-traces 3, sometimes compound: stipule-scars very unequal.

Parrotia persica is markedly different from other trees referred to the Hamamelidaceae in its conspicuously exfoliating bark and nearly black buds. Its winter-characters are pictured by Schneider, f. 96.

Parrotia agrees with *Hamamelis* and differs from *Fothergilla* in bearing its fruits in compact short clusters. It is rather tenderer than either of the others but is entirely hardy farther north than Washington.

An interesting characteristic of the family is that when the woody capsules dehisce the pressure of their walls upon the smooth seeds forces these out much as a melon-seed may be snapped from between finger and thumb.

Twigs brown: buds blackish-puberulent. (1). P. persica.
Twigs olive: buds dingy puberulent. P. Jacquemontiana.

The winter-characters of *Disanthus cercidifolia*, of the Hamamelidaceae, are pictured by Shirasawa, 254, pl. 6.

FOTHERGILLA.
(Family Hamamelidaceae).

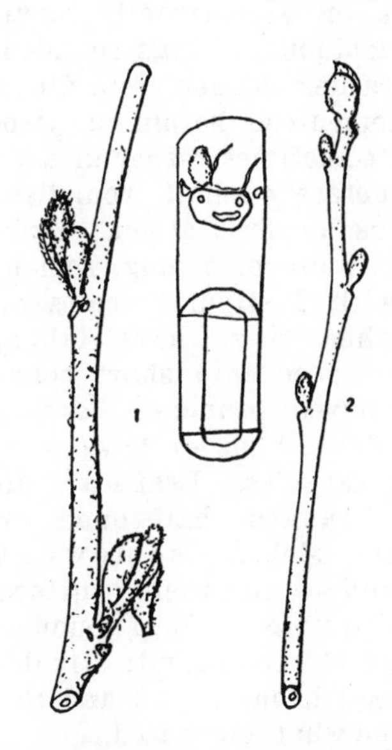

Shrubs: Deciduous. Twigs rounded, zig-zag, slender, dingy stellate-tomentose or more or less glabrescent: pith rather small, somewhat angular, continuous, for a time greenish. Buds moderate or small, stalked, oblique, obovate or oblong, with 2 caducous scales, often collaterally branched, the end-bud largest. Leaf-scars alternate, 2-ranked, half-round or deltoid, slightly raised, small: bundle-traces 3, more or less compound or confluent: stipule-scars unequal, one short and the other elongated. Capsules often present.

Though the vegetative characters of *Fothergilla* are much like those of *Hamamelis*, the flowers and capsules are borne in elongated clusters in the former and in short groups in the latter. This character is usually available in winter.

The winter-characters of *Fothergilla carolina*—or *F. Gardenii* as it is called here—are pictured by Schneider, f. 107.

1. Very low and suckering: gray-puberulent. F. parvifolia.
   Rather tall: buds yellowish or tawny. 2.
2. Openly branched. 3.
   Pyramidal. F. monticola.
3. Capsules long-beaked, over 10 mm. long: stout. (1). F. major.
   Capsules short (scarcely 10 mm.): twigs often slender. (2). F. Gardenii.

HAMAMELIS. Witch Hazel. Bead-tree.
(Family Hamamelidaceae).

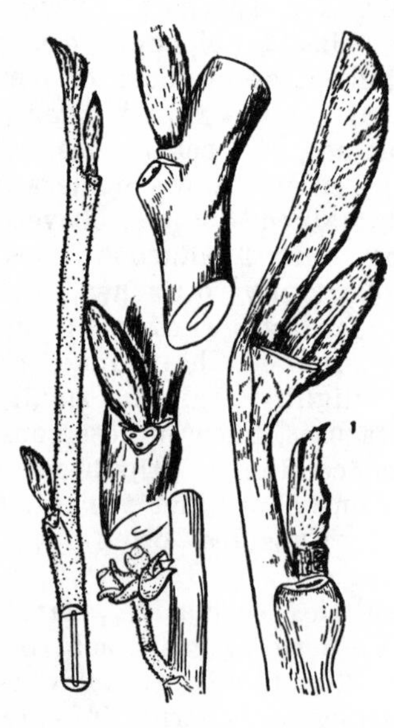

Shrubs or exceptionally small trees: deciduous. Twigs rounded, zig-zag, rather slender, from dingy stellate-tomentose becoming glabrate and sometimes rather glossy: pith moderately small, roundish, continuous, at first green. Buds moderate, stalked, oblong, tomentulose, with 2 stipular scales or naked when these have fallen, often developed into short collateral recurved branches bearing about 3 flower-buds or flowers or incipient capsules. Leaf-scars alternate, 2-ranked, half-round or somewhat 3-lobed, somewhat raised and with their surface again falling in spring: bundle-traces 3, often compound: stipule-scars unequal, one round and the other somewhat elongated.

The curious double abscission of the petiole forms the subject of a note by Foerste in the Bulletin of the Torrey Botanical Club for 1884.

Winter-character references:—*Hamamelis japonica.* Shirasawa, 267, pl. 9.—*H. virginiana.* Blakeslee & Jarvis, 331, 478, pl.; Brendel, pl. 4; Schneider, f. 96.

1. Buds long (fully 10 mm. including stalk). H. japonica.
   Buds short (5-8 mm. including stalk). 2.
2. Flowering in autumn. (1). H. virginiana.
   Flowering in late winter. 3.
3. Pubescence scurfy. H. vernalis.
   Pubescence long. H. mollis.

CORYLOPSIS.
(Family Hamamelidaceae).

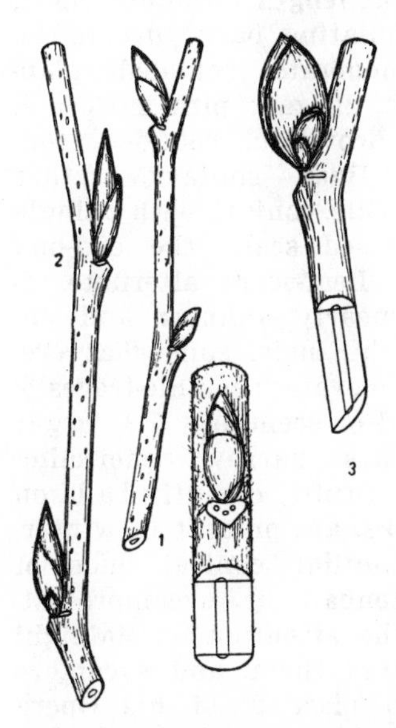

Shrubs: deciduous. Twigs rounded, zig-zag, moderate or slender, mostly glabrescent: pith rather small, somewhat angular, continuous. Buds rather large, sessile and solitary or finally short-stalked and collaterally branched, directly in the axil, fusiform or ovoid, with about 3 glabrous scales, the end-bud somewhat larger. Leaf-scars alternate, 2-ranked, half-round or 3-sided, slightly raised, small: bundle-traces 3; stipule-scars equal, elongated.

Fothergilla, *Hamamelis* and *Parrotia* posses a marked general resemblance in bud and twig characters; and their woody fruits, which require a year for maturing, are much alike. Neither *Liquidambar* nor *Corylopsis* bears the slightest resemblance to them in these respects, so far as general appearance is concerned. Winter-characters of *Corylopsis* have been studied by Schneider (*C. spicata*,—f. 96); and Shirasawa (*C. pauciflora* and *C. spicata*,—262, pl. 8).

1. Lateral buds fusiform. 2.
   Buds ovoid. 3.
2. Second scale half the length of bud. (1). C. spicata.
   Second scale longer. (2). C. Willmottiana.
3. Buds large (10 mm. long). (3). C. Veitchiana.
   Buds moderate (7 mm. long), purplish. C. Gotoana.
   Buds small (5-7 mm. long). C. pauciflora.

PLATANUS. Sycamore.
(Family Platanaceae).

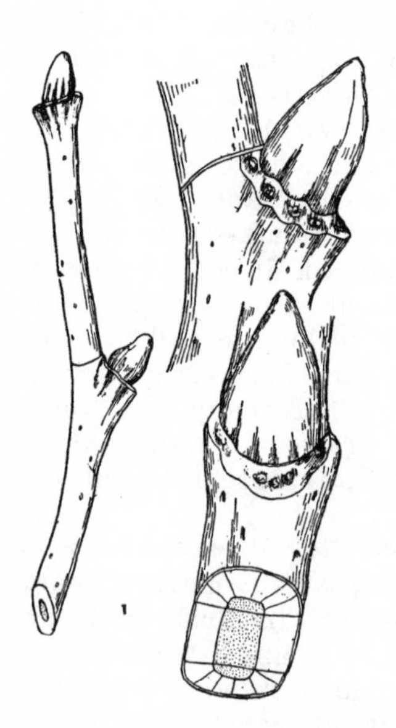

Trees, at length large and open, with exfoliating bark: deciduous. Twigs moderate, rounded, glabrous, buff, zig-zag: pith moderate, pale or brownish, rounded, continuous. Buds solitary, rather large, sessile, conical, with a single glossy closed scale, the end-bud lacking. Leaf-scars alternate, 2-ranked, nearly annular and encircling the buds, somewhat crenate and elevated: bundle-traces 5, compound or seemingly 7-9, large: stipule-scars narrow, encircling the twig. Fruits, in fluffy balls on long stalks, are present in winter.

The familiar conical buds of the buttonball or sycamore attracted the attention of Malpighi who figured them, and sycamore wood, on plate 9 of his Opera Omnia as early as 1687. Each of the three caps within which a bud is enclosed represents a pair of stipules united by their edges. The gum that bathes these caps is the product of a type of secretion-glands known as colleters.

Winter-character references:—*P. occidentalis*. Blakeslee & Jarvis, 330, 482, pl.; Brendel, pl. 3; Hitchcock (1), 4; (3), 17; (4), 138, f. 95-8; Otis, 140; Ward, 1:35, f. 19-20; 118, f. 59; 214, f. 109; Willkomm, 4, 8, 19, f. 13.—*P. orientalis*. Schneider, f. 107.

Fruit-ball mostly solitary on the stalk. (1). P. occidentalis
Fruit-balls mostly 2 on the stalk. P. acerifolia.
Fruit-balls characteristically 3 on the stalk. P. orientalis.

PHYSOCARPUS. Ninebark.
(Family Rosaceae).

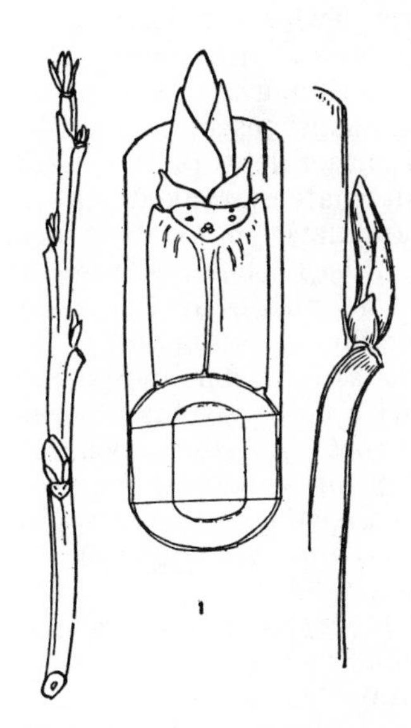

Loosely branching shrubs with quickly shredding brown bark: deciduous. Twigs terete but 5-lined from the nodes, moderately slender, somewhat zig-zag: pith relatively large, brownish, round, homogeneous. Buds rather small, solitary, sessile, conical-oblong or ovoid, with about 5 rather loose brown scales. Leaf-scars alternate, half-elliptical or somewhat 3-lobed, raised on a distinct cushion bearing the small stipule-scars: bundle-traces 5, unequal, the lower one distinctly larger. Fruit, as clustered small follicles, may be present in winter. Sometimes united with *Spiraea* or referred to *Neillia* or *Opulaster*.

Winter character references:—
P. amurensis. Schneider, f. 152.
P. opulifolius. Bösemann, 76; Schneider, f. 152; Willkomm, 11.

Novices frequently have difficulty in distinguishing between ninebark and the common snowball (*Viburnum Opulus*). Fundamental distinctions lie in its alternate leaves or short broad leaf-scars, and in its sessile buds with several scales; the *Viburnum* having narrow opposite leaf-scars and stalked plump buds with a closed outer sac.

1. Puberulent: buds ovoid, spreading. P. amurensis.
   Twigs glabrous: buds pointed, appressed. 2.
2. Follicles puberulent. P. intermedius.
   Follicles glabrous. (1). P. opulifolius.

NEILLIA.
(Family Rosaceae).

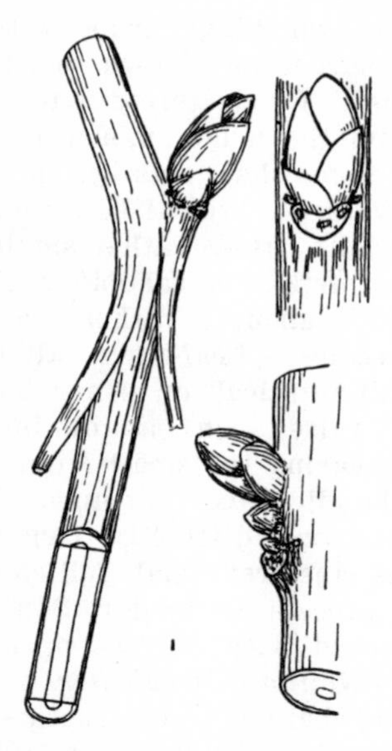

Small loosely branched shrubs: deciduous. Twigs slender, zig-zag quickly terete: pith small, light brown, continuous. Buds moderate, often superposed, ovoid, with about 4 rather loose scales. Leaf-scars alternate, 2-ranked, rather small, angularly crescent-shaped, slightly raised: bundle-traces 3: stipule-scars small, at the upper angles of the leaf-scar.

Neillias are slender spiraea-like shrubs with no particular differentials except in the technical characters on which the genus is segregated. Winter-characters of *N. thyrsiflora* are figured by Schneider, f. 71.

As with *Stephanandra*, the habit of *Neillia* fits it for blending down stiffer shrubbery.

Bark glabrous, shredding: buds large. N. sinensis.
Bark not shredding: buds small. (1). N. thyrsiflora.

Winter-character references to *Rubus*:—*R. caesius*. Bösemann, 39; Fant, 26.—*R. fruticosus*. Bösemann, 39; Fant, 25, f. 22; Ward, 1:202, f. 103.—*R. idaeus*. Bösemann, 39; Fant, 25, f. 22; Schneider, f. 146; Willkomm, 6, 37, f. 56.—*R. incisus*. Shirasawa, 250.—*R. Koehleri*. Bösemann, 39.—*R. occidentalis*. Foerste, Botanical Gazette, 20:78, pl. 6; Hitchcock (3), 14; (4), 136, f. 59-63.—*R. odoratus*. Bösemann, 39; Schneider, f. 146.—*R. phoenicolasius*. Schneider, f. 146.—*R. saxatilis*. Bösemann, 39.—*R. trifidus*. Shirasawa, 257.—*R. villosus*. Hitchcock (3), 14; (4), 136, f. 64-68.

STEPHANANDRA.
(Family Rosaceae).

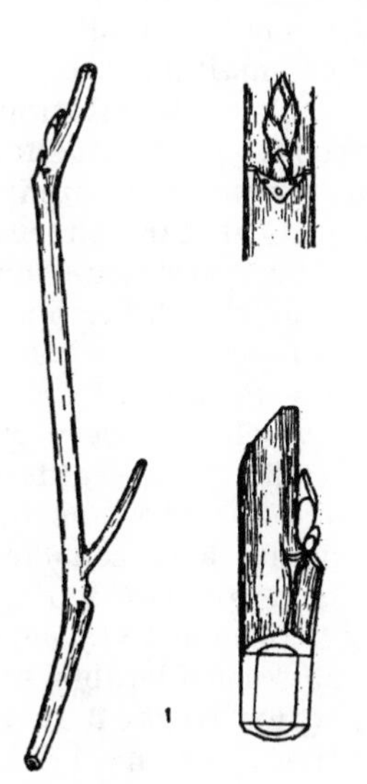

Small shrubs, loosely branched: deciduous. Twigs terete or somewhat 5-lined from the nodes, slender, zig-zag, red: pith small, pale or light brown, continuous. Buds small, superposed, the upper of each series often developing the first season or slightly stalked, ovoid or oblong, with about 4 scales. Leaf-scars alternate, 2-ranked, small, half-round or triangular, slightly raised: bundle-traces 3 or subconfluent: stipule-scars relatively large.

Stephanandras are slender spiraea- or kerria-like shrubs differing from the former in some small respects and from the latter in their red and not bright green twigs. Winter-characters of *S. flexuosa* are given by Shirasawa. 247, pl. 4, and of *S. incisca* by Schneider, f. 137.

Buds ovoid. S. incisa

Buds elongated. (1). S. Tanakae.

SPIRAEA.
(Family Rosaceae).

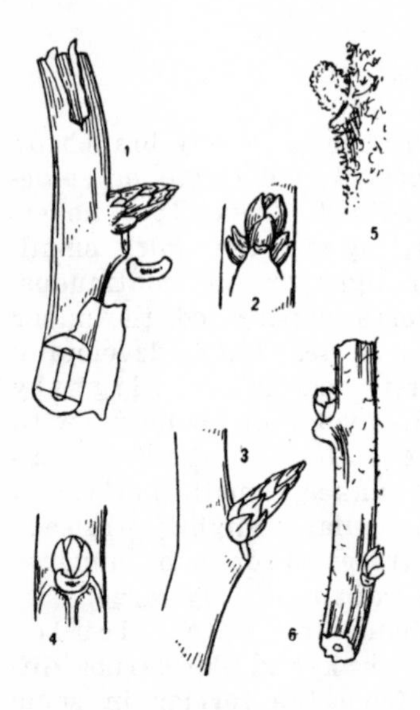

Shrubs, usually low and little branched or else with wand-like branches: deciduous. Twigs terete or angled from the nodes, often very slender, more or less zig-zag: pith small, roundish, continuous. Buds small, solitary or in a few cases collaterally multiplied, sessile, globose to subfusiform, mostly with some half-dozen exposed scales. Leaf-scars alternate, half-round or crescent-shaped, minute, often much raised: bundle-trace 1: stipule-scars not evident.

Spiraea, like *Pyrus* and *Prunus*, is a genus which has been very differently defined by different botanists, for some of whom it includes the plants here considered under the genera *Neillia*, *Physocarpus*, *Sorbaria* and *Stephanandra*. The most concise winter-key to any considerable number of its species is that of Bösemann, which treats it in this broader and older sense. The comparatively few species that enter into ordinary American planting and are considered here differ for the most part in several distinctive ways, and their buds belong to several unmistakable types.

Winter-character references:—*S. ariaefolia.* Bösemann, 76.—*S. betulaefolia.* Shirasawa, 244, pl. 4.—*S. cana.* Schneider, f. 175—× *S. cantoniensis.* Shirasawa, 246, pl. 4.—*S. chamaedryfolia.* Bösemann, 75.—*S. crenata.* Schneider, f. 174.—*S. discolor.* Schneider, f. 179.—*S. hypericifolia.* Bösemann, 77; Schneider, f. 175.—*S. japonica.* Shirasawa, 274, pl.

4.—*S. laevigata.* Schneider, f. 133.—*S. media.* Schneider, f. 176.—*S. prunifolia.* Bösemann, 76; Shirasawa, 247.—*S. salicifolia.* Bösemann, 76; Willkomm, 37, f. 57.

1. Buds with 2 valvate scales. 2.
   Buds with several exposed scales when mature. 3.
2. Buds short. S. canescens.
   Buds long and slender. S. longigemmis.
3. Buds conical: twigs terete, slender. (1). × S. Vanhouttei.
   Buds ovoid, or else shrubs low. 4.
4. Buds often collaterally multiplied. (2). S. prunifolia.
   Buds solitary. 5.
5. Twigs glabrous. 6.
   Twigs pubescent. 10.
6. Twigs terete. 7.
   Twigs more or less distinctly angled. 8.
7. Twigs dark: buds elongated. (3). × S. cantoniensis.
   Twigs bright red-brown. S. corymbosa.
8. Angles evanescent: rather low and simple. 9.
   Angles pronounced: tall and bushy. S. chamaedryfolia.
9. Vestiges of inflorescence corymbose. S. betulaefolia.
   Vestiges of inflorescence paniculate. (4). S. latifolia
10. Pubescence gray or merely dingy, usually velvety. 11.
    Pubescence often rusty and woolly. (5). S. tomentosa.
11. Twigs more or less distinctly angled. 12.
    Twigs terete: inflorescence corymbose. S. japonica.
12. Twigs neither excessively slender nor numerous. 13.
    Twigs filiform. (6). S. Thunbergii.
13. Inflorescence corymbose. 14.
    Inflorescence paniculate. 15.
14. Stems slightly glaucous. S. virginiana pubescens.
    Stems not glaucous. × S. Bumalda.
15. Pubescence abundant. S. Douglasii.
    Pubescence scanty. S. alba.

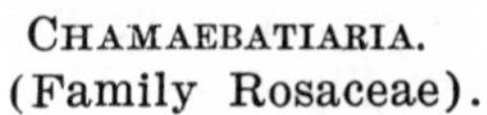

CHAMAEBATIARIA.
(Family Rosaceae).

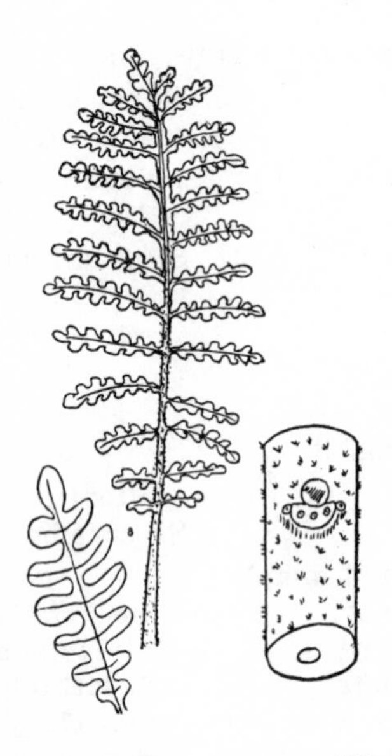

Small shrubs, stellate and varnished: evergreen. Twigs terete, rather slender: pith small, roundish, continuous. Buds small, promptly developing into short leafy spurs. Leaf-scars alternate, small, half-round or somewhat 3-angled, low, concave: bundle-traces 3, impressed: stipule-scars relatively large, concave, confluent with the leaf-scar, each with a distinct impressed bundle-trace. Leaves petioled, elliptical, twice pinnatifid or almost bipinnate, with minute somewhat separated blunt segments.

Though they are not very closely related in the family Resaceae, *Chamaebatiaria* and *Chamaebatia* are rather similar in their very finely divided fern-like foliage. They are readily distinguished by the leaves of the former being not quite twice pinnate, while those of the latter are essentially thrice pinnate. No other plant among these here considered has a leaf-scar nearly divided into three parts, as that of *Chamaebataria* seems to be.

Twigs reddish-brown: leaf- and stipule-scars white.
C. Millefolium.

SORBARIA.
(Family Rosaceae).

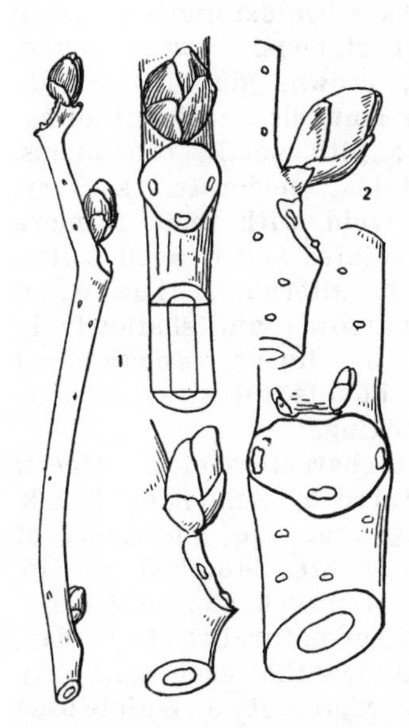

Low and little-branched shrubs: deciduous. Twigs terete, somewhat zig-zag, stout for the size of the plant, glabrous: pith relatively large, rounded, brown, continuous. Buds ovoid, moderate and sessile, with about 4 exposed scales, or quickly developing so as to become large, open, stalked and collaterally multiple; the end-bud lacking. Leaf-scars alternate, rather large, half-round to round or elliptical, more or less angled or truncate, little raised: bundle-traces 3, large: stipule-scars lacking.

Sorbaria has been considered a part of the genus *Spiraea* by many botanists, and on the other hand those who seregate it sometimes use the generic name *Basilima* for its species. The following winter-character references may be given:—*S. alpina*. Schneider. f. 133.—*S. sorbifolia*. Bösemann, 76; Schneider, f. 133. The reason why no terminal bud is found in *Sorbaria*, and the structure of its buds, are considered in an extensive article on buds published by Ohlert in the journal Linnaea for 1837.

1. Twigs and buds red-brown. (1). S. Lindleyana.
   Twigs and buds gray-brown. 2.
   Twigs purple: capsules glabrous. S. Aitchisoni.
2. Capsules glabrous. (2). S. sorbifolia.
   Capsules loosely hairy. S. stellipila.

EXOCHORDA. Pearl Bush.
(Family Rosaceae).

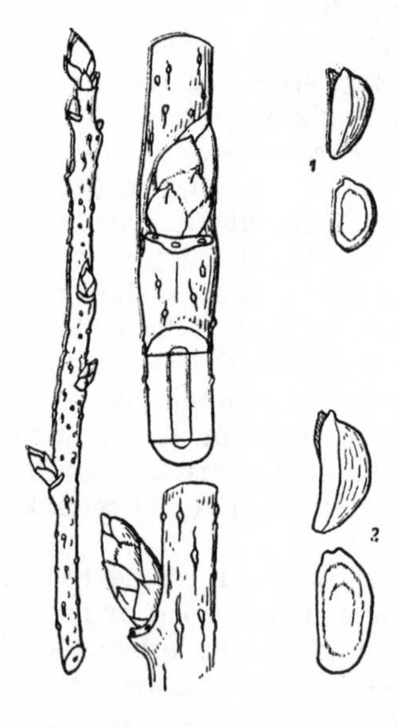

Shrubs with exfoliating brown bark: deciduous. Twigs round, slender, brown, glabrous, roughened by lenticels and longitudinal fissures; pith small, continuous, pale. Buds moderate, solitary, sessile, ovoid, with about 10 more or less pointed and fringed scales. Leaf-scars alternate, clustered above, narrowly and shallowly U-shaped or linear, somewhat raised: bundle-traces 3: stipule-scars lacking.

Winter-characters of *E. Alberti* are pictured by Schneider, f. 138.

Noting that the bud-scales of *Exochorda* are 3-toothed at tip, Sir John Lubbock, the most eminent amateur naturalist of our day, took the view that each scale may perhaps represent a petiole-base with adnate stipules, although distinguishable stipules do not accompany many of the developed leaves.

Lubbock's many and carefully made observations on the buds of a great variety of plants were published first in the botanical section of the Journal of the Linnean Society—*Exochorda* being noted on p. 494 of the thirtieth volume of this series. They subsequently formed the foundation for a convenient and very instructive volume On Buds and Stipules.

Fruit depressed, short (7-8 mm. long). (1). E. grandiflora.
Fruit obovoid, longer (12 mm.). (2). E. Alberti.

PYRACANTHA. Fire Thorn.
(Family Rosaceae).

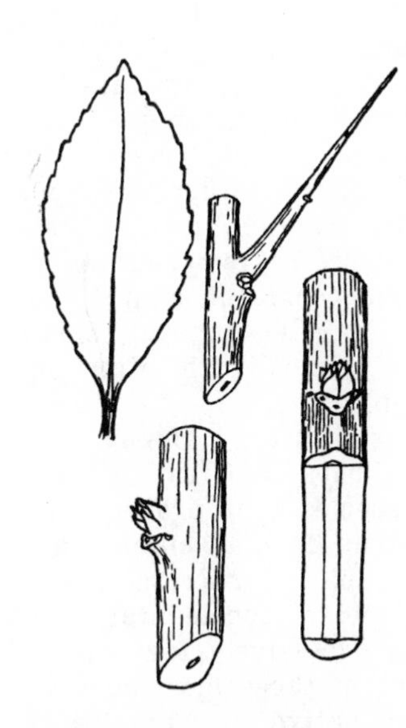

Compactly branched shrubs, sometimes grown against walls or other supports, with very sharp spiny twigs: evergreen. Twigs rather slender, subterete: pith small, continuous. Buds solitary or collaterally branched in spine formation, sessile, round-ovoid, with some half-dozen pointed dry scales. Leaf-scars alternate, narrowly crescent-shaped or 3-lobed, somewhat raised: bundle-traces 3: stipule-scars minute. Leaves oblanceolate, glandular-crenulate. (*Crataegus*).

The fire-thorn is one of the many Rosaceae with apple-like fruit which are separated into technically well-defined genera with great difficulty. Though it is usually considered to belong to a different genus from the red-haws, many gardeners still speak of it as *Crataegus Pyracantha.* Where it can be grown, it is an effective shrub for evergreen hedges.

Twigs red, somewhat hairy, or glabrate. P. coccinea.

COTONEASTER.

(Family Rosaceae).

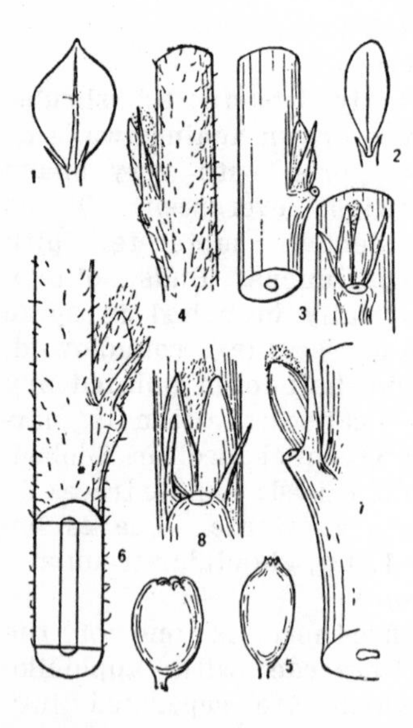

Shrubs: deciduous or evergreen. Twigs slender, subterete: pith small, rounded, continuous. Buds solitary, sessile, ovoid or oblong, the 2 outer scales mostly parted and exposing the hairy interior. Leaf-scars alternate, minute, elliptical, raised: bundle-trace 1, indistinct: stipules rather persistent on the leaf-cushion, leaving narrow indistinct scars when fallen. Leaves when present simple, entire. Fruit, often present, small drupe-like pomes with often incurved sepals.

Cotoneasters are among the favorite shrubs of Great Britain, but the species that prove so effective in an insular climate are rarely capable of successful cultivation under continental conditions even though not subjected to excessively low winter temperatures. A considerable number of those most successfully grown in the United States are native to countries of relatively dry climate, and some of the best of them are of recent introduction.

The few winter-character references are:—*C. integerrimus* (or *vulgaris*). Bösemann, 78; Fant, 19; Ward, 1:231, f. 118; Willkomm, 6, 7, 32, f. 42.—*C. nigra* and *C. tomentosa*. Schneider, f. 151.

1. Evergreen: low and spreading. 2.
   Deciduous: larger and mostly erect. 3.

2. Leaves round: twigs strigose. (1). C. horizontalis.
   Leaves obovate, pubescent beneath. (2). C. microphylla.
3. Buds small (2-3 mm.) or glabrate. 4.
   Buds larger (4-5 mm.) or persistently hairy. 10.
4. Buds glabrate: fruit red. 5.
   Buds at first silky: fruit glaucous. (3). C. racemiflora.
   Buds persistently hairy. 7.
5. Twigs very slender (1 mm.). C. hupehensis.
   Twigs stouter (2 mm.). 6.
6. Buds short (3 mm.): fruit glaucous. C. rosea.
   Buds larger (4-5 mm.): fruit not glaucous. C. acuminata.
7. Fruit black. 8.
   Fruit red. 9.
8. Twigs red-brown. C. nitens.
   Twigs buff or light brown. (4). C. acutifolia.
9. Twigs glabrescent: fruit oblong: sepals erect. (5). C. divaricata.
   Twigs dingy-hairy: fruit obovoid: sepals incurved. (6). C. obscura.
10. Fruit red. 11.
    Fruit blackish red. (7). C. multiflora.
    Fruit black. 14.
11. Fruit small (6-8 mm.). C. Dielsiana.
    Fruit large (10 mm.). 12.
12. Outer bud-scales glabrescent. (8). C. integerrima.
    Buds very yellow-hairy. 13.
13. Fruit glabrous. C. bullata.
    Fruit somewhat cottony. C. tomentosa.
14. Buds subglabrescent. 15.
    Buds persistently hairy. C. lucida.
15. Fruit very glaucous, small (7-8 mm.). C. melanocarpa.
    Fruit scarcely glaucous. 16.
16. Fruit small (7-8 mm.). C. moupinensis.
    Fruit larger (8-10 mm.). C. foveolata.

CYDONIA. Quince.
(Family Rosaceae).

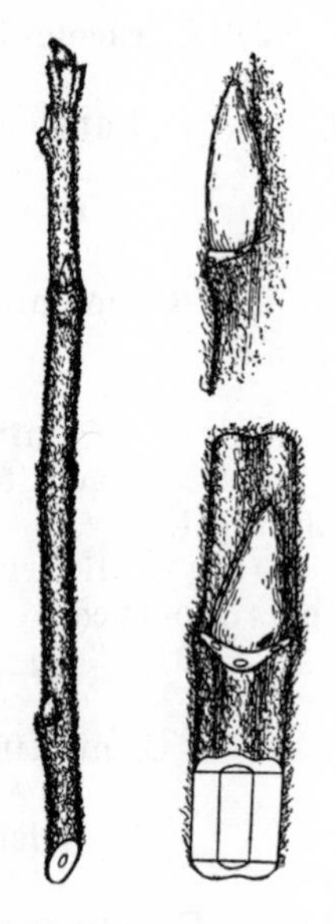

Shrubs or small bushy trees finally with somewhat flaking bark: deciduous. Twigs rather slender, somewhat fluted: pith small, pale, rounded, continuous. Buds solitary, moderate, sessile, conical-oblong, appressed, with 1 or 2 exposed brown scales, the end-bud lacking. Leaf-scars alternate, small, shallow, U-shaped, somewhat raised: bundle traces 3: stipule-scars rather small, elongated.

Only a few winter-character references are to be noted:— Blakeslee & Jarvis, 334, 490, pl.; Bösemann, 50; Schneider, f. 171; Willkomm, 33, 45.

The quince was placed formerly in the genus *Pyrus*. In a systematic study of the anatomy of the Pomaceae, as the group of Rosaceae to which this genus belongs is called, Burgerstein in volume 104 of the Sitzungsberichte of the Vienna Academy of Sciences showed that the structure of its wood is intermediate between the pear and apple components—*Pyrus* and *Malus*—of that still complex genus.

Twigs gray-woolly: buds glabrate. C. oblonga

CHAENOMELES. Japanese Quince.
(Family Rosaceae).

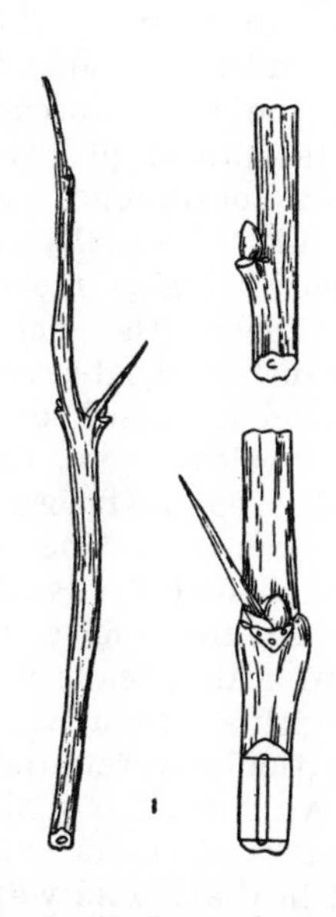

Rather closely branched and small shrubs with slender terminal and axillary twig spines: deciduous. Twigs very slender, round or somewhat angled from the nodes: pith small, pale, rounded, continuous. Buds solitary, small, sessile, round-ovoid, with few exposed scales, collaterally branching in spine-formation, the end-bud lacking. Leaf-scars alternate, small, linear or crescent-shaped or narrowly triangular, strongly raised: bundle-traces 3, minute: stipule-scars somewhat elongated. (*Cydonia*).

The Asiatic or "flowering" quinces, which differ from the true quince in having a considerable number of seeds in each of the rather large core-cavities of their fruit, have been placed in the genus *Cydonia* very commonly. Their winter-characters are discussed by Bösemann, 49; and Schneider, f. 128. The species hybridize.

In an article on the winter-storage of food in the tissues of woody plants, published in the second volume of the Memoirs of the Torrey Botanical Club, Halsted discusses the spines of *C. japonica* as such food-reservoirs.

Twigs glabrous: leaf-scars narrow. (1). C. japonica.
Twigs somewhat hairy: leaf-scars broader. C. chinensis.

PYRUS. Pear. Apple.
(Family Rosaceae).

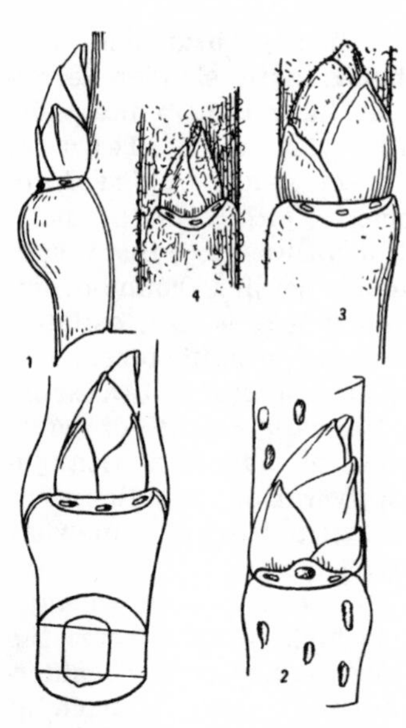

Shrubs or usually moderate-sized trees: deciduous. Twigs moderate, rounded or somewhat angled from the nodes, occasionally ending in spines: pith somewhat angular, continuous. Buds moderate, solitary, sessile, with about 4 exposed scales more or less keeled above, the end-bud sometimes wanting. Leaf-scars alternate, somewhat raised or the nodes swollen below them, linear or U-shaped: bundle-traces 3: stipule-scars lacking. The first two species represent *Pyrus* in *the* restricted sense, the apples often being segregated in a genus *Malus*.

Dwarf fruiting branches or spurs are particularly familiar in this genus. An extensive study of the winter storage of starch, begun on the apple, is published by Halsted in the second volume of Memoirs of the Torrey Botanical Club.—References under *Raphiolepis*.

1. Glabrous: bud-scales submucronate, not margined. 2.
   Buds, at least, often pubescent, their scales sometimes margined. 3.
2. Twigs olive: lenticels inconspicuous. (1). P. communis.
   Twigs red-brown: lenticels conspicuous. (2). P. sinensis.
3. Buds blunt-ovoid: scales subobtuse. (3). P. Malus.
   Buds conical-oblong: scales acute. (Wild Crabs). 4.
4. Twigs glabrate. P. coronarius.
   Persistently woolly. (4). P. ioensis.

ARONIA. Chokeberry.
(Family Rosaceae).

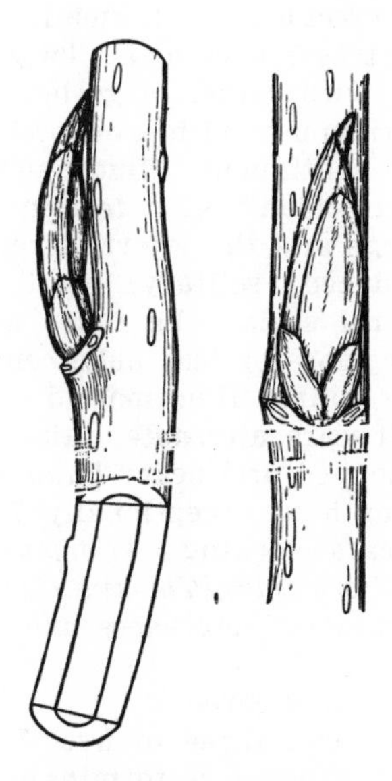

Shrubs: deciduous. Twigs moderate, roundish, glabrous, brown: pith moderate, rounded, pale, subcontinuous. Buds solitary, sessile, oblong, flattened and appressed, with about 5 often abruptly short-pointed more or less glandular-denticulate scales. Leaf-scars alternate, U-shaped, low: bundle-traces 3: stipule-scars lacking. (*Pyrus*).

Aronia, like *Sorbus*, is segregated from *Pyrus* by the less conservative botanists and retained in that genus by those who are more conservative. In common with the firethorn and several other diverse types, it has found lodgment at one time or another in the genus *Mespilus*, now by common consent restricted to the German medlar, *M. germanica.* The only winter-character reference, to *A. arbutifolia*, is Schneider's f. 147.

In curious contrast with the absence of apple-pear hybrids, several crosses are known to occur between mountain-ash (*Sorbus*) and chokeberry (*Aronia*) variously considered to be distinct genera or sections of *Pyrus*: for these the generic name × *Sorbaronia* may be used appropriately.

1. Twigs and buds glabrous.
   (Black chokeberry). (1). A. melanocarpa.
   Twigs more or less woolly. 2.
2. Buds quickly glabrous. (Purple c.) A. atropurpurea.
   Buds somewhat woolly. (Red chokeberry). A. arbutifolia.

SORBUS. Mountain Ash.
(Family Rosaceae).

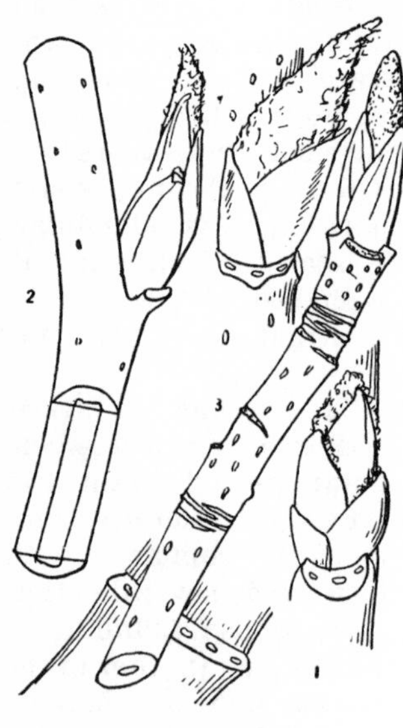

Rather erect-branched, small or moderate trees: deciduous. Twigs moderate, with rather large lenticels, continuous: pith roundish, brownish, continuous. Buds subconical or oblong, the terminal rather large and the lateral often much reduced, solitary, sessile, with several scales, the inner of which are more or less pubescent with long hairs often matted in gum, Leaf-scars alternate, raised, crescent-shaped or linear: bundle-traces 3 or 5 or exceptionally 7: stipule-scars lacking. (*Cormus*, *Hahnia*, *Micromeles*, *Torminaria*). Winter-character references under *Photinia*.

1. Bundle-traces three. 2.
   Bundle-traces three to five. 7.
2. Buds subglobose. S. torminalis.
   Buds elongated. 3.
3. Scales dark-margined. 4.
   Scales not dark-margined. 6.
4. End-bud enlarged. S. Chamaemespilus.
   End-bud scarcely larger than lateral. 5.
5. Buds of equal size. S. latifolia.
   Buds markedly unequal. (White Beam). (1). S. Aria.
6. Scales with scarious-margins. S. Mougeotii.
   Scales not scarious-margined. S. alnifolia.
7. Bundle-traces 3 or 4 or 5: buds woolly. (2). × S. hybrida.
   Bundle-traces five. 8.
8. Buds woolly, not gummy. (Rowan Tree). S. Aucuparia.
   Buds gummy. (Mountain Ash). (3). S. americana.

RAPHIOLEPIS.
(Family Rosaceae).

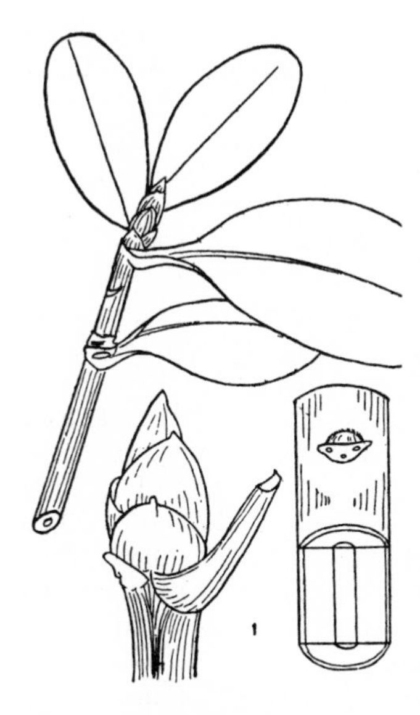

Large tender shrubs: evergreen. Twigs moderate, fluted above: pith rather small, rounded, continuous. Buds solitary, sessile, the lateral minute or suppressed, the terminal moderately large, ovoid, with about 4 abruptly pointed scales. Leaf-scars alternate, clustered toward the tip, half-round or the lower much narrower, scarcely raised: bundle-traces 3: stipule-scars lacking Leaves simple, entire or somewhat toothed.

Winter-character references to *Pyrus*:—*P. amygdaliformis* Schneider, f. 178. *P. baccata.* Bösemann, 52. *P. cathayensis* Shirasawa, 254, pl. 6. *P. communis.* Blakeslee & Jarvis, 330, 334, 484, pl.; Bösemann, 52; Fant, 22, f. 20; Schneider, f. 14, 179; Ward, 1:240, f. 124; Willkomm, 33, f. 46. *P. coronaria.* Otis, 144. *P. ioensis.* Brendel, pl. 3; Hitchcock (1), 5, (3), 14. *P. japonica.* Shirasawa, 252, pl. 5. *P. Malus.* Blakeslee & Jarvis, 330, 334, 486, pl.; Fant, 22, f. 19; Schneider, 148, f. 151; Ward, 1:230, f. 117. *P. Malus austera.* Bösemann, 51, *P. Malus silvestris.* Bösemann, 51; Willkomm, 34, f. 48. *P. mitis.* Bösemann, 51. *P. nivalis.* Bösemann, 52; Schneider, f. 178; Willkomm. 4, 9, 34, f. 47. *P. praecox.* Bösemann, 52. *P. salicifolia.* Schneider, f. 178. *P. sinensis.* Shirasawa, 252, pl. 5. *P. spectabilis.* Schneider, f. 152. *P. Toringo incisa.* Shirasawa, 255, pl. 5.

Glabrous: leaves obovate, pale beneath. R. umbellata.

ERIOBOTRYA. Loquat. Nespera.
(Family Rosaceae).

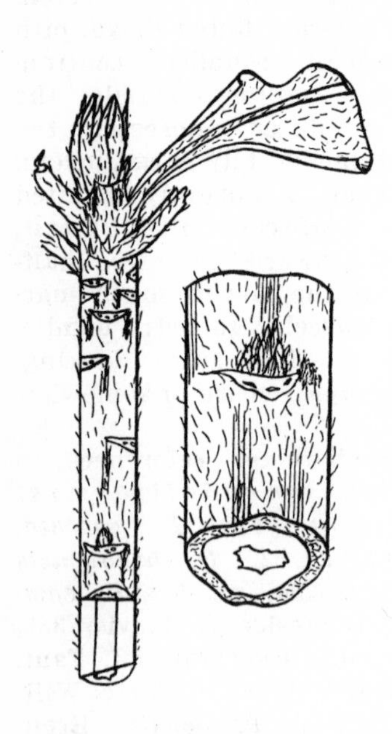

Small tender trees: evergreen. Twigs stout, fluted: pith large, angular, continuous. Buds solitary, sessile, indistinguishable in the pubescense, the terminal ovoid with many paired acute very hairy stipular scales. Leaf-scars alternate, crowded toward the tip, narrowly crescent-shaped or triangular, low: bundle-traces 3: stipule-scars forming linear prolongations of the leaf-scar. Leaves large, oblanceolate, serrate.

Though grown under glass only, in the North, the loquat or nespera is one of the frequent fruit trees in some of the warmer parts of the world and its acid fruits are much liked by those who have come to know them. As a decorative plant, it has nothing to commend it.

Very rusty-hairy, the leaves glabrous above. E. japonica.

The following genus, *Photinia*, in addition to the deciduous species characterized and figured here, contains evergreens with less elevated leaf-scars and lenticels. One such glabrous evergreen is *P. serrulata;* another is the beautiful Californian Christmas-berry, *P. arbutifolia*, which is known often as *Heteromeles*.

PHOTINIA.
(Family Rosaceae).

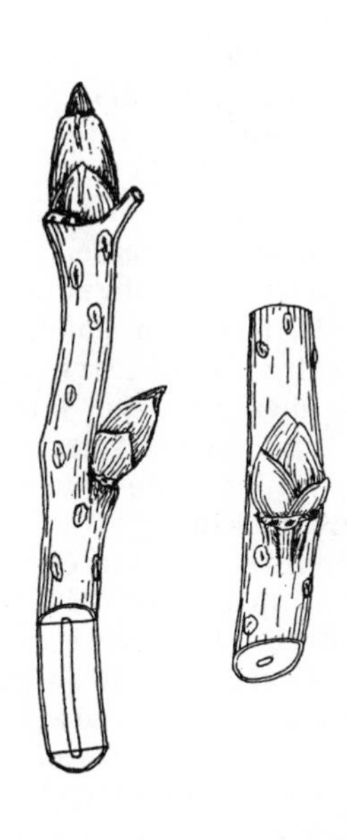

Shrubs: deciduous. Twigs moderate or rather slender, rounded, with large lenticels: pith rather small, continuous. Buds sessile, solitary, ovoid, acute, with about 4 somewhat keeled and mucronate scales, the end-bud lacking. Leaf-scars alternate, 2-ranked, linear-crescent-shaped or somewhat 3-lobed, somewhat raised: bundle-traces 3: stipule-scars lacking.

Photinia has been figured in its essentials by Schneider, f. 74.

Glabrescent. P. villosa.

Winter-character references to *Sorbus*:—*S. americana*. Blakeslee & Jarvis, 488; Otis, 146. *S. Aria*. Bösemann, 78; Fant, 14, f. 8; Ward, 1:237, f. 122-123; Willkomm, 34, f. 49. *S. Aria kamaoensis*. Shirasawa, 251, pl. 5. *S. Aucuparia*. Blakeslee & Jarvis, 488, pl.; Bösemann, 78; Fant, 12, f. 3; Schneider, f. 36; Ward, 1:226, f. 114-115; Willkomm, 11, 35, f. 52. *S. avellana*. Fant, 3, f. 4. *S. Chamaemespilus*. Schneider, f. 170; Willkomm, 35, f. 50. *S. domestica*. Bösemann, 78; Schneider, f. 136; Willkomm, 36, f. 53. × *S. hybrida*. Bösemann, 78; Fant, 13; Schneider, f. 136; Willkomm, 6, 36, f. 54. *S. latifolia*. Schneider, f. 167. *S. Miyabei*. Shirasawa, 257, pl. 5. *S. Mougeotii*. Schneider, f. 170. *S. sambucifolia*. Shirasawa, 248, pl. 5. *S. scandica*. Fant, 13. *S. sitchensis*. Blakeslee & Jarvis, 488. *S. torminalis*. Bösemann, 78; Schneider, f. 18, 167; Ward, 1:236, f. 121; Willkomm, 7, 35, f. 51.

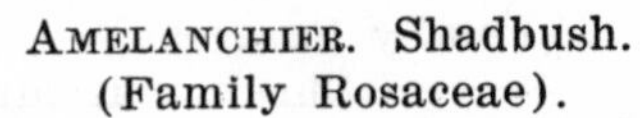

AMELANCHIER. Shadbush.
(Family Rosaceae).

Shrubs or open trees: deciduous. Wood hard, reddish brown, ring-porous with minute ducts. Twigs rather slender, zig-zag, nearly terete: pith somewhat 5-sided, continuous, pale. Buds moderate, solitary, elongated, sessile, with half-a-dozen sometimes twisted scales. Leaf-scars alternate, sometimes 2-ranked, more or less elevated, narrowly crescent- or U-shaped: bundle traces 3: stipule-scars lacking.

Winter-character references:—*A. asiatica.* Shirasawa, 247, pl. 4. *A. canadensis.* Blakeslee & Jarvis, 331, 334, 492, pl.; Brendel, pl 3; Hitchcock (1), 4; Otis, 148; Schneider f. 171.—*A. rotundifolia.* Bösemann, 79; Schneider, f. 171; Willkomm, 32, f. 44. *A. spicata.* Schneider, f. 71.

Buds red-brown or straw-color, slender.
Eastern. (1). A. canadensis.
Buds blackish, stout. Western. A. alnifolia.

Winter-characters of Rosaceae not considered here:—*Mespilus cuneata.* Shirasawa, 252, pl. 5. *M. germanica.* Bösemann, 51; Schneider, f. 74; Willkomm, 32, f. 43. *Peraphyllum ramosissimum.* Schneider, f. 71. *Pourthiaea villosa.* Shira sawa, 247, pl.

CRATAEGUS. Haw. Red Haw.
(Family Rosaceae).

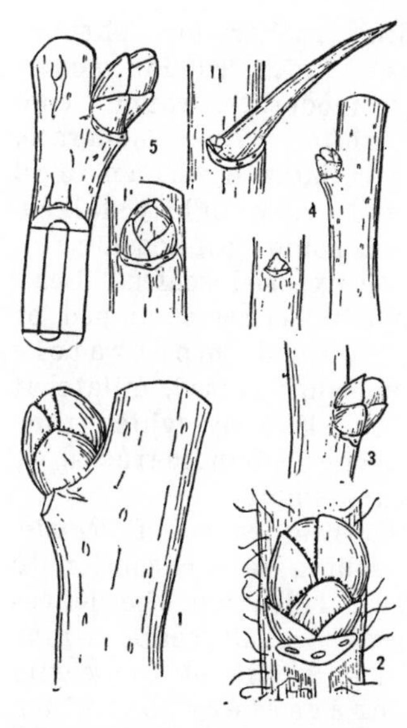

Shrubs or trees, usually with well-developed twig-spines: deciduous. Twigs moderate or rather slender, terete: pith rather small. continuous, roundish. Buds solitary or collaterally branched in spine formation, sessile, round or oblong-ovoid, with some half-dozen exposed fleshy and often bright red scales. Leaf-scars alternate, narrowly crescent-shaped, somewhat raised: bundle-traces 3: stipule-scars small.

A complex aggregate of minor species incapable as yet of delimitation in winter even if they may be known when found with foliage, flowers and fruit: though the pointed habit of growth of *C. Phaenopyrum* (the Washington Thorn), the open round-headed form of *C. mollis* (the common Red-Haw of the prairie region,—1) and its thornless variety *inermis*,—2, the stratified branching of *C. Crus-galli* (the Cockspur Thorn,—3) and *C. punctata*, and the ash-gray outer bark, flaking from the buff-orange inner layer of *C. viridis* (the River Haw,—4) joined to the obvious bud-differences figured, suggest that the task of segregating the more commonly cultivated forms in winter may be less hopeless than it appears at first sight. The European Hawthorns of the gardens are in part *C. oxyacantha* and in part the very similar *C. monogyna*,—5. Winter character references under *Purshia*, p. 123.

RHODOTYPOS.

(Family Rosaceae).

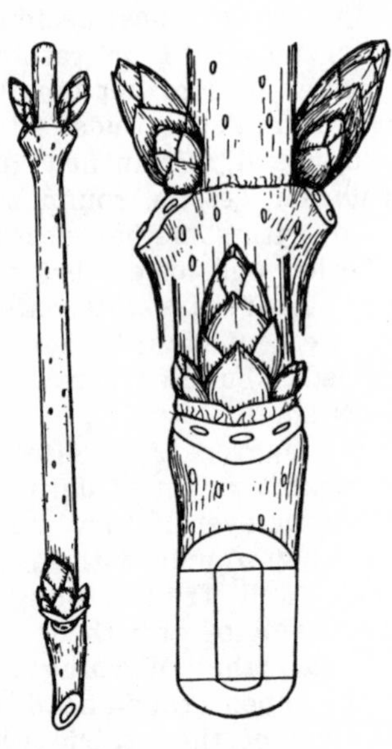

Spreading rather low shrubs: deciduous. Twigs round, moderate: pith moderate, round, continuous, white. Buds moderate, becoming collaterally branched and at length very slightly stalked, ovoid, with some half-dozen pairs of glabrate exposed scales. Leaf-scars opposite, crescent-shaped or somewhat 3-sided, moderately small, somewhat raised, ciliate at top like the line by which they are connected: bundle-traces 3: stipule-scars small.

The opposite leaves of *Rhodotypos* present a rare exception to the general rule that the leaves of Rosaceae are alternate, which to a novice is one of the easily learned characters by which woody Rosaceae may be distinguished at a glance from woody Saxifragaceae, to which they bear a close resemblance sometimes.

From a study of the vascular arrangement in multiple buds, Baldacci and Filipucci have shown in the second volume of the Bulletin of the Boissier Herbarium that in *Rhodotypos*, as in *Coriaria* and many other cases, the supernumerary buds are derivatives of the normal axillary bud and not independent structures.

Winter-characters are figured by Schneider, f. 137.

Twigs olive-brown, glabrate. R. kerrioides.

KERRIA. "Corchorus."
(Family Rosaceae).

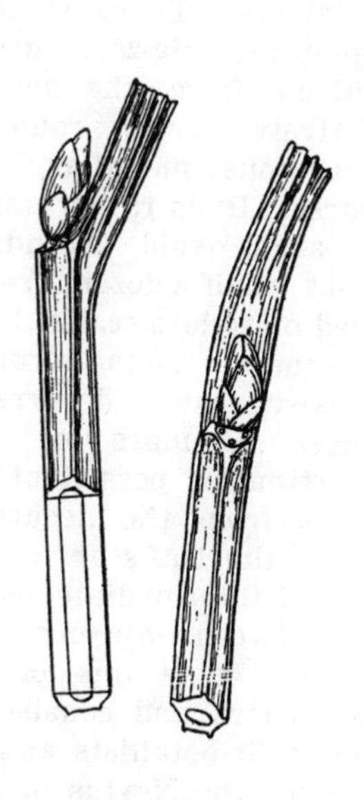

Small shrubs: deciduous. Twigs somewhat 5-angled or ridged, very slender, zig-zag: pith relatively large, white, continuous. Buds solitary, sessile, oblong, with about 5 exposed scales. Leaf scars alternate, often 2-ranked, crescent-shaped or three-sided, somewhat raised, small: bundle-traces 3: stipule-scars small.

Like *Philadelphus*, *Kerria* illustrates the tenacity of Latinized plant names when once established as vernacular names. Introduced as a *Corchorus* — the genus to which the jute plant belongs, the plant still finds corchorus clinging to it as its garden name; just as syringa stands in popular parlance for the mock orange and not for the lilac, which belongs to the genus *Syringa*.

Few people have difficulty in recognizing it at sight, after having made its acquaintance once, for its very slender zig-zag angled bright green twigs are unlike those of anything else that is likely to be seen. Its winter-characters are given by Schneider, f. 137; and Shirasawa, 254.

Twigs green, glabrous: buds subappressed. K. japonica.

NEVIUSIA.

(Family Rosaceae).

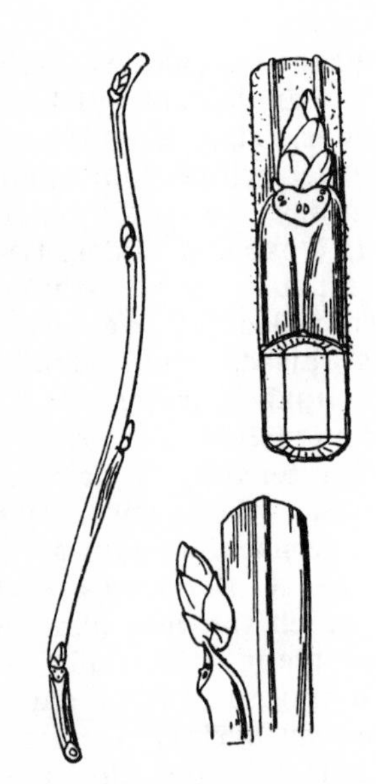

Loosely branched shrubs resembling *Spiraea* and *Physocarpus*: deciduous. Twigs slender. long, somewhat zig-zag, decurrently ridged from the nodes: pith relatively large, rounded, white, continuous: medullary rays rather coarse. Buds rather small, solitary, sessile, ovoid, ascending, with about half-a-dozen somewhat keeled or striate scales. Leaf-scars alternate, round-cordate: slightly raised and decurrent: bundle-traces 3, more or less doubled: stipules persistent as small scales from the decurrent ridges above the leaf-scar.

Neviusia is intermediate in appearance between *Spiraea* and *Physocarpus*. It is one of the very local genera and consists of a single species which was made known to botanists and introduced into cultivation by the reverend Dr. Nevius of Alabama, who sent to the Missouri Botanical Garden the plant from which the accompanying sketch was made.

Winter-characters of *N. alabamensis* are given by Schneider, f. 137.

Twigs golden-brown, puberulent: buds glabrate.
N. alabamensis.

RUBUS. Bramble.
(Family Rosaceae).

Rather soft-wooded simple low shrubs, mostly armed with prickles, occasionally trailing or scrambling over supports: deciduous, or in warm regions more or less evergreen. Shoots moderate, often 5-angled: pith relatively large, brownish, crenately round or sharply 5-angled, continuous. Buds moderate, sessile, oblong, ovoid, commonly superposed with the upper developing the first year or the second smaller and covered by the petiole, and occasionally collaterally branched, with some half-dozen exposed scales. Leaf-scars alternate, torn and irregularly shriveled on the much-raised persistent petiole base: bundle-traces not discernible, but 3 bundles evident when the crescent- or U-shaped petiole remnant is cut across at its base: stipule-scars lacking, but the stipules often persistent at top of the petiole remnant.—Winter-character references under *Neillia*, p. 94.

The brambles, or raspberries and blackberries as they are called usually in this country, vegetatively similar to the roses, present one of the rare instances of deciduous leaves which do not disarticulate by a cleancut abscission but tear away in the autumn. Growers of small-fruit are familiar, too, with the fact that they do not stop their seasonal growth at a definitely limited point but, like many willows, a number of them continue to produce unmatured shoots until stopped by the approach of winter so that their canes, as these long-shoots are called, may die back nearly or quite to the base. In this failure to make advance provision for the winter they stand in marked contrast with such genera as *Ailanthus* and *Tilia*, where, early in the season, a starveling tip of each branch is cut off cleanly by a self-healed scar.

The chief types of *Rubus*,—flowering raspberries, high-bush blackberries, dewberries, red raspberries and black-cap raspberries,—are easily known at any season of the year, but the individual species and their hybrids are much confused.

1. Bark shredding: unarmed.
   (Flowering raspberry). (1). R. odoratus.
   Bark not shredding: trailing or fountain-like. 2.
2. Trailing. (Dewberries). 3.
   Forming open or recurving bushes. 4.
3. Slender and very soft-wooded. R. hispidus.
   Stouter: strong and woody. R. procumbens.
4. Stems characteristically rooting at tip, mostly very glaucous. 5.
   At most exceptionally stoloniferous. 6.
5. Prickles strongly hooked. (Blackcap). R. occidentalis.
   Prickles straighter: canes purple.
   (Purple cane). (2). × R. neglectus.
6. Shoots very glandular-hairy as well as prickly.
   (Wineberry). R. phoenicolasius.
   Scarcely glandular-hairy. 7.
7. Nearly unarmed: dwarf. R. idaeus anomalus.
   Very prickly or else moderately tall. 8.
8. Unarmed.
   Prickly. 9.
9. Prickles bristle-like, often represented by warts in winter. (Red raspberries). 10.
   Prickles stout and persistent. (3). R. allegheniensis.
10. Shoots red, brown, orange or purple. (4). R. strigosus.
    Shoots straw-colored. European. R. idaeus.

POTENTILLA. Cinquefoil.

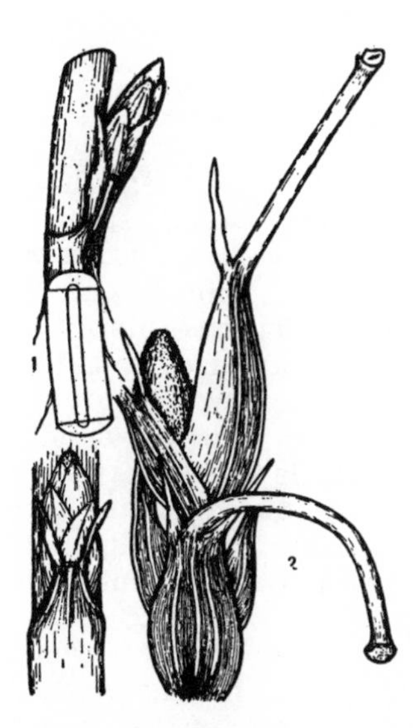

Small scraggly shrubs or mostly herbs: deciduous. Twigs slender, subterete, with quickly exfoliating bark: pith small, roundish, brown, rather spongy. Buds relatively large, solitary, sessile, oblong, with about 4 somewhat striate exposed scales, the inner gray-hairy when visible. Leaf-scars much raised on a clasping 3-nerved base bearing the persistent stipules at top, (or in the second at tip of the persistent petiole), minute, round: bundle-trace 1.

The two woody cinquefoils considered here show interesting morphological features. *P. fruticosa*—the winter-characters of which are described by Bösemann, 74, and Schneider, f. 71—forms ordinary winter buds, of large size for the plant; and these stand in the axils of the persistent stipule-bearing leaf-bases, at top of which small abscission scars have been formed. The buds of *P. tridentata* are to be compound with the hibernacula or subterranean buds in which the growing tips of many perennial herbs pass the winter. As in *Nandina*, disarticulation takes place at a distance above the point where the stipules separate from the winged base of the petiole.

Low-bushy, internodes elongated. (*Dasiphora*: *Sibbaldiopsis*).
(1). P. fruticosa.

Stems very dwarf and tufted, covered by the leaf-bases.
(2). P. tridentata.

FALLUGIA. Apache Plume.
(Family Rosaceae).

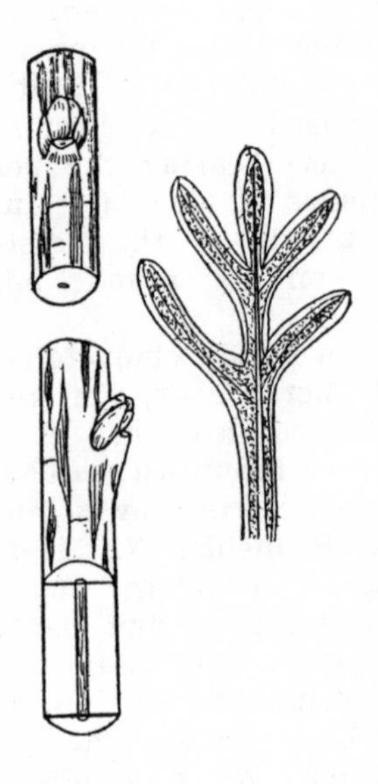

Small shrubs: evergreen. Twigs terete, slender, with splitting creamy outer cortex, becoming red-brown: pith minute, round. Buds small, solitary, sessile, ovoid, with 2 widely parted outer scales. Leaf-scars alternate, half-round minute, much raised. bundle-trace, 1: stipule-scars lacking or indefinite at top of the leaf-cushion. Leaves small, pinnately 3- or 5- lobed, very revolute, not glandular.

Fallugia differs from *Cowania* and *Purshia* in having normal buds, while those of the latter genera usually develop into spurs that remain covered by the bases of fallen leaves as in the hybrid barberry. It is attractive when bearing its plumed fruits, but is not commonly seen in gardens.

Twigs glabrescent: leaves often loosely hairy. F. paradoxa.

COWANIA.
(Family Rosaceae).

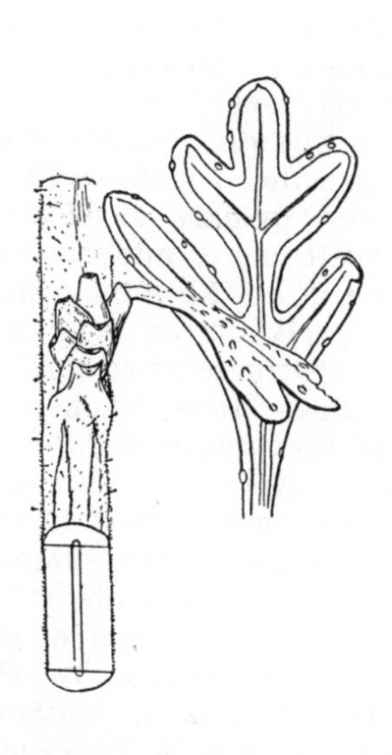

Shrubs: evergreen. Twigs terete, slender, from brown becoming gray with scurfy outer cortex: pith minute, round. Buds solitary, sessile, at first ovoid with 2 outer scales but rather quickly developing short branches sheathed by overlapping leaf-bases. Leaf-scars alternate, half-round, minute, much raised on thin winged bases topped by the rather persistent stipules: bundle-trace 1, indistinct. Leaves as in *Fallugia* but very glandular-warty, or in one species (*C. ericaefolia*) minute, entire, and pungent.

Cowania, *Fallugia*, and *Purshia* are three genera with rather similar leaves. As in *Potentilla*, these disarticulate from the top of a dilated persistent base corresponding to the lower part of the petiole with stipules attached to its sides. Leaf-bases of this sort, which are found in a number of Rosaceae, are more frequent in the related family Leguminosae, and transitions may be found between extreme cases like these and the less produced but otherwise comparable leaf-cushion found in the greater number of rosaceous and leguminous genera.

Twigs from bristly and puberulent glabrescent.

C. Stansburiana

CERCOCARPUS. Mountain Mahogany.
(Family Rosaceae).

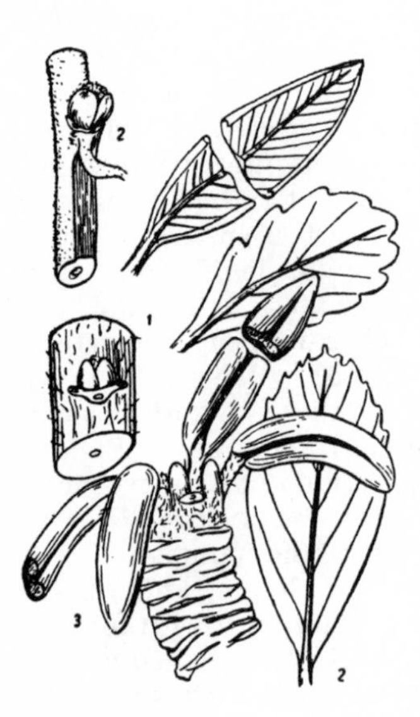

Shrubs or small trees: evergreen. Twigs terete, rather slender, commonly forming dwarf spurs closely covered by old leaf-scars: pith minute, rounded. Buds solitary, sessile, round, with 2 outer scales, quickly developing. Leaf-scars alternate, minute, half round, at top of the stipule-base, or transversely linear and low with 3 bundle-traces after the fall of this base. Leaves obovate, flat and toothed, or lanceolate, revolute and entire.

No one who has walked in the western mountains in late summer can have failed to have his attention drawn to one or other of the species of *Cercoparpus* by the clematis-like clusters of feathery fruits that terminate its short twigs, and from which the name of the genus has been derived. There is a marked contrast between the leaves of the first two species and of the other two.

1. Leaves toothed and nearly flat. 2.
   Leaves entire and very revolute, varnished. 3.
2. Teeth rounded: Rocky Mountains. (1). C. parvifolius.
   Teeth pointed: California. (2). C. betulaefolius.
3. Leaves minute (1 × 5 mm.), teretely revolute. (3). C. intricatus.
   Leaves larger (25 mm. long), revolute at margin. (4). C. ledifolius.

PURSHIA. Antelope Brush.
(Family Rosaceae).

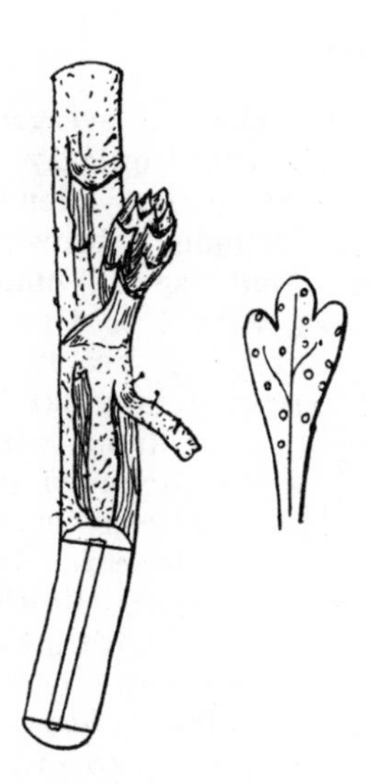

Spreading rather rigidly branched shrubs. Twigs somewhat fluted, becoming terete, slender, with quickly flaking cortex: pith minute, angular, continuous, light brown. Buds solitary, sessile, ovoid, with several more or less ciliate scales, rather quickly developing into short branches covered by the overlapping leaf-bases. Leaf-scars alternate, half-round, with 1 bundle-trace, minute, much raised on thin winged bases topped by the stipules, or these finally falling and their linear scars encircling the stem. (*Tigarea; Kunzia*).

Purshia is hardly to be counted a decorative plant.

Twigs at first somewhat hairy and bristly. P. tridentata

Winter-character references to *Crataegus*:—*C. azarolus*. Bösemann, 50; Schneider, f. 172. *C. coccinea*. Hitchcock (1). 4, (3), 15, (4), 137, f. 71-73. *C. crus-galli*. Bösemann, 50; Schneider, f. 173. *C. monogyna*. Bösemann, 50; Fant, 20; Schneider, f. 110, 172. *C. mollis*. Hitchcock (1), 4, (3), 15. *C. nigra*. Schneider, f. 174. *C. Oxyacantha*. Bösemann, 50; Fant, 26, f. 23; Schneider, f. 174; Ward, 1:194, f. 97-98; Willkomm, 8, 10, 31, f. 41. *C. punctata*. Otis, 150. *C. sanguinea*. Schneider, f. 172. *C. tanacetifolia*. Schneider, f. 173. *C. tomentosa*. Brendel, pl. 3; Hitchcock (1), 4.

CHAMAEBATIA.

(Family Rosaceae).

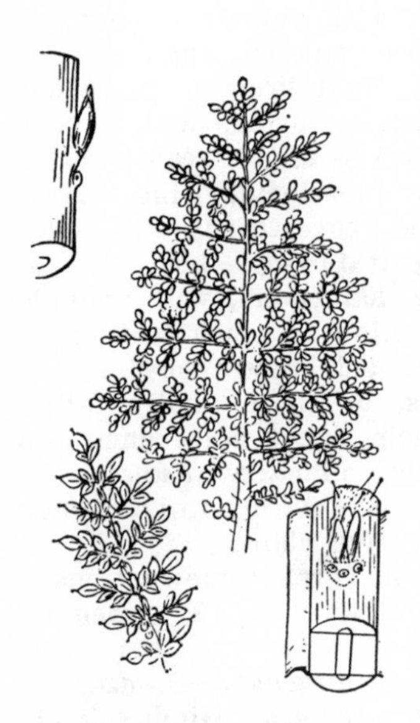

Small hairy shrubs: evergreen. Twigs terete with quickly exfoliating bark, rather slender: pith small, rounded, brownish, continuous. Buds small, oblong, acute, 2-edged, with 2 or 4 scales Leaf-scars alternate, nearly encircling the twig, triangular, obliterated by the deciduous cortex but evident on the denuded twig as 3 subconfluent circles, each a bundle-trace: stipule-scars lacking. Leaves subsessile, elliptical-ovate, thrice pinnate, with minute overlapping rather acute leaflets.

Chamaebatia, like *Chamaebatiaria*, is a delicate evergreen with fern-like leaves cut into minute leaflets. It is easily distinguished from the latter genus in its more decompound foliage with the very small leaflets glandular-mucronate. Neither genus is approached in delicacy of foliage by any other flowering plant likely to be seen by the ordinary observer.

Twigs glandular-bristly, very smooth when denuded.
C. foliolosa.

ROSA.
(Family Rosaceae).

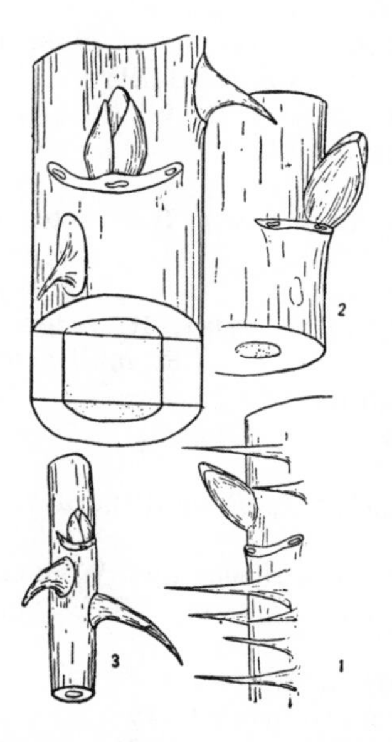

Shrubs, mostly armed with prickles, occasionally trailing or scrambling: deciduous or exceptionally evergreen. Shoots moderate, terete: pith relatively large, brownish, rounded. Buds rather small, solitary, sessile, ovoid, with 3 or 4 exposed scales, sometimes a litle above the axil. Leaf-scars alternate, low, narrowly and shallowly U-shaped or almost linear: bundle-traces 3: stipule-scars lacking. Suckers are usually more prickly than the ordinary branches, from which characters are taken here.

Winter-character references: — *Rosa alpina*. Bösemann, 44. *R. arvensis*. Bösemann, 44. *R. baltica*. Bösemann, 44. *R. canina*. Bösemann, 45; Fant, 23, f. 21; Ward, 1:201, f. 102; Willkomm, 36, f. 55. *R. carelica*. Fant, 24. *R. centifolia*. Bösemann, 45. *R. centifolia muscosa*. Bösemann, 45. *R. cinnamomea*. Böseman, 45, Fant, 24. *R. collina*. Fant, 24. *R. coriifolia*. Fant, 24. *R. gallica*. Bösemann, 44. *R. inodora* Fant, 23. *R. lucida*. Bösemann, 44. *R lutea*. Bösemann, 45. *R. mollissima*. Fant, 24. *R. multiflora*. Shirasawa, 250. *R. pimpinellaefolia*. Bösemann, 44. *R. pomifera*. Bösemann, 45; Fant, 24. *R. pratincola*. Hitchcock (3), 14, (4), 136, f. 69-70. *R. pumila*. Bösemann, 45. *R. rubiginosa*. Bösemann, 46; Fant, 23; Schneider, f. 147. *R. spinosissima*. Schneider, f. 147. *R. tomentosa*. Fant, 24. *R. turbinata*. Bösemann, 44.

Though they often present marked and characteristic differences when really comparable parts are compared, the roses differ so greatly in their individual branches that any effort to key the species out on vegetative characters must be taken with a large degree of allowance for fallibility.

1. Prostrate: evergreen. (Memorial rose). R. Wichuraiana.
   Scrambling or climbing, or fountain-like. 2.
   Bushy: deciduous. 4.
2. Evergreen: very prickly. (Macartney rose). R. bracteata.
   Deciduous. 3.
3. Forming fountain-like clumps. (Prairie rose). R. setigera.
   High climbing. (Ramblers). R. multiflora.
4. Small (scarcely a half-meter high as a rule). 5.
   Taller (usually 1-2 m. high). 6.
5. Prickles widened at base. (Baby rambler). R. multiflora var.
   Prickles needle-like. (Wild roses). R. acicularis, humilis, pratincola and Woodsii.
6. Essentially unarmed except the suckers. R. blanda.
   Characteristically prickly. 7.
7. Prickles needle-like, nearly straight. 8.
   Prickles flattened at base or strongly hooked. 10.
8. Stems stout: planted everywhere. (1). R. rugosa.
   Stems rather slender. 9.
9. Rather dwarf. (Scotch rose). R. spinosissima.
   About 2 m. high. (Yellow rose). R. foetida.
10. Stems green. 11.
    Stems red or purple. 12.
11. Prickles much dilated. (Dog rose). (2). R. canina.
    Prickles not greatly dilated. (Sweetbrier). (3). R. rubiginosa.
12. Stems rather pink and glaucous. R. rubrifolia.
    Stems purple. R. cinnamomea.

OSMARONIA. Osoberry.
Family Rosaceae).

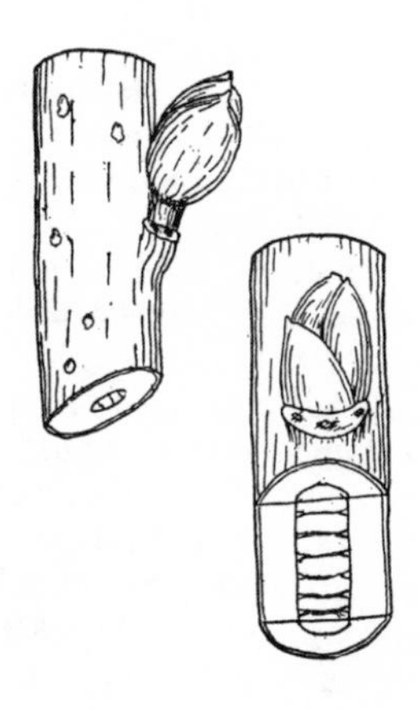

Shrubs or subarborescent: deciduous. Twigs moderate, terete: pith rather large, rounded, pale, chambered. Buds sessile or more or less supra-axillary or stalked. ovoid, obtuse, with about 3 exposed mucronulate scales. Leaf-scars alternate, somewhat-crowded at tip, shallow U-shaped or narrowly crescent-shaped, little raised: bundle-traces 3: stipule-scars lacking. (*Nuttallia*).

The winter-characters of *Osmaronia* (or *Nuttallia*) *cerasiformis* are given by Schneider, f. 74.

Osmaronia is a distinctively Californian genus locally differentiated into distinguishable forms but in the minds of conservative botanists doubtfully divisible into as many species.

Glabrous: twigs purplish: buds green. O. cerasiformis.

MADDENIA.

(Family Rosaceae).

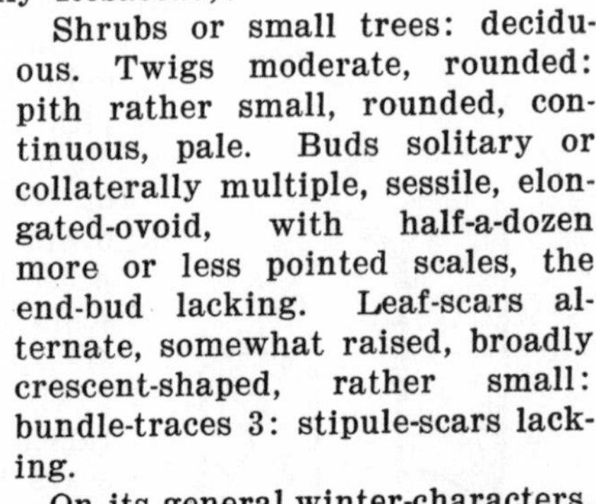

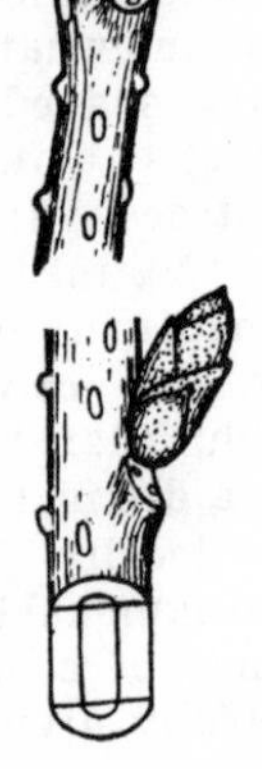

Shrubs or small trees: deciduous. Twigs moderate, rounded: pith rather small, rounded, continuous, pale. Buds solitary or collaterally multiple, sessile, elongated-ovoid, with half-a-dozen more or less pointed scales, the end-bud lacking. Leaf-scars alternate, somewhat raised, broadly crescent-shaped, rather small: bundle-traces 3: stipule-scars lacking.

On its general winter-characters, *Maddenia hypoxantha* would be taken for a species of *Prunus* lacking the terminal bud as the plums do, but with the peculiar pitted marking of its bud-scales shown by the common choke-cherry of the Eastern States. Several Asiatic species are known, of which one has been introduced to a small extent in this country.

Glabrescent: bud-scales brown, pitted. M. hypoxantha.

PRUNUS. Plum, Cherry, etc.
(Family Rosaceae).

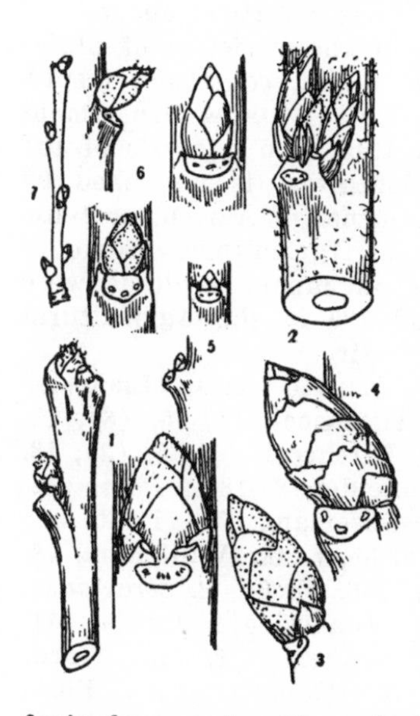

Shrubs or trees: deciduous, or the cherry laurels evergreen. Twigs slender or moderate, subterete or somewhat angled from the nodes, occasionally spine tipped: pith roundish or angled, pale or brown, continuous. Buds solitary or collaterally multiple, sessile, subglobose or mostly ovoid, with usually a half-dozen exposed scales, the end-bud lacking in certain groups (apricots, plums). Leaf-scars alternate, raised on a cushion flanked by the stipule vestiges or scars, half-round or half-elliptical, small: bundle-traces 3, usually minute.

Leaves of the evergreens are simple, mostly entire, and with round nectar-disks on the back.

Like *Pyrus*, this genus is confusingly complex through inclusion of such diverse forms as the evergreen cherry-laurels and the deciduous types represented by peach, apricot, plum, cherry and bird-cherry, which nevertheless do not segregate by characters satisfactory to many botanists.

Though the different cherries are sufficiently distinct from one another, the American plums are almost as troublesome as the red haws. Only the most distinct of their types are differentiated in the key here given.

A classified bibliography of *Prunus* is given by Rehder in volume three of the Bradley Bibliography, compiled by him at the Arnold Arboretum.

The most sumptuous American publication on *Prunus* is contained in Hedrick's large volumes on The Cherries of New York and The Plums of New York. Critical analysis of our native species of *Prunus* and of the varieties of plums derived from American species, by Wight, constitute respectively Bulletins 179 and 172 of the United States Department of Agriculture,—both published in 1915. An analysis of the pubescent-fruited species of the Southwest is published by Mason in the first volume of the Journal of Agricultural Research, issued by the Department of Agriculture. Some of Professor Bailey's earlier opinions on Japanese plums were published in Bulletins 62, 106, and 139 of the Agricultural Experiment Station at Cornell University.

Winter-characters of *Prunus*:—*P. americana*. Blakeslee & Jarvis, 508, pl.; Brendel, pl. 3; Hitchcock (1), 5, (3), 13, (4), 136, f. 54-58. *P. angustifolia*. Hitchcock (1), 5, (3), 13, *P. Armeniaca*. Bösemann, 53; Schneider, f. 183. *P. avium*. Blakeslee & Jarvis. 341, 502, pl.; Bösemann, 53; Fant, 21; Schneider, f. 185; Ward, 1:50, f. 32, 69, f. 48; Willkomm, 38, f. 60. *P. Buergeriana*. Shirasawa, 256, pl. 6. *P. cerasoides*. Shirasawa, 256, pl. 6. *P. Cerasus*. Blakeslee & Jarvis, 341, 504, pl.; Bösemann, 53; Fant, 21; Schneider, f. 185; Ward, 1:245, f. 128; Willkomm, 39, f. 61. *P. Chamaecerasus*. Bösemann, 53. *P. chicasa*. Hitchcock (1), f. 9-10, (4), 136, f. 49. *P.* (*Amygdalus*) *communis*. Schneider, f. 184. *P. domestica*. Blakeslee & Jarvis, 508, pl.; Bösemann, 52; Fant, 21, f. 16; Schneider, f. 188; Ward, 1:243, f. 126; Willkomm, 3, 39, f. 62. *P. fruticosa*. Schneider, f. 187. *P. Grayana*. Shirasawa, 256, pl. 6. *P. insititia*. Bösemann, 53; Fant, 22, f. 17; Schneider, f. 188; Willkomm, 39, f. 63. *P. intermedia*. Schneider, f. 187. *P. japonica*. Shirasawa, 245, pl. 6. *P. Mahaleb*. Bösemann, 53; Schneider, f. 41, 128; Willkomm, 38, f. 59. *P. Miqueliana*. Shirasawa, 255, pl. 6. *P. Mume*. Shirasawa, 253. *P. Myrobalana*. Schneider, f. 186. *P. nana*. Bösemann, 75; Schneider, f. 184. *P. nigra*. Blakeslee & Jarvis, 341, 506, pl.; Otis

160. *P. Padus.* Bösemann, 53; Fant, 20, f. 15; Schneider, f 184; Ward, 1:241, f. 125; Willkomm, 3, 38, f. 58. *P. pennsylvanica.* Blakeslee & Jarvis, 332, 341, 500, pl.; Otis, 158. *P. Persica.* Blakeslee & Jarvis, 332, 334, 341, 512, pl.; Bösemann, 74; Price, Bulletin 39, Texas Agr. Exper. Station, 828, f. 13-15; Schneider, f. 183; Shirasawa, 253. *P. pseudocerasus.* Shirasawa, 256, pl. 6. *P. pumila.* Schneider, f. 186. *P. serotina.* Blakeslee & Jarvis, 341, 496, pl.; Brendel, pl. 3; Hitchcock (1), 5; Otis, 154; Schaffner & Tyler, Ohio Naturalist, 1:31; Schneider, f. 48, 183. *P. spinosa.* Bösemann, 53; Fant, 22, f. 17; Schneider, f. 96, 186; Ward, 1:245, f. 127; Willkomm, 4, 9, 40, f. 64. *P. tomentosa.* Shirasawa, 253, pl. 6. *P. triflora.* Blakeslee & Jarvis, 508, pl. *P. triloba.* Schneider, f. 185. *P. virginiana.* Blakeslee & Jarvis, 341, 498, pl.; Hitchcock (3), 14; Otis, 156.

1. Evergreen: leaves entire or slightly toothed. 2.
   Deciduous. 3.
2. Tree: leaves rather lanceolate, about 3 × 8 cm.
   (American cherry laurel). P. caroliniana.
   Subarborescent: leaves rather ovate, about 4 × 10 cm.
   (European cherry laurel). P. Laurocerasus.
3. End-bud present. 4.
   End-bud deciduous. (Plums; apricot). 14.
4. Twigs green or red. 5.
   Twigs brown or gray. 6.
5. Buds hairy: tree. (Peach). (1). P. Persica.
   Buds glabrous: twigs slender: low shrubs.
   (Flowering almond). P. nana.
6. Stipules persistent or broken above the base: shrub. 7.
   Stipules deciduous from the leaf-cushion. 8.
7. Loosely hairy: stipules setaceous. (2). P. tomentosa.
   Glabrate or puberulent: stipules deeply fimbriate.
8. Twigs more or less velvety. 9. P. triloba.
   Twigs glabrous. 10.

9. Buds round-ovoid, spreading. P. Mahaleb.
   Buds oblong, appressed, glabrous. P. Padus.
10. Buds dull brown, ovoid: scales rough. (3). P. virginiana.
   Buds clear brown or glossy. 11.
11. Buds conical, light brown. P. Maackii.
   Buds ovoid. 12.
12. Buds small (2 × 4 mm.), glossy: scales rather fleshy. (Wild black cherry). P. serotina.
   Buds large (3 × 5-7 mm.). 13.
13. Buds glossy, ovoid-fusiform. (Sweet cherry). (4). P. avium.
   Buds duller or darker, round-ovoid. (Sour cherry). P. Cerasus.
14. Buds scarcely longer than thick. 15.
   Buds more elongated. 16.
15. Buds half-covered by the ciliate leaf-cushion, twigs slender, red. (Southern plum). (5). P. angustifolia.
   Buds protruding: twigs velvety, very spiny. P. spinosa.
16. Buds broadly ovoid. 17.
   Buds ovoid-fusiform. 19.
17. Buds dark: scales ciliate. (Apricot). P. Armeniaca.
   Buds light brown, puberulent. (European plums). 18.
18. Twigs glabrous. P. domestica.
   Twigs velvety. (Damson). P. insititia.
19. Twigs velvety. 20.
   Twigs glabrous. 21.
20. Low and spreading: buds velvety. P. maritima.
   Tall. P. americana mollis.
21. Buds velvety: twigs slender. (7). P. cerasifera.
   Buds glabrous: twigs stouter or stiff. (Wild plums). 22.
22. Buds red-brown, short (3-4 mm.). (6). P. americana.
   Buds black or gray, large (4-5 mm.) and subconical. P. nigra.

PRINSEPIA.
(Family Rosaceae).

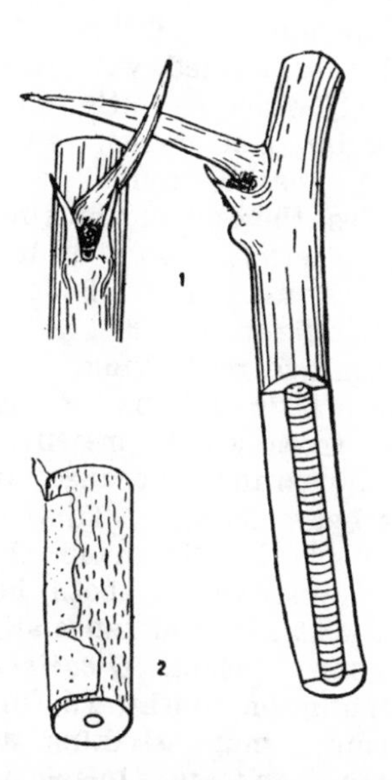

Shrubs, with rather short supra-axillary spines somewhat constricted at base: deciduous. Twigs long and slender, round: Pith moderate, round, yellowish, chambered or finally hollowed out except for annular lines about the cavity. Buds solitary (or the spine representing a second), small, indistinctly scaly, concealed in brown hairs that line the stipules and fill the axil, the end-bud lacking. Leaf-scars alternate, small, half-round, raised: bundle-trace 1: stipules rather large becoming firm and persistent at top of the swollen leaf-cushion.

Prinsepia, unlike most Rosaceae, which have solid pith, has its pith chambered or finally excavated, as Solereder indicates in his Systematic Anatomy of the Dicotyledons. Mention of this discovery is made in a paper on chambered or discoid pith by Foxworthy in the Proceedings of the Indiana Academy of Science for 1903. It is one of a small group differing in a number of respects from other Rosaceae.

Some Prinsepias are sometimes called *Plagiospermum*, but the two genera are not considered sufficiently distinct for segregation by other botanists. They are among the earliest shrubs to come into leaf in spring.

Twigs becoming brown. (1). P. sinensis.
Twigs persistently gray. (2). P. uniflora.

ALBIZZIA.
(Family Leguminosae).

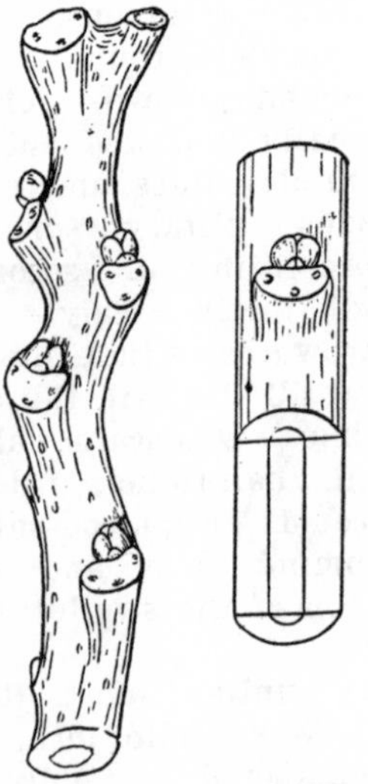

Trees: deciduous. Twigs moderately slender, angled, with rather evident lenticels: pith moderate, angular, continuous. Buds superposed, sessile, round, with 2 or 3 scales, the end-bud lacking. Leaf-scars alternate, more or less 2-ranked, somewhat 3-lobed, raised: bundle-traces 3, rather large: stipule-scars lacking.

The julibrissin is one of the distinctive trees which present a tropical appearance because of their feathery foliage. This is most seen in the North in the locust and rose acacia, both belonging to *Robinia*, and especially in the honey locust, *Gleditsia*. From Washington southward, this effect becomes more striking as the still more delicate *Albizzia* is encountered, and as subtropical and tropical conditions are reached the variety of trees of this type increases. A somewhat similar effect is produced by a few genera like *Zizyphus* and *Coriaria* which bear simple leaves but produce clusters of slender leafy twigs each year which simulate tufts of compound leaves.

In the West Indies, a graceful tree of this genus (*A. Lebbek*) is much planted under the name of woman's tongue,—its thin clustered legumes rustling pleasingly on every impulse.

Twigs brownish. A. Julibrissin.

ACACIA.
(Family Leguminosae.)

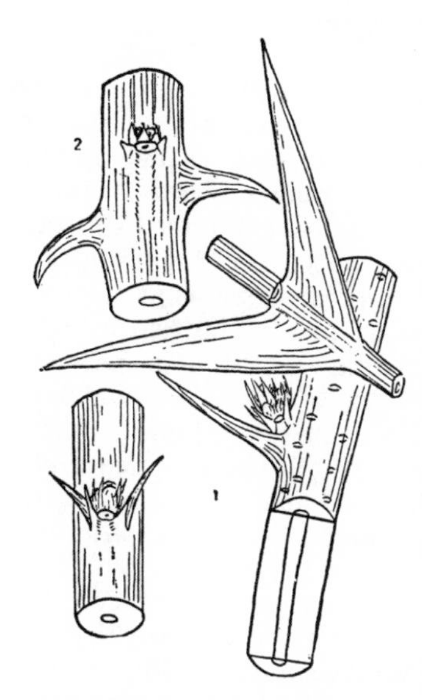

Tender shrubs or small trees, usually with stipular spines or with strong prickles away from the nodes: more or less evergreen. Twigs slender, zig-zag, somewhat angular: pith small. roundish, continuous. Buds solitary, sessile, small, usually quickly developing into short spurs covered by leaves or their bases and sometimes bristling with pungent stipules, the end-bud lacking. Leaf-scars alternate, small, elliptical, somewhat raised: bundle-trace 1: stipules sometimes present as strong sometimes greatly enlarged spines, which in many tropical species are inhabited by pugnacious ants. An account of these (contributed by Safford) is to be found under the caption bull-horn in the Standard Cyclopedia of Horticulture. Leaves, if present, bipinnate (in Australian species reduced to their dilated vertical petioles or phyllodia).

1. Unarmed: stems very angular, hairy. A. filicina.
   Armed with pungent stipules or prickles. 2.
2. Stipules strong and pungent. 3.
   Stipules weak: stems with strong hooked prickles. 4.
3. Spines short or swollen. (1). A. Farnesiana.
   Spines becoming long (3-4 cm.) and slender. A. constricta.
4. Twigs brown: leaflets 3×10 mm. (2). A. Roemeriana.
   Twigs becoming gray: leaflets small (2×5 mm.).
   (Texas Mimosa). A. Greggii.

LEUCAENA. White Popinac.
(Family Leguminosae).

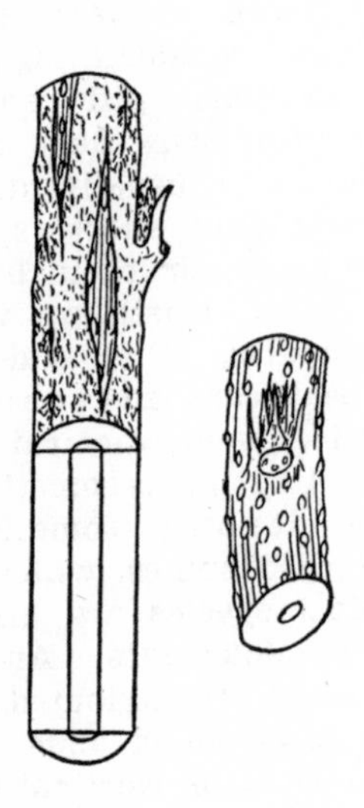

Tender graceful trees: evergreen. Twigs moderate or rather slender, terete: pith rather small, round, continuous, white. Buds solitary, sessile, ovoid, with stipular scales only. Leaf-scars alternate, 2-ranked, somewhat elevated, rather small, half-elliptical: bundle-traces 3: stipules persistent at top of the leaf-cushion. Leaves abruptly bipinnate with numerous small oblong inequilateral whitened leaflets. The fruit, when present, is of long thin legumes.

Winter-character references to Leguminosae not considered here: *Caesalpinia sepiaria*. Shirasawa, 234, pl. 2. *Calycotome spinosa*. Schneider, f. 82. *Dorycnium suffruticosum*. Schneider, f. 140 *Hedysarum multijugum*. Schneider, f. 72. *Indigofera Gerardiana*. Schneider, f. 134. *Lespedeza bicolor*. Schneider, f. 73. *Ononis fruticosa*. Schneider, f. 70. *Petteria* (*Laburnum*) *ramentacea*. Schneider, f. 72.

Twigs light brown, warty, for a time puberulent. L. glauca.

PROSOPIS. Mesquite.
(Family Leguminosae).

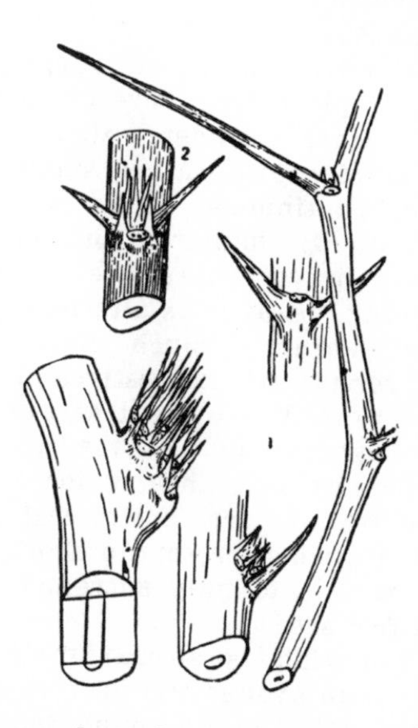

Shrubs or small trees. Twigs moderate, zig-zag: pith minute, angular, continuous. Buds minute, rather quickly developing into stout spurs bristling with stipules and frequently flanked by a solitary spine or mostly a pair of terete nearly straight spines, the end-bud lacking. Leaf-scars alternate, often 2-ranked, somewhat raised, rounded or elliptical: bundle-traces 3: stipules long persistent. Leages of 2 pinnate leaflets terminating the petiole, or of 4 such leaflets. (Includes *Strombocarpa*).

Notwithstanding its compound leaves, their characteristic drooping position and the openly branched top of the tree cause a grove of mesquite to suggest a peach orchard to many people when they see it for the first time. As in many other Leguminosae the stipules of *Prosopis* persist, even when they are not converted into spines; and their presence gives a peculiar shaggy appearance to the axillary spurs on which the foliage is clustered.

The screw-bean or tornillo, *P. pubescens*, is separated frequently from the other species under the generic name *Strombocarpa*.

1. Stipules becoming spines: downy. (1). P. pubescens.
   Spines not representing the nodal stipules. 2.
2. Glabrous. (Common mesquite). (2). P. glandulosa.
   Leaves, and twigs above, gray-pubescent. P. velutina.

TAMARINDUS. Tamarind.
(Family Leguminosae).

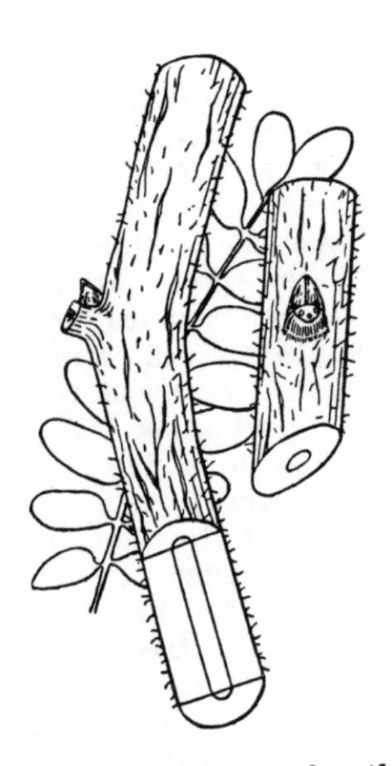

Large round-topped rough-barked tropical tree: evergreen. Twigs rather slender, zig-zag, nearly terete: pith rather small, rounded, continuous. Buds solitary, sessile, triangular, with 2 or 3 exposed brown scales, the end-bud lacking. Leaf-scars alternate, 2-ranked, abruptly much elevated, half-round: stipule vestiges or scars more or less evident at top of the leaf-cushion. Leaves abruptly pinnate with about a dozen pairs of inequilateral entire leaflets. Fruit, when present, a short legume with acid pulp surrounding the few seeds.

The tamarind is sometimes planted as an avenue tree in tropical countries, and its round top and dense fleecy foliage make it unusually effective for this use.

Like the chick-pea, its foliage is reputed to produce an acid which renders the dew or rain that drips from them, or water that stands on them after they have fallen, so extremely caustic as to disintegrate fabrics on which it falls; and the Hindus are said to be afraid to sleep under the trees.

Twigs dull brown, sparingly soft-hairy. T. indica.

CERCIS. Redbud. Judas Tree.
(Family Leguminosae).

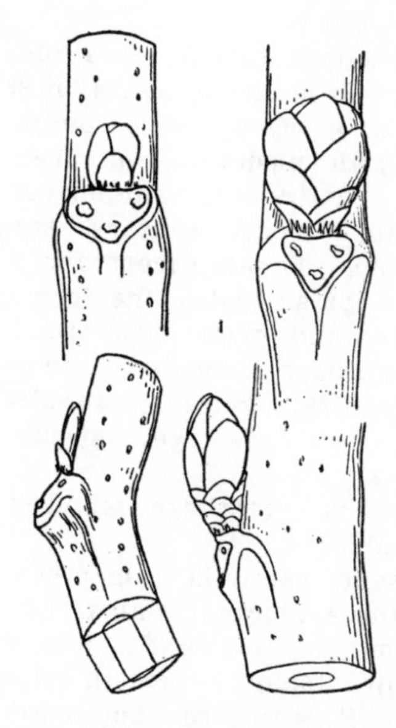

Shrubs or small trees: deciduous. Twigs moderate, zig-zag, subterete: pith roundish, continuous, pale or pinkish. Buds glabrous, superposed, the upper slightly stalked, the lower sessile and covered by the top of the leaf-scar, ovoid or obovoid, with 2 or, in case of flower-buds, several often keeled scales, the end-bud lacking. Leaf-scars alternate, 2-ranked, somewhat raised, obtusely triangular, with decurrent ridges, fringed at top: bundle-traces 3: stipule-scars lacking.

Winter-character references: — *C. canadensis*. Blakeslee & Jarvis, 332, 518, pl.; Brendel, 27, 30, pl. 4; Hitchcock (1), 4, (3), 12, (4), 185, f. 41; Otis, 166; Schneider, f. 91. *C. chinensis*. Shirasawa, 245, pl. 4. *C. Siliquastrum*. Schneider, f. 91.

Though the Old World species of *Cercis* are not successfully grown in the interior of the country, the native redbud (*C. canadensis*) is much planted, and, with *Cornus florida*, it makes a most effective combination in the native forest.

1. Buds short (2-3 mm.). 2.
   Buds elongated (5 mm.), closely appressed, acute.
   (Judas tree). C. Siliquastrum.
2. Buds ovoid or obovoid, blunt: twigs reddish.
   (Redbud). (1). C. canadensis.
   Buds acute: twigs greenish.

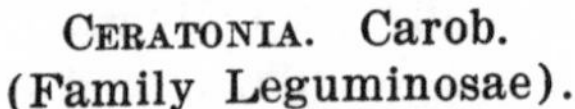

CERATONIA. Carob.
(Family Leguminosae).

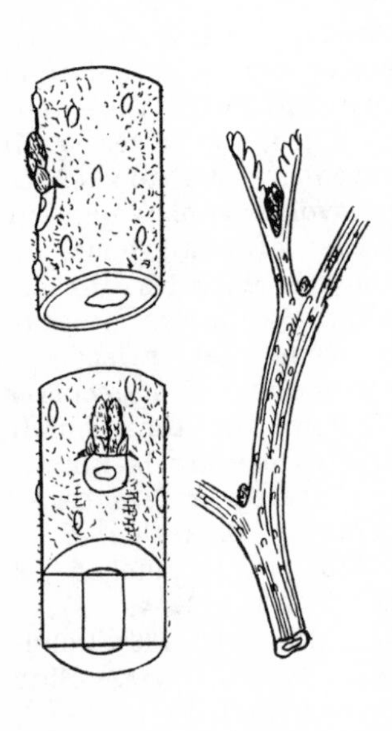

Round-topped tender trees: deciduous. Twigs moderate, at first somewhat grooved but becoming terete: pith moderate, obscurely angled, continuous, salmon-colored. Buds small, solitary, sessile, oblong, naked except for a pair of stipular scales, the terminal larger and more open. Leaf-scars alternate, 2-ranked, suborbicular, little raised: bundle-trace 1, rather large: stipule scars small.

Winter-characters are pictured by Schneider, f. 73.

The name carob is a modification of the Arabic name algaroba: it is commonly called St. John's bread, or Johannisbrot in the German cities where the sweet pulp of its pods is much liked by children. It is said to be an important forage plant in the Mediterranean region, and under favorable cultural conditions to produce a greater food yield per acre than alfalfa, averaging several hundred pounds of pods to the tree each year and in some cases producing over a ton to the tree. Efforts are being made to introduce it into the warmer parts of the United States as a staple crop.

Twigs gray-velvety, with large brown lenticels. C. Siliqua.

GLEDITSIA. Honey Locust.
(Family Leguminosae).

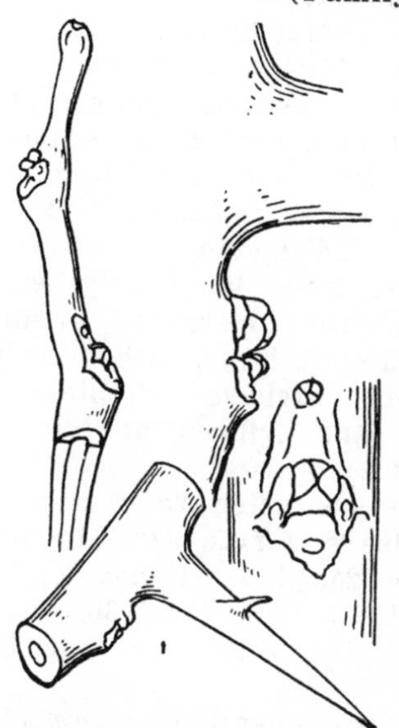

Trees, often large and spreading, usually armed with often horridly compound spines arising above the axils and persisting on the trunk. Twigs moderate, somewhat nodose and zig-zag, irregularly terete: pith rounded, continuous, pale or pinkish. Buds glabrous, sessile, superposed, the uppermost often developing into a spine or replaced by an inflorescence-scar, the others more or less covered by the torn margin of the leaf-scar, with few scales, the end bud lacking. Leaf-scars alternate, rather large, irregularly shield-shaped, little raised: bundle-traces 3: stipule-scars lacking.

Winter-character references: — *G. japonica.* Shirasawa, 239, pl. 2. *G. triacanthos.* Blakeslee & Jarvis, 330, 333, 516, pl.; Bösemann, 51; Brendel, 28, pl. 3; Hitchcock (1), 4, (3), 13, (4), 136, f. 46-8; Otis, 164; Schneider, f. 22, 68.

1. Unarmed. 2.
   Spiny. 3.
2. Large tree. (Thornless honey l.). G. triacanthos inermis.
   Shrub. G. triacanthos elegantissima.
3. Spines terete. 4.
   Spines flattened. 5.
4. Tree. G. sinensis.
   Shrub. G. sinensis nana.
5. Pods elongated, with many seeds. (1). G. triacanthos.
   Pods short, with 1-3 seeds. G. aquatica.

GYMNOCLADUS. Coffee Tree.
(Family Leguminosae).

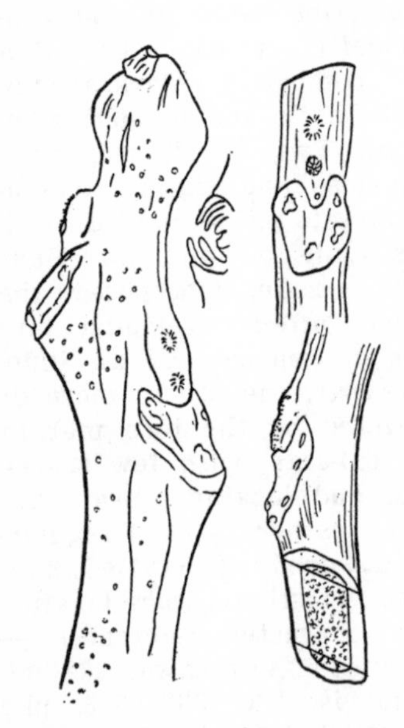

Large rough-barked tree: deciduous. Twigs stout, terete or irregularly 3-sided above: pith large, round, continuous, salmon-colored. Buds superposed in raised silky craters, indistinctly scaly, the end-bud lacking. Leaf-scars alternate, large, irregularly heart-shaped, little elevated: bundle-traces 3 or 5, large, rather indefinite and divided: stipule-scars minute and fringed at top, or lacking.

Winter-character references: — Blakeslee & Jarvis, 333, 514, pl.; Brendel, 28, pl. 3; Hitchcock (1), 4, f. 11, (3), 13, (4), 136, f. 43-45; Otis, 162; Schneider, f. 13, 33, 72, 139.

Like the allanthus, *Gymnocladus* presents unmistakable evidence of the absence of a true terminal bud on its stout twigs. Von Mohl has published on this abscission in the Botanische Zeitung of 1848 and 1860, and it is figured by Foerste in volume 20 of the Botanical Gazette. The large leaf-scars afford a particularly good opportunity for observing the progressive obliteration of self-healed wounds, and the changes in the leaf-scars in successive years were described by von Mohl in the Botanische Zeitung for 1849. The mechanism of leaf-fall is described by van Tieghem and Guignard in the Bulletin de la Société Botanique de France for 1882.

Twigs with whitening epidermis and fine lenticels. G. dioica.

PARKINSONIA.
(Family Leguminosae).

Small trees with brown trunk and greenish twigs: evergreen or deciduous. Twigs moderate, 3-sided and more or less striate. pith moderate, roundish, continuous. Buds solitary, or superposed with the lower developing into an inflorescence, minute, indistinctly few-scaled. Leaf-scars alternate, somewhat raised, 3-lobed or broadly crescent-shaped, with 3 indistinct bundle-traces; or the spinescent rachis persistent, bearing spiny stipules and marked by leaflet-scars below. Leaves, when present, with a few pairs of long narrow pinnae with flat rachis and many small oblong pinnules.

Like *Caragana*, *Parkinsonia* has the rachis of its compound leaf transformed into a persistent spine, and on this the former position of the fallen leaflets is marked during the winter by the scars caused by their abscission.

Glabrous: evergreen. (Jerusalem Thorn.) (1). P. aculeata.
Puberulent: deciduous. (Retama). P. Torreyana.

CERCIDIUM. Palo Verde.
(Family Leguminosae).

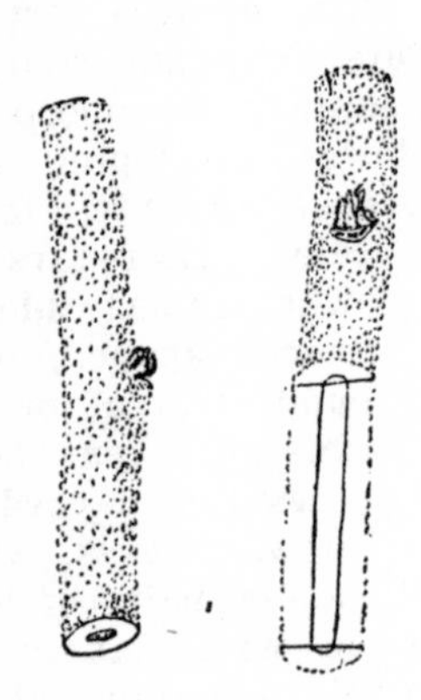

Green-barked glabrous small trees of the Southwest, sometimes with axillary spines: deciduous. Twigs slender, subterete, somewhat zig-zag, finely but distinctly granular-roughened: pith moderate, roundish, continuous. Buds solitary and sessile, or collaterally branching in spine formation or becoming somewhat stalked in developing, minute, obscurely few-scaled. Leaf-scars alternate, little elevated, crescent-shaped or transversely almost linear, minute; bundle-traces 3, indistinct: stipule-scars minute, at the angles of the leaf-scar.

The palo verde or green tree is one of the particularly striking and unusual trees of the Southwest because of its smooth green bark. Though characteristically spiny, it is sometimes nearly or quite unarmed.

Of Arizona and arid California (1). C. Torreyanum.
Of Texas. C. floridum.

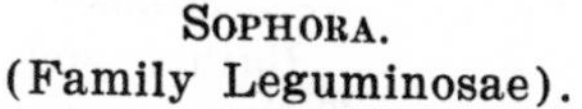

SOPHORA.
(Family Leguminosae).

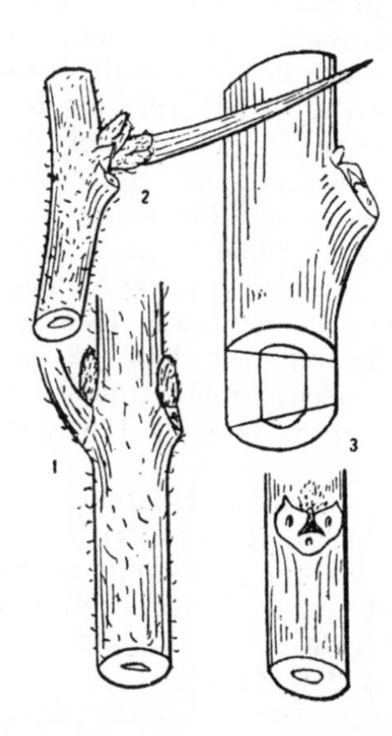

Small trees or shrubs for our purpose: deciduous or exceptionally evergreen. Twigs moderate, swollen at the nodes, more or less zig-zag with elongated internodes, subterete or angled; pith somewhat 3-sided, continuous, pale or greenish. Buds woolly, superposed, sessile, sometimes small and at first concealed by the leaf-scar, the end-bud lacking. Leaf-scars usually alternate, raised, from nearly round or deltoid becoming narrowly U-shaped by tearing of the articular membrane: bundle-traces 3: stipule-scars or remnants minute, at the upper angles of the leaf-scar.

Winter-character references: — *Sophora japonica.* Schneider, f. 91; Shirasawa, 238, pl. 2.

1. Buds covered by the articular membrane: twigs green. 2.
   Buds evident in the axils. 4.
2. Native of the Southwest. (2). S. affinis.
   Cultivated rather generally. 3.
3. Not weeping. (Pagoda Tree). S. japonica.
   Weeping. S. japonica pendula.
4. Unarmed: twigs greenish: evergreen. (3). S. secundiflora.
   With axillary spines: twigs purple. (1). S. viciifolia.

CLADRASTIS. Yellow-wood.
(Family Leguminosae).

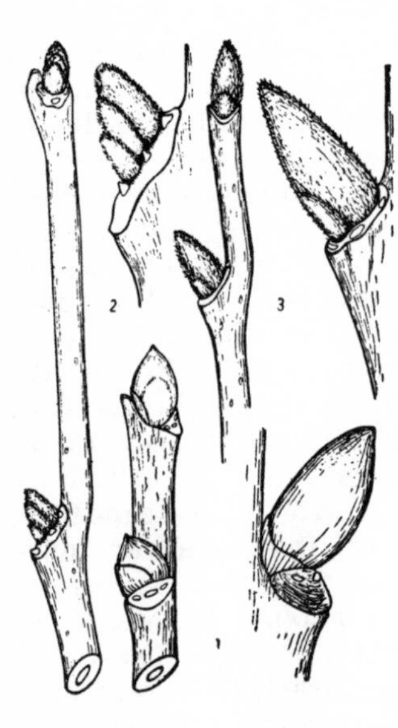

Rather small trees: deciduous. Twigs moderate, terete, sometimes zig-zag: pith moderate, round, continuous, usually pale. Buds sessile, either solitary and evidently scaly (1) or not distinctly scaly and in superposed aggregates resembling single buds (2, 3), the end-bud lacking. Leaf-scars alternate, 2-ranked, half-round (1) or narrowly C-shaped and encircling the bud (2, 3), slightly raised: bundle-traces 3 to 7: stipule-scars lacking. (Includes *Maackia*).

Winter-character references: — *C. amurensis.* Schneider, f. 70. *C. amurensis floribunda.* Shirasawa, 245, pl. 4. *C. lutea.* Blakeslee & Jarvis, 331, 334, 520, pl.; Schneider, f. 4, 63, 70.

The two groups represented respectively by *Cladrastis* (or *Maackia*) *amurensis* and by *C. lutea* and *C. sinensis*, show a very marked difference in winter-characters, though on technical taxonomic grounds they are now united under a single generic name.

1. Buds with 2 exposed pale-margined scales.
   (1). C. (Maackia) amurensis.

   Buds not evidently scaly: leaf-scars narrow. 2.

2. Twigs red-brown: buds short (scarcely 5 mm.).
   (2). C. lutea.

   Twigs buff: buds conical, 7-10 mm. long. (3). C. sinensis.

SPARTIUM. Spanish Broom.
(Family Leguminosae).

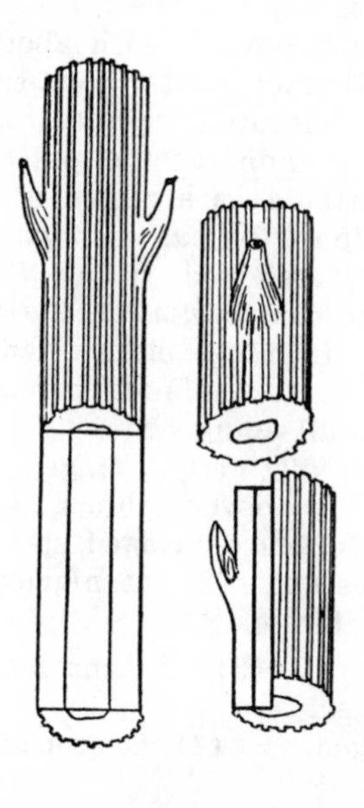

Shrubs with elongated rush-like stems: deciduous. Shoots moderately slender, terete, striate-ridged: pith rather large, somewhat angular, white, continuous. Buds small, solitary, shorter than the much elongated leaf-cushion, the end-bud lacking. Leaf-scars opposite or more commonly those of a pair widely separated, minute; bundle-trace 1, indistinct when the leaf-base is shriveled: stipule-scars lacking.

Spartium, which is called *Spartianthus* sometimes, represents an extreme case of the persistence of a prolonged leaf-cushion or petiole-base, which here far exceeds in length the subtended bud. The condition is figured by Lubbock, On Buds and Stipules, 81, r, 124; and Schneider, f. 75.

Glabrous, green, not pungent, though tapered at end.
S. junceum.

CYTISUS. Broom.
(Family Leguminosae).

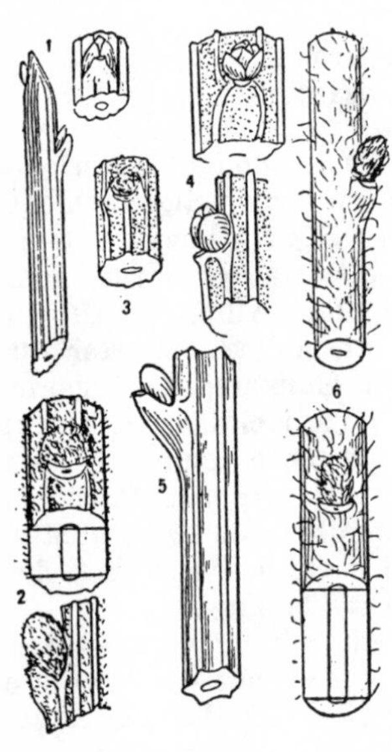

Shrubs, usually rather small: commonly deciduous. Twigs slender, terete or more usually ribbed or grooved: pith small, roundish, continuous: Buds small, solitary, sessile, round-ovoid, with about 4 often indistinct scales. Leaf-scars alternate, elevated, minute: bundle-trace 1, indistinct: stipules or minute stipule-scars at top of the leaf-cushion. *Cytisus scoparius* is frequently referred to as *Spartium;* and *Laburnum*, as *Cytisus*.

1. Twigs forming blunt slender spines. (1). C. pungens.
   Not at all spiny. 2.
2. Twigs distinctly ridged or angular, never villous. 3.
   Twigs obscurely ridged, staring-pubescent. (2). C. nigricans
   Twigs terete. 6.
3. Twigs narrowly ridged. (3). C. canariensis.
   Twigs prominently angled or ridged. 4.
4. Twigs finely granular, almost winged. (4). C. scoparius
   Twigs not granular. 5.
5. Twigs glabrescent or appressed-pubescent. (5). C. glabrescens.
   Twigs quite glabrous. C. purpureus.
6. Pubescence rather short and appressed. C. leucanthus.
   Pubescence long and loose. 7.
7. Erect C. hirsutus.
   Low and spreading. C. supinus.

References under Laburnum, on p. 150

GENISTA. Whin.
(Family Leguminosae).

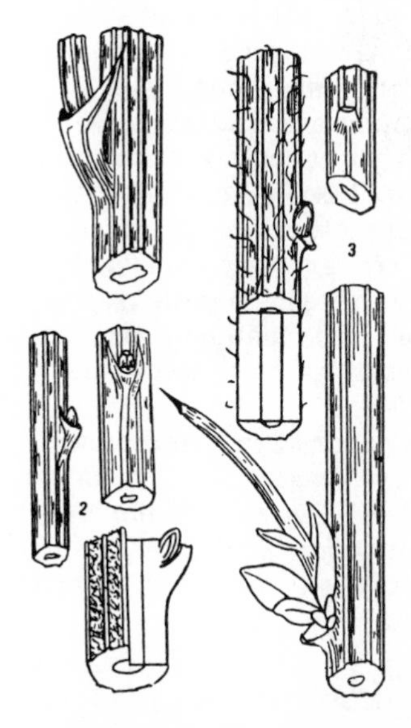

Small shrubs, sometimes spiny: deciduous. Twigs slender, ribbed or grooved: pith small, rounded, continuous. Buds small, solitary, sessile, ovoid, sometimes developing the first season or collaterally branched and producing a green grooved spine, with some half-dozen scales. Leaf-scars alternate, much raised, minute: bundle-trace 1, indistinct: stipules at top of the leaf-cushion, or their scars indistinct.

Winter-character references:—*Genista anglica.* Bösemann, 34. *G. dalmatica.* Schneider, f. 78. *G. germanica.* Bösemann, 34. *G. pilosa.* Bösemann, 34. *G. radiata.* Schneider, f. 89. *G. tinctoria.* Bösemann, 34; Schneider, f. 78 *G. triangularis.* Schneider, f. 89.

1. Stipules persistent: twigs not spiny. (1). G. tinctoria.
   Stipules deciduous. 2.
2. Without spines: twigs tomentulose: prostrate. (2). G. pilosa.
   With short spines: Villous or glabrate: erect. (3). G. germanica.

LABURNUM. Golden Chain.
(Family Leguminosae).

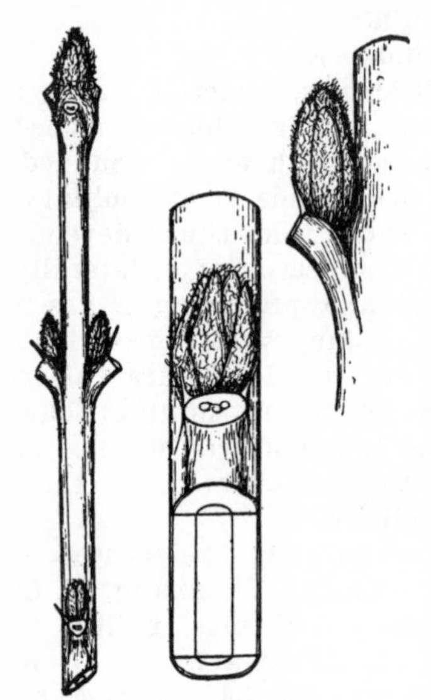

Shrub or small tree: deciduous. Wood somewhat ring-porous with tangential wood-parenchyma pattern. Twigs rather slender, terete or slightly fluted: pith moderate, roundish, continuous, white. Buds moderate, solitary, sessile, ovoid, with about 4 exposed silvery-haired scales scarred at top. Leaf-scars alternate or rarely opposite, transversely elliptical, small, elevated: bundle-traces 3, more or less confluent or indistinct: stipules persistent on the leaf-cushion.

Winter-character references:—*Laburnum anagyroides* (commonly called *Cytisus Laburnum*). Bösemann, 54; Schneider, f. 140; Willkomm, 42, f. 70; Zuccarini, 32, pl. 18.

Not weeping. L. anagyroides.
Weeping. L. anagyroides pendulum.

Winter-character references to *Cytisus*:—*C. alpinus*. Schneider, f. 68; Willkomm, 4, 42, f. 71; Zuccarini, pl. 18. *C. austriacus* [f. 6]. Schneider, f. 177. *C. hirsutus*. Bösemann, 54; Schneider, f. 76; Willkomm, 42, f. 69. *C. nigricans*. Bösemann, 54. *C. purpureus*. Schneider, f. 75. *C. ratisbonensis*. Schneider, f. 76. *C. scorparius* (often referred to *Sarothamnus* or *Spartium*). Bösemann, 38; Fant, 30, f. 32; Schneider, f. 75; Willkomm, 43, f. 73. *C. sessilifolius*. Schneider, f. 76. *S. supinus*. Schneider, f. 177.

ULEX. Furze.
(Family Leguminosae).

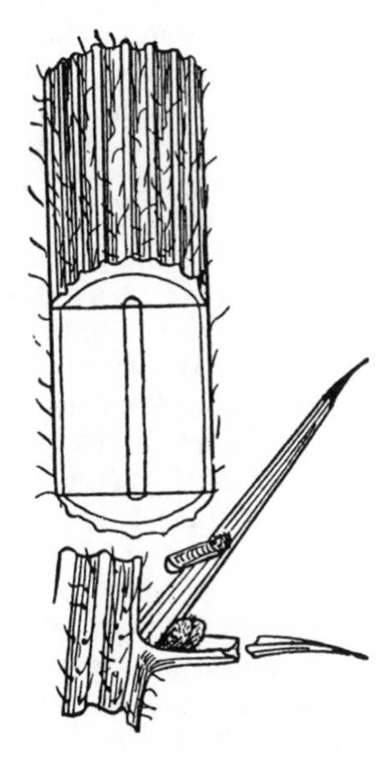

Small very twiggy and spiny shrubs, the triangular leaf-spines persistent. Twigs short, slender, tapering into spines, fluted, the stouter branches loosely hairy and often papillate: pith minute, continuous. Buds small, usually superposed with the upper developing promptly and the lower flattened between it and the leaf, with about 4 rather indistinct scales. Leaves alternate, narrowly triangular, keeled, very pungent: stipules lacking.

It is unusual to find the equivalent of leaves as well as twig-branches of the stem converted into spines: as a rule when one is spinescent the other is not. *Ulex* presents both cases. Like other plants in which the leaves are changed into spines, it does not form leaf-scars, for the modified leaves do not disarticulate.

Though a plant of dry sandy regions, the furze grows naturally where rain or mist is frequent. In hedges, or massed, it is attractive, especially when flowering, but for the perfection of its beauty symmetrical single plants should be seen in the early morning or after a gentle rain, when the moisture-laden down with which they are covered gives a new meaning to the colloquial word fuzzy.

Twigs green: buds tomentulose. U. euopaeus.

AMORPHA. False Indigo.
(Family Leguminosae).

Shrubs: deciduous. Twigs rather slender, slightly angled below the nodes: pith moderate, roundish, continuous, pale. Buds rather small, sometimes superposed, ascending, with 2 or 3 exposed scales. Leaf-scars alternate, somewhat triangular-crescent-shaped, elevated: bundle-traces 3: stipule-scars small, at the upper angles of the leaf-scars.

Winter-character references: —
A. canescens. Hitchcock (3), 12.
A. fruticosa. Brendel, 27, pl. 3; Hitchcock (3), 12, (4), 135, f. 40; Schneider, f. 82.

The common lead plant is believed by some people to grow only where it finds a considerable amount of lead in the soil and to the extent to which this belief is held it is considered indicative of the occurrence of mineral, like *Eriogonum* in the western silver mountains. Little useful dependence is to be placed on such indications, though there is some foundation for the credence placed in some of them. A paper on such indicative plants was published by Rossiter W. Raymond in volume 15 of the Transactions of the American Institute of Mining Engineers.

1. Buds superposed: twigs glabrate: stipule-scars evident. (1). A. fruticosa.
   Buds solitary: stipule-scars minute. 2.
2. Twigs glabrate. A. microphylla.
   Twigs white-woolly. (Lead plant). (2). A. canescens.

WISTERIA. Wistaria.
(Family Leguminosae).

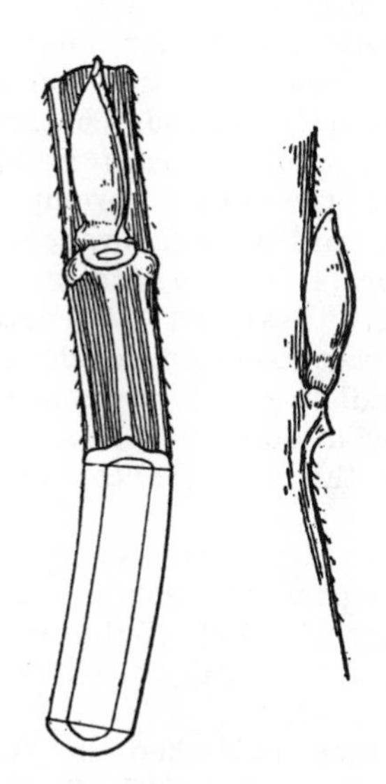

Woody twiners: deciduous. Stems moderate, somewhat angled: pith moderate, white or becoming brown, round, continuous. Buds moderate, solitary, sessile, narrowly oblong, very acute, nearly surrounded by the outer scale. Leaf-scars alternate, transversely elliptical, much raised and with a horn- or wart-like prominence at each side: bundle-trace 1, transverse: stipule-scars lacking.

Winter-character references:—*Wisteria brachybotrys*. Shirasawa, 260, pl. 7, *W. polystachya*. Schneider, f. 81.

The different species of *Wisteria* are not easily named except when they are in flower. The most beautiful of them are the Asiatic species, *W. sinensis* and *W. floribunda*, the latter especially extensively grown near the coast; in the interior the native species, of which *W. macrostachys* is one, succeed better, though they are far less attractive.

Wisteria or *Wistaria* as it was intended to be written and as it has passed into popular parlance, was named in honor of Dr. Caspar Wistar, one of a number of American physicians forming the subject of a little volume on some American medical botanists commemorated in our botanical nomenclature, published in Troy by Dr. Howard A. Kelley in 1914.

Stems somewhat retrorsely hairy. W. macrostachys.

COLUTEA. Bladder Senna.
(Family Leguminosae).

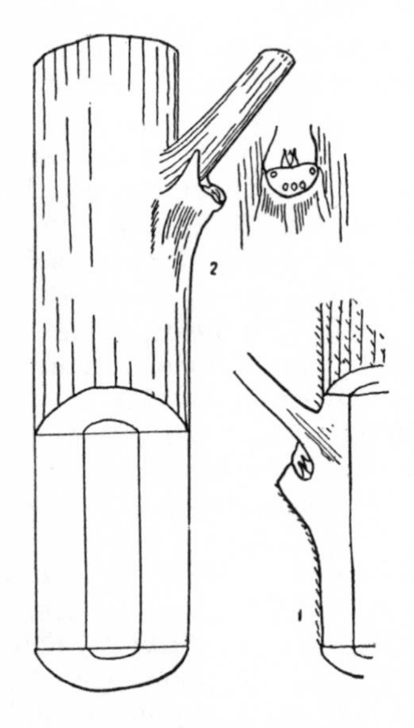

Shrubs: deciduous. Twigs moderate, terete except for shortly decurrent lines from the nodes: pith moderate, rounded, continuous. Buds small, usually superposed and the upper promptly developing into slender branches with 2 or 4 visible scales or leaves. Leaf-scars alternate, broadly crescent-shaped, much elevated: bundle-traces 1 or 3, or the middle one divided: stipules persistent on the sides of the leaf-cushion.

Winter-character references: — *C. arborescens.* Bösemann, 54; Schneider, f. 81, 139; Willkomm, 3, 7, 42, f. 69. *C. orientalis.* Schneider, f. 81.

In a paper published in the journal Linnaea in 1837, Ohlert shows that *Colutea* produces some thirty internodes in a year's twig-growth. Half-a-dozen of these are preformed in the bud: the remainder developed during the growing season. He notes the striking contrast between this and the behaviour of, for instance, *Tilia*, in which more preformed leaves are found in the bud than are to be counted on the developed branch because of the abscission of its terminal parts.

Appressed-pubescent. (1). C. arborescens.

Glabrescent. (2). C. cilicica.

HALIMODENDRON. Salt Tree.
(Family Leguminosae).

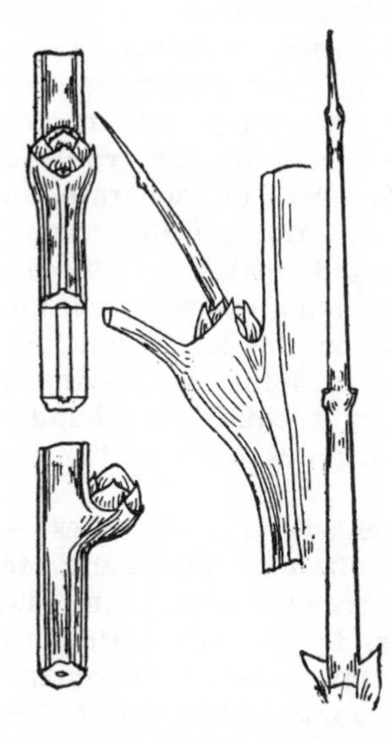

Shrubs with more or less pungent stipules and frequent persistent spine-tipped leaf-axes, otherwise deciduous. Twigs slender or often forming globose spurs invested by the many persistent bud scales, angular: pith rather small, somewhat angular, continuous. Buds usually thicker than the twig, solitary, sessile, globose, with some half-dozen exposed acute scales. Leaf-scars alternate, much raised, minute: bundle-trace 1: stipules erect beside the bud, on the leaf-cushion.

Halimodendron differs from other commonly seen plants with a much raised persistent leaf-base in that this spreads almost horizontally from the stem, in this way making place for the globose relatively large buds. These frequently develop ino short leafy spurs, on the leaf-bases of which spines sometimes persist. As in *Parkinsonia* and *Caragana*, the spines are persistent axes, marked with scars from which leaflets have fallen. The winter-characters of *H. halodendron* are pictured by Schneider, f. 72.

Outer bud-scales dark, the inter pale. H. halodendron.

CARAGANA. Pea Tree.
(Family Leguminosae).

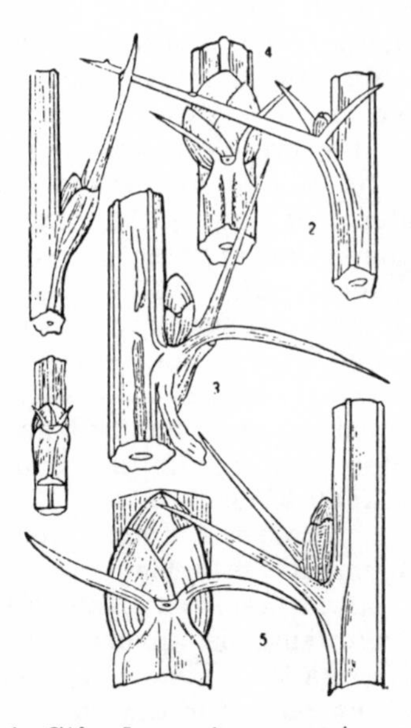

Shrubs, exceptionally subarborescent or grafted as standards; somewhat spiny: deciduous. Twigs moderate or rather slender: angled from the nodes: pith moderate, somewhat angular, continuous. Buds small or moderate, apparently solitary, sessile, with 3 or 4 exposed scales. Leaf-scars alternate, much raised, minute, half-round or the leaf-rachis persistent as a spine or leaving a round scar if this falls: bundle-trace 1: stipules persistent, often pungent.

Winter-character references: — *Caragana altanga.* Bösemann, 46. *C. arborescens.* Bösemann, 46; Schneider, f. 134. *C. frutescens.* Bösemann, 46. *C. mollis.* Bösemann, 46. *C. spinosa.* Schneider, f. 134.

1. Stipules not pungent: spine falling. (1). C. frutex.
   Stipules and rachis both spinescent. 2.
   Stipules very pungent: rachis falling. 4.
2. Twigs slender (1-2 mm.). 3.
   Twigs coarse, with many subglobose spurs. C. spinosa.
3. Leaflet-scars crowded near end of the spine. C. pygmaea.
   Two scars near the middle of the spine. (2). Chamlagu.
4. Buds small: bark exfoliating. (3). C. decorticans.
   Buds relatively large (4-6 mm. long). 5.
5. Stipule-spines short (3-4) mm.). (4). C. microphylla
   Stipule-spines moderate or long (5-10 mm.). 6.
6. Twigs, spines and buds green or olive. C. arborescens.
   Twigs, spines and buds dull red. (5). C. Boisii

CALOPHACA.
(Family Leguminosae).

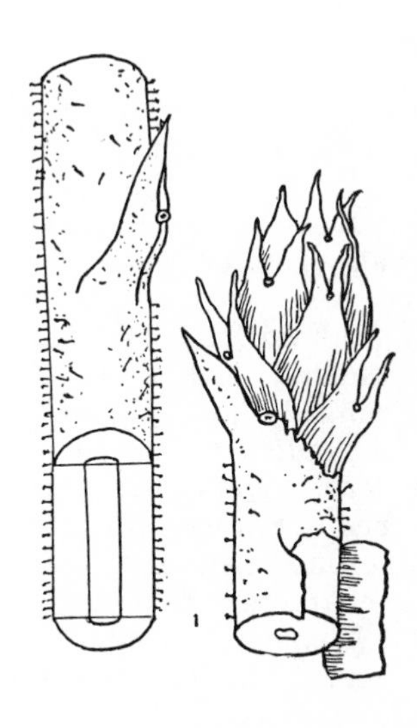

Shrubs, or grafted as weeping trees: deciduous. Twigs moderate, terete: cortex exfoliating: pith small, roundish, continuous. Buds solitary, sessile, concealed by the leaf-cushion, often developing the first season, with numerous leaf-base scales evident as the bud expands. Leaf-scars alternate, minute, round or elliptical, at the top of a greatly dilated base that half-encircles the stem: bundle-trace 1: stipules large, brown.

Calophaca is one of a considerable number of Leguminosae in which the leaves disarticulate from a much elongated and dilated base which persists on the stem. Usually such persistent leaf-bases are crowned by persistent stipules. In *Calophaca* these are exceptionally large. Its winter-buds are sheathed in similar notched leaf-bases so that they resemble those of hybrid barberry,—× *Mahoberberis*. The winter-characters of *C. wolgarica* are pictured by Schneider, f. 73.

Stipules long (10 mm.): loosely hairy. C. grandiflora.
Stipules shorter (scarcely 6 mm.): puberulent. (1). C. wolgarica.

CORONILLA.
(Family Leguminosae).

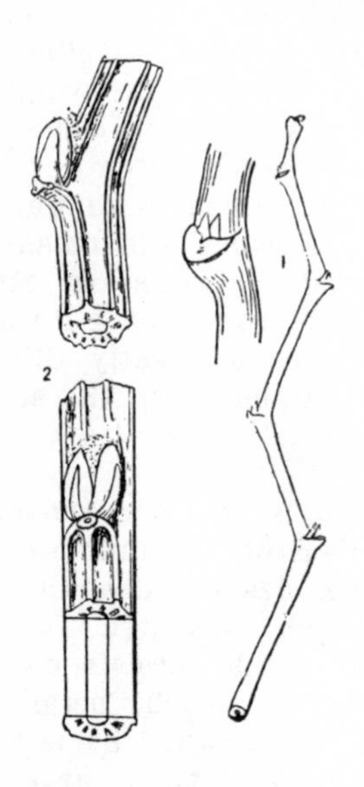

Shrubs (or often herbs): deciduous. Twigs moderate or slender, zig-zag, angled or ribbed, glabrous, green: pith round, white, very soft (and sometimes chambered?). Buds solitary, sessile, with a pair of outer scales, ovoid, more or less covered by the strongly 3-ribbed leaf-cushion, the end-bud lacking. Leaf-scars alternate, 2-ranked, much raised, rounded: bundle-trace 1: stipules persistent as supplementary scales of the bud or forming narrow transverse lines on the stem.

Winter-character references: — *Coronilla Emerus.* Fant, 27, f. 25; Schneider, f. 70, 139; Willkomm, 7, 44, f. 74.

1. Low and trailing. C. viminalis.
   Bushy, 2.
2. Twigs very slender (1 mm.), glaucous. (1). C. glauca.
   Twigs stouter, green. 3.
3. Twigs sharply lined or fluted.
   (Scorpion senna). (2). C. Emerus.
   Twigs less evidently lined. C. emeroides.

ROBINIA. Locust.
(Family Leguminosae).

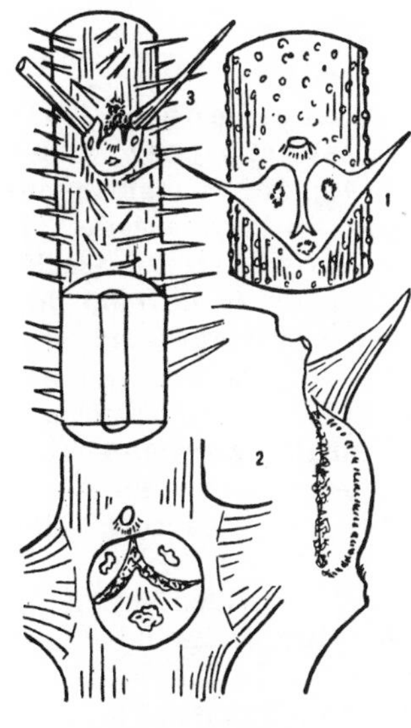

Trees or shrubs: deciduous. Wood hard, yellow or brown, ring-porous. Twigs zig-zag, more or less angled: pith round, continuous, brown. Buds small, superposed beneath a membrane left after leaf-fall, the end-bud lacking. Leaf-scars alternate, broadly triangular or 3-lobed, consisting of a membrane that splits open later: bundle-traces 3. Stipules bristle- or prickle-like.

Winter-character references:—*Robinia hispida.* Blakeslee & Jarvis, 522; Bösemann, 47; Brendel, 28; Hitchcock (1), 4, (3), 12; Otis, 168; Schneider, f. 67; Shirasawa, 230, pl. 1; Ward, 1:197, f. 99; Willkomm, 36, 41, f. 68. *R. viscosa.* Blakeslee & Jarvis, 522; Bösemann, 47; Schneider, f. 139.

A note on the stipular spines of *Robinia* is to be found under *Zanthoxylum*.

1. Trees. 2.
   Shrubs. 4.
2. Twigs glandular. — (1). R. viscosa.
   Twigs not glandular. 3.
3. With spines. (Black locust). — (2). R. Pseudacacia.
   Unarmed. — R. Pseudacacia inermis.
4. Twigs both viscid and bristly. — R. neo-mexicana.
   Twigs without viscid glands. 5.
5. Twigs very bristly. (Rose acacia). — (3). R. hispida.
   Twigs not bristly. — R. Kelseyi.

ERYTHROXYLON. Coca.
(Family Erythroxylaceae).

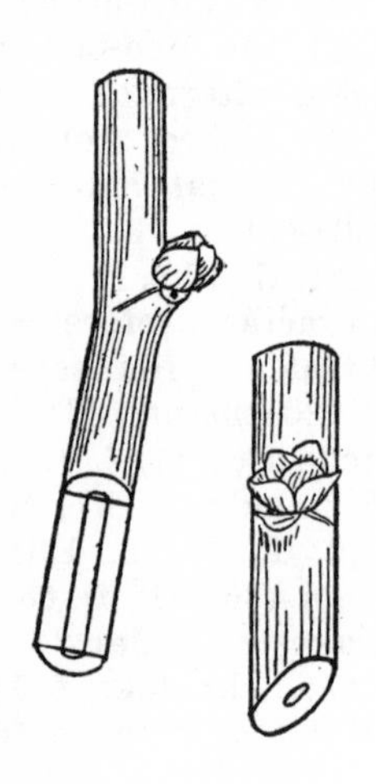

Shrubs: deciduous. Twigs slender, somewhat zig-zag, round: pith moderate, round, continuous, pale. Buds solitary, sessile, globose with a pair of stipular-scales, or those that are to develop flowers quickly compound and with numerous chaffy scales, the end-bud lacking. Leaf-scars alternate, 2-ranked, small, crescent-shaped, low: bundle-trace 1, indistinct: stipule-scars very narrow, elongated.

Erythroxylon, which is of no decorative value, is included here only because it is the source of the important anaesthetic alkaloid cocaine. The leaves of the plant are imported from Bolivia and Peru chiefly, though it is cultivated also in the East Indies. As with the opium poppy, it produces a number of distinct active principles.

Glabrous: twigs brown. E. Coca.

GUAIACUM. Lignum Vitae.
(Family Zygophyllaceae).

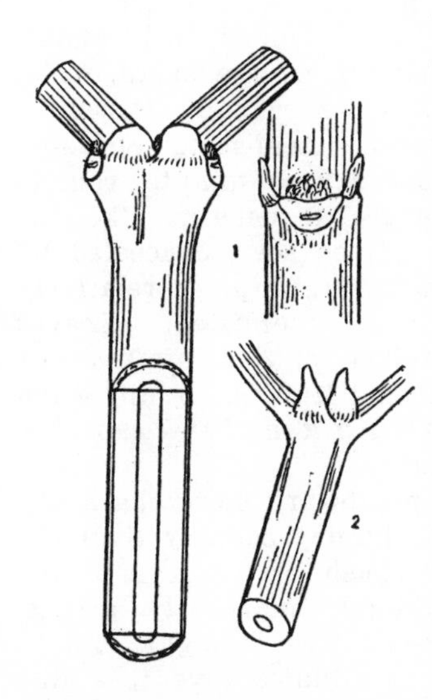

Trees with very hard yellow wood and resinous bark: evergreen. Twigs rather slender. forking at short intervals, green, subterete: pith small, round, continuous, white. Buds scarcely discernible, not evidently scaly except as the abortive end-bud may show several stipules. Leaf-scars opposite but the pairs not decussating, broadly crescent-shaped, somewhat elevated by the swollen nodes: bundle-trace 1, indistinct: stipules rather persistent, one of each pair overlapping the other. Leaves abruptly pinnate, with several pairs of rather large entire leaflets.

In his collected essays On Buds and Stipules Sir John Lubbock—who subsequently became Lord Avebury—pictures twigs of *Guaiacum* which have the leaf-pairs decussating in the normal manner.

Stipules blunt: leaflets prominently veiny. (1). G. officinale.
Stipules pointed: leaflets obscurely veiny. (2). G. sanctum.

COVILLEA. Creosote Bush.
(Family Zygophyllaceae).

Odoriferous small shrubs exuding balsam where wounded: evergreen. Twigs 4-angled, becoming round in age, with short internodes: pith 4-sided, continuous. Buds solitary, sessile, small, ovoid, with 2 scales, usually imbedded in balsam. Leaf-scars opposite, somewhat raised, minute, round: bundle-trace 1, usually, like the outline of the scar, concealed by the exudation: stipules relatively large, brown, persistent. Leaves short-stalked, of 2 falcate more or less parallel leaflets. Fruit, when present, long-hairy capsules (*Larrea*).

Few plants are more characteristic of the dry country than the creosote bush or, as it is called often though improperly, greasewood, and none is more readily recognized at sight. As in lignum vitae, the evident persistent stipules give it a distinctive character. In an account of the native trees and shrubs published as Bulletin 87 of the New Mexico Agricultural Experiment Station, Wooton speaks of the characteristic bright color of *Covillea* in contrast with the prevailing gray of other vegetation.

Twigs at first green, puberulent. C. tridentata.

ZANTHOXYLUM. Prickly Ash.
(Family Rutaceae).

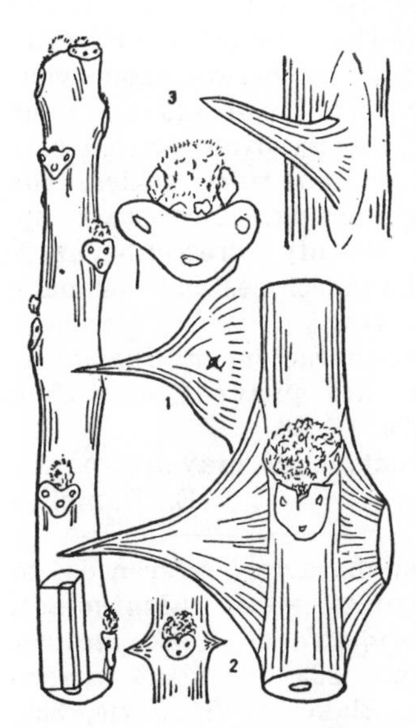

Small trees or shrubs, aromatic or pungently acrid, usually armed with detachable prickles which sometimes occur paired at the nodes: deciduous. Twigs moderate or stout, subterete: pith rounded, continuous, very creamy white. Buds moderate, superposed, sessile, globose, woolly and indistinctly scaly. Leaf-scars alternate, broadly triangular or 3-lobed, little raised, sometimes with a conspicuous articular membrane: bundle-traces 3: stipule-scars lacking. Winter-character references under *Evodia*, p. 164.

The strong prickles beside the leaf-scar in *Zanthoxylum* present a puzzling question as to their morphology. If they represent stipules, they should be called spines: if they are superficial outgrowths of the cortex, they are truly prickles. Position is not a safe guide. The pungent outgrowth of gooseberry and rose are prickles: they are stipules in the locust, and, like other stipules, are connected with the vascular system of the stem at least in their early stages. They are believed to be prickles in *Zanthoxylum*.

1. Prickles broad and acuminate. (1). Z. Bungei.
   Prickles not acuminate even when widened. 2.
2. Nodal prickles often widened: articular-membrane often conspicuous: buds red-rusty. (2). Z. americanum.
   Prickles not greatly dilated nor articular-membrane developed: buds glabrous. (3). Z. Clava Herculis.

EVODIA.
(Family Rutaceae).

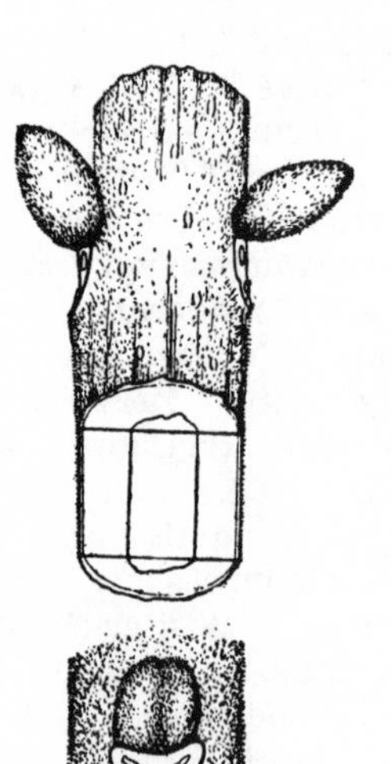

Trees: deciduous. Twigs round or somewhat 4-angled or wrinkled: pith moderate, somewhat angular, firm, continuous. Buds solitary, sessile, ovoid, with 1 pair of rather indistinct scales, the end-bud lacking. Leaf-scars opposite, broadly crescent-shaped, low: bundle-traces 3: stipule-scars lacking.

Winter-characters of *Evodia rutaecarpa* are pictured by Shirasawa, 270, pl. 10.

Puberulent: buds gray-brown.
E. Daniellii

Winter-character references to *Zanthoxylum*: — *Z. ailanthoides*. Shirasawa, 237, pl. 3. *Z. alatum*. Shirasawa, 239, pl. 3. *Z. americanum*. Blakeslee & Jarvis, 330, 522, pl.; Brendel, 31, pl. 3; Hitchcock (1), f, (3), 8, (4), 134, f. 12-13; Schneider, f. 85. *Z. Bungei*. Schneider, f. 85. *Z. piperatum*. Shirasawa, 239, pl. 2. *Z. schinifolium*. Shirasawa, 239, pl. 3.

Foerste states in the Botanical Gazette for 1892 that vascular strands are found beneath the usual position of the larger prickles of *Xanthoxylum* even when these are aborted. Specialized outgrowths from a plant member are sometimes distinguished under the name emergences, particularly when they contain vascular elements.

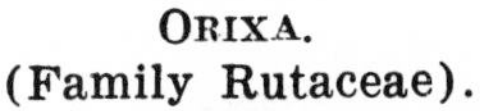

ORIXA.
(Family Rutaceae).

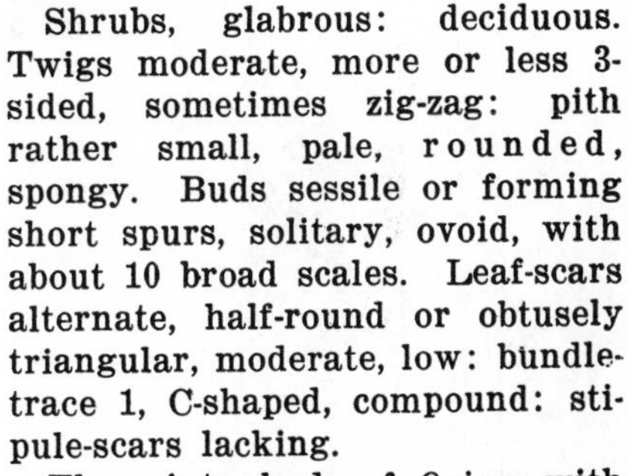

Shrubs, glabrous: deciduous. Twigs moderate, more or less 3-sided, sometimes zig-zag: pith rather small, pale, rounded, spongy. Buds sessile or forming short spurs, solitary, ovoid, with about 10 broad scales. Leaf-scars alternate, half-round or obtusely triangular, moderate, low: bundle-trace 1, C-shaped, compound: stipule-scars lacking.

The winter-buds of *Orixa*, with the conspicuous pale margin of their scales, are quite unlike those of any other shrub or tree likely to be encountered. The winter-characters of *O. japonica* are pictured by Schneider, f. 97, and Shirasawa, 254, pl. 6. At different times it has been placed in *Celastrus*, *Ilex* and *Othera*.

Like other Rutaceae, *Orixa* produces an essential oil in its various parts that gives it a characteristic odor. Sometimes, as in *Citrus*, such odors are pleasant to our senses: sometimes, as in the rue, they are very disagreeable. *Orixa* is of the odoriferous rather than the aromatic type.

Twigs olive: bud-scales with pale ciliate margin. O. japonica.

PTELEA. Hop Tree.
(Family Rutaceae).

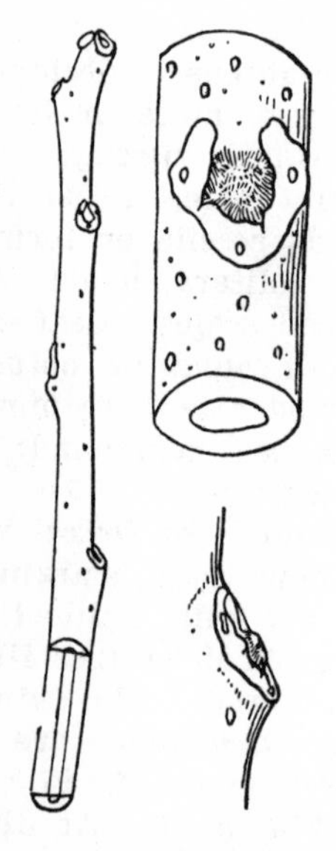

Shrubs or small trees: deciduous. Twigs moderate, warty and dotted, terete: pith rather large, roundish, continuous, white. Buds moderate, closely superposed in pairs, very low-conical, sessile, breaking through the leaf-scars, not distinctly scaly, silvery-silky, the end-bud lacking. Leaf-scars alternate, somewhat raised, rather large, horseshoe-shaped when torn by the buds: bundle-traces 3: stipule-scars lacking.

Winter-characters: — *Ptelea trifoliata*. Bösemann, 56; Brendel, 27, 30, pl. 3; Hitchcock (1), 4, f. 3; Schneider, f. 97.

To some persons, notwithstanding its blue-green foliage, *Ptelea* resembles *Staphylea* when growing, but its alternate leaves or leaf-scars and very different buds afford a ready and sure means of recognition. In winter it is much more likely to be mistaken for its relative, *Phellodendron*.

The importance of twig-characters, observance of which need not be restricted to the winter months, is pointed out by Greene in the tenth volume of Contributions from the United States National Herbarium, where he segregates 59 nominal western and southwestern species of *Ptelea*,—in addition to an earlier subdivision (Torreya, 5:100) of what is here called *P. trifoliata*.

Twigs glabrous, buff. (Wafer ash). P. trifoliata.
Twigs puberulent. P. trifoliata mollis.

PHELLODENDRON. Cork Tree.
(Family Rutaceae).

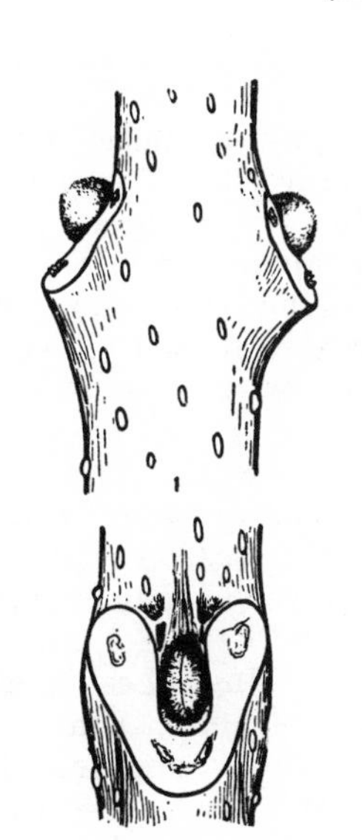

Small trees with spongy soft bark: deciduous. Twigs moderate, rounded: pith moderate, brown, continuous: bark yellow when cut. Buds solitary, sessile, half-ellipsoid, compressed from the sides, silky with red or bronzed hairs so as to mask the overlapping of the 2 scales. Leaf-scars opposite or the pairs separated, horseshoe-shaped, raised, rather large: bundle-traces 3, often compound.

Winter-characters of *Phellodendron amurense* are pictured by Schneider, f. 97; and Shirasawa, 272, pl. 10.

Phellodendron and *Evodia* differ from the other Rutaceae here considered in having their leaf-scars opposite or in broken decussating pairs, and not alternate on the stems. Winter twigs of *Ptelea*, which might be mistaken for those of the cork tree, are easily distinguished by this character.

Though in some respects well suited to cultivation, the cork trees possess the great demerit of holding their black berry-like fruits late into the season so that, like the black cherry in summer, they become an unusual nuisance until the last fruit has fallen.

1. Twigs orange: bark of trunk corky. P. amurense.
   Twigs red or purple-brown: bark of trunk not corky. 2.
2. Twigs glabrous. (1). P. sachalinense.
   Twigs somewhat hairy above. P. chinense.

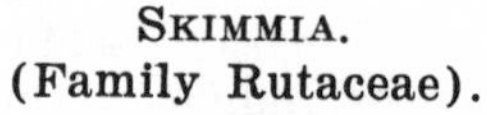

SKIMMIA.
(Family Rutaceae).

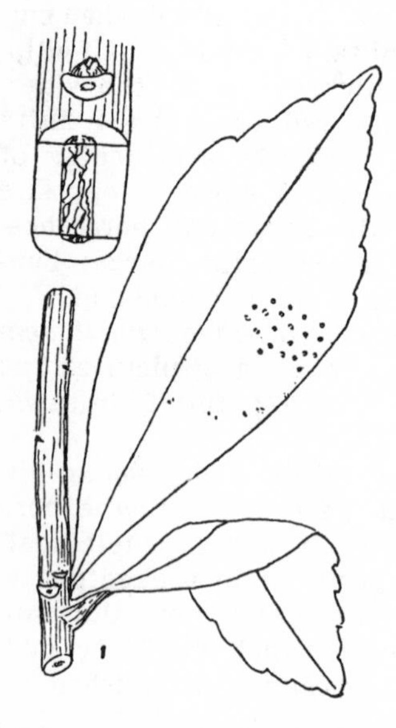

More or less aromatic tender shrubs: evergreen. Twigs moderate, green, terete, smooth except for oil-papules: pith relatively large, round, spongily excavated. Buds solitary, small, round-conical, with 2 or 3 small scales, for the most part suppressed. Leaf-scars alternate, low, half-round, crowded toward the end of the season's growth, separated, narrower and reduced elsewhere: bundle-trace 1, round: stipule-scars lacking. Leaves simple, slightly revolute, somewhat crenate above the middle. The small red or black berry-like fruits are often present in winter.

Skimmias are tender and can be grown only in the South, where they are counted among the best evergreen shrubs for smoky cities.

Leaves oblanceolate, blunt-pointed: fruit scarlet.
(1). S. japonica.

Leaves more lanceolate and acuminate: fruit crimson.
S. Fortunei.

TRIPHASIA. Limeberry.
(Family Rutaceae).

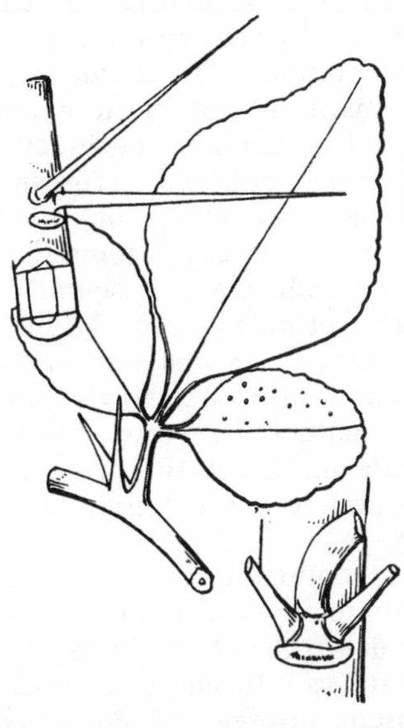

Tender shrubs with paired needle-like branch-spines: evergreen. Twigs terete, rather slender: pith small, white, more or less angular, homogeneous. Buds minute, solitary, sessile, depressed-globose, obscure or developed into the short-flower-stalk, the end-bud absent. Leaf-scars very small, alternate, half-elliptical, low: bundle-trace 1, crescent-shaped, compound: stipule-scars lacking. Leaves short-stalked, digitate, pellucid-dotted.

The limeberry is used for hedges and shrubbery where the winters are sufficiently mild, and is said to be tolerant of a considerable amount of salt in the soil.

The generic name *Limonia* has been used for *Triphasia*, which is considered separable from that genus. The limeberry is spoken of sometimes as a citrus, which is proper only when the name is used in the most general sense and even then may lead to confusion with the deciduous hardy orange, *Poncirus*, which has been called *Citrus trifoliata.*

Glabrescent: leaflets. 3. T. trifolia.

CITRUS. Orange, Lemon.
(Family Rutaceae).

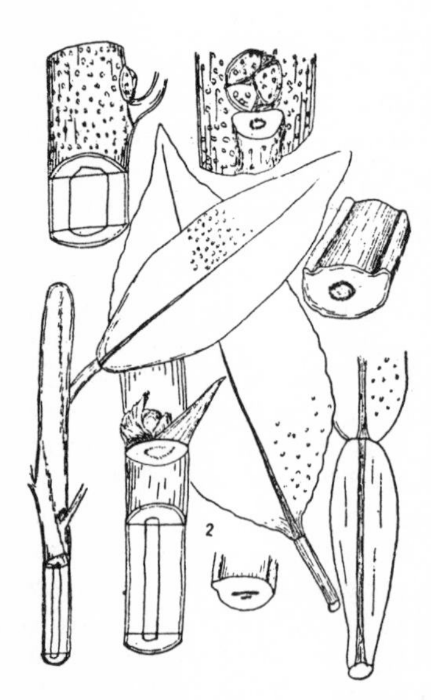

Aromatic shrubs or small trees, often with axillary spines: evergreen. Twigs moderate, green, more or less 2-sided: pith small, 3-sided, continuous. Buds solitary, sessile, small, round, with about 3 scales, the end-bud deciduous. Leaf-scars alternate, crescent-shaped or half-round or lens-shaped, rather small, somewhat elevated: bundle-trace 1, round or elliptical: stipules and stipule-scars lacking. Leaves appearing simple but really of a single low-crenate pellucid-punctate leaflet disarticulating from the typically winged petiole. (Including *Fortunella*).

Like the plum, olive and many other commonly cultivated fruit-trees and shrubs, the citrus species present a great variation in spininess. In addition to the "citrange" hybrids between the common orange and *Poncirus*, crosses have been effected between the Tangerine type (*C. nobilis*) and the grape fruit (*C. grandis*), which are called "tangelos"; and between the lime (*C. aurantifolia*) and the kumquat (*C. japonica*).

1. Leaves ovate, pubescent: petiole winged. C. grandis.
   Leaves lanceolate, glabrous. 2.
2. Petiole moderately winged. (Orange). (1). C. Aurantium
   Petiole narrowly winged. 3.
3. Leaves and fruit large. (Lemon). (2). C. Limonia.
   Leaves and fruit small. (*Fortunella*). (3). C. japonica.

PONCIRUS. Hardy Orange.
(Family Rutaceae).

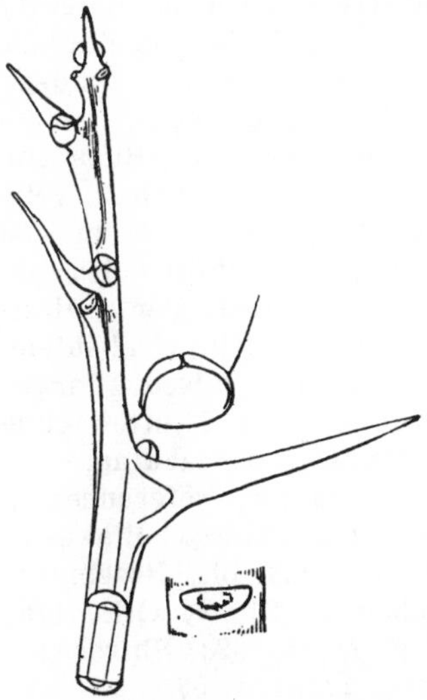

Shrubs with branch-spines: deciduous. Twigs triangular, dilated into the thorns at the nodes, rather stout: pith rather large white, homogeneous. Buds rather small, solitary, sessile, subglobose, with about 3 exposed scales, the end-bud absent. Leaf-scars very small, alternate, 5-ranked, half-elliptical, scarcely raised: bundle-trace 1, crescent-shaped, evanescent: stipule-scars lacking. (*Aegle*, *Citrus*).

The hardy orange, capable of growth even in the North as an effective and attractive hedge-plant, presents another instance of the occasional occurrence of hybridization between different genera, and at the same time emphasizes the closeness of the relationship of such genera. *Poncirus* gives hybrids, more or less intermediate in character, with the grape fruit belonging to the evergreen unifoliolate genus for which the name *Citrus* is now reserved; but it has been considered itself to belong to that genus by botanists for whom generic characters might be drawn a little more broadly than they are under the prevailing custom. Its winter-characters are pictured by Schneider, f. 85.

For the hybrid "citranges" the generic name × *Poncirocitrus* might find appropriate use.

Twigs glabrous, glossy green: buds glabrous, blood-red.
P. trifoliata.

AILANTHUS. Tree of Heaven.
(Family Simarubaceae).

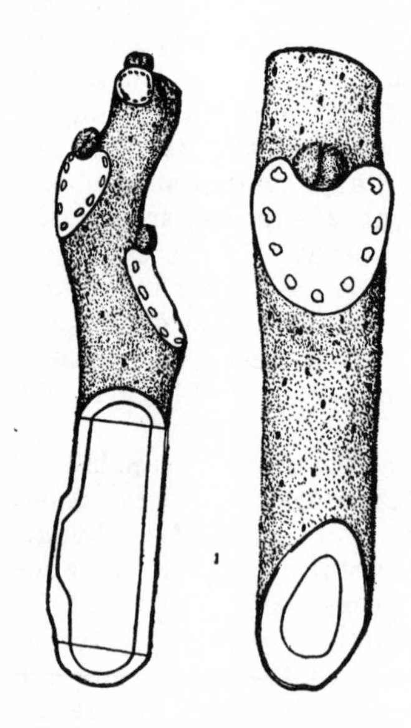

Rather smooth-barked loosely branched trees with persistently prominent lenticels: deciduous. Twigs coarse, somewhat 3-sided: pith large, homogeneous, roundish, becoming colored. Buds solitary, sessile, hemispherical, relatively small, with 2 or 4 exposed scales, the end-bud fallen, leaving a large scar. Leaf-scars alternate cordately elliptical-shield-shaped, slightly raised, large: bundle-traces about 9, often compound: stipule-scars lacking.

Winter-character references:— *Ailanthus glandulosa*. Blakeslee & Jarvis, 334, 524, pl.; Bösemann, 61; Hitchcock (3), 9; Otis, 170; Schneider, f. 35, 99; Shirasawa, 236; Ward, 1:118, f. 59.

Like *Gymnocladus*, *Ailanthus* offers exceptionally good opportunities for recognizing that year after year the branches of certain trees are continued by development of axillary or lateral buds, the tip of each year's growth disappearing early by a cleancut abscission.

Mr. Swingle, after reviewing the early European history of *Ailanthus*, shows that the commonly cultivated species should be called *A. altissima*, in the Journal of the Washington Academy of Sciences, of August 19, 1916.

1. Twigs prickly. A. Vilmoriniana.
   Unarmed. 2.
2. Twigs puberulent. (1). A. glandulosa.
   Twigs glabrescent. A. glandulosa pendulifolia

BURSERA. West Indian Birch.
(Family Burseraceae).

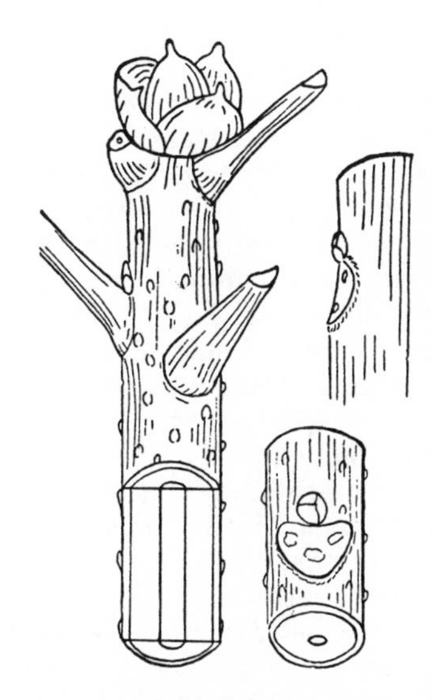

Tender resinous trees with papery-flaking red or brown bark and extremely light, soft and utterly worthless wood: subdeciduous. Twigs glabrous, moderate, terete: pith round, continuous, light brown. Buds solitary, sessile, small, depressed globose, with about 3 more or less short-pointed scales. Leaf-scars alternate, half-round, low: bundle-traces 3: stipule-scars lacking. Leaves, if present, like the twigs closely resemble those of mahogany, from which in bark, wood and habit it greatly differs, as it does in the technical characters of flowers and fruit.

An effective contrast of the bark of *Bursera* and *Swietenia* is afforded in figures 9 and 10 of the text accompanying part 13 of Hough's American Woods, of which thus far 325 species have been distributed in cross section, and tangential and radial longitudinal sections.

Twigs light brown, warty. (Gumbo limbo). B. Simaruba.

SWIETENIA. Mahogany.
(Family Meliaceae).

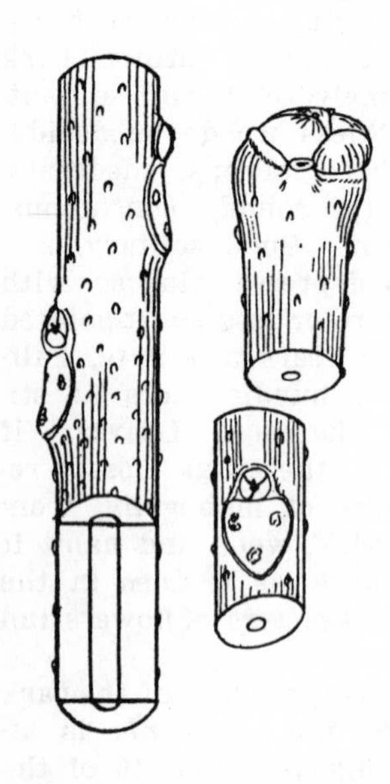

Tender trees, often of large size and then with buttressed trunks: subevergreen. Twigs glabrous, moderate, terete: pith round, continuous, light brown. Buds solitary, sessile, small, depressed globose, with about 3 more or less abruptly pointed exposed scales, the end-bud lacking. Leaf-scars alternate, half-round or somewhat shield-shaped, little raised: bundle-traces 3: stipule-scars lacking. Leaves, if present, pinnately compound.

Mahogany, which furnishes the most important cabinet wood exported from the tropics where it occurs as scattered individual trees in a mixed forest, is rather effective as a shade tree where temperatures are favorable. In twigs, buds and foliage it resembles the preceding closely but differs in its compact bark and excellent wood.

An idea of the buttressed trunk of a mature mahogany tree is given by the plate facing p. 463 of Gibson's American Forest Trees.

Twigs light brown, warty. S. Mahagoni.

CEDRELA. False Cedar.
(Family Meliaceae).

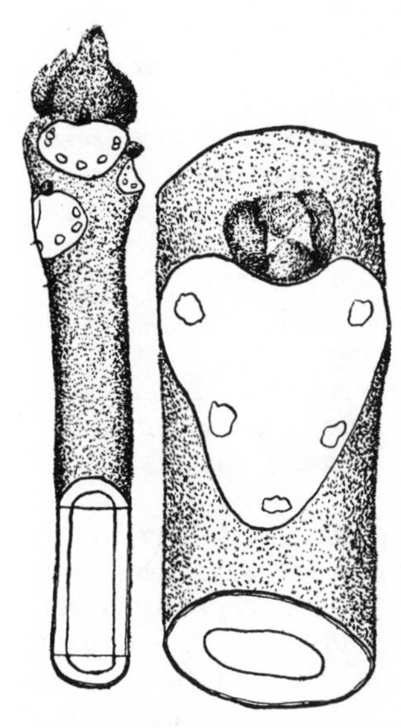

Rather smooth-barked loosely branched trees: deciduous. Twigs coarse, terete: pith large, homogeneous, roundish, from white becoming colored. Buds solitary, sessile, short-ovoid, with about 4 short-pointed exposed scales, the end-bud much larger. Leaf-scars alternate, cordately elliptical-shield-shaped, slightly raised, large: bundle-traces 5: stipule-scars lacking.

Wood of the West-Indian and Central American cedar, *C. odorata*, out of which the better cigar boxes are made, resembles mahogany in many respects. The cheap grade of cigar boxes is made of sycamore wood, the heavy medullary rays of which are very characteristic. The Asiatic hardy cedrela presents much the appearance of ailanthus. The winter-characters of *C. sinensis* are considered by Schneider, f. 99; and Shirasawa, 232, pl. 2.

Twigs puberulent. C. sinensis.

MELIA. China Berry.
(Family Meliaceae).

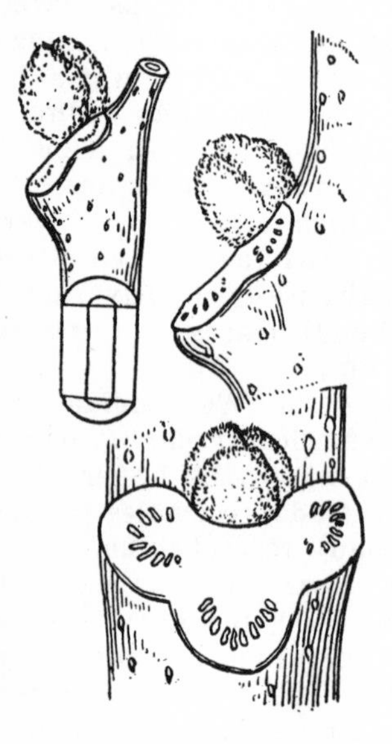

Moderate-sized trees: deciduous. Twigs rather stout, terete: pith moderate, continuous, rounded, white. Buds solitary, sessile, globose, moderate, with 3 exposed scales, the end-bud absent. Leaf-scars alternate, 3-lobed, elevated, large: bundle-traces in 3 compound C-shaped groups: stipule-scars lacking.

Winter-character references:— *Melia Azedarach.* Schneider, f. 94. *M. japonica.* Shirasawa, 236, pl. 2.

Though the China berry is usually connected with the South Atlantic region, where it is planted as a shade tree, it stands the drought of the Southwest, and, especially in its round-topped form, it proves very effective where green foliage is uncommon.

Twigs olive with many small pale lenticels. M. Azedarach.

ANDRACHNE.

(Family Euphorbiaceae).

Small shrubs: deciduous. Twigs 5-angled or terete; the youngest very slender, the older with somewhat flaking bark: pith small, rounded, continuous. Buds small, collaterally multiple, with several ciliate scales, the axils often occupied by pedicel-scars. Leaf-scars alternate, minute, half-round, low: bundle-trace 1: stipules more or less persistent at the side.

Neither *Andrachne* nor *Securinega* is of much merit, but the rarity of woody Euphorbiaceae outside of the tropics makes them a little puzzling when they are encountered. Winter-characters of *Securinega ramiflora* are given by Schneider, f. 125. As typical of many anatomical studies to which reference is not made in this book, may be cited a paper on the phyllanthoid Euphoribiaceae by Rothdauscher, published in volume 68 of the Botanisches Centralblatt.

Twigs terete, glabrous. (1). A. colchica.
Twigs 5-lined, somewhat hairy. (2). A. phyllanthoides.

SECURINEGA.
(Family Euphorbiaceae).

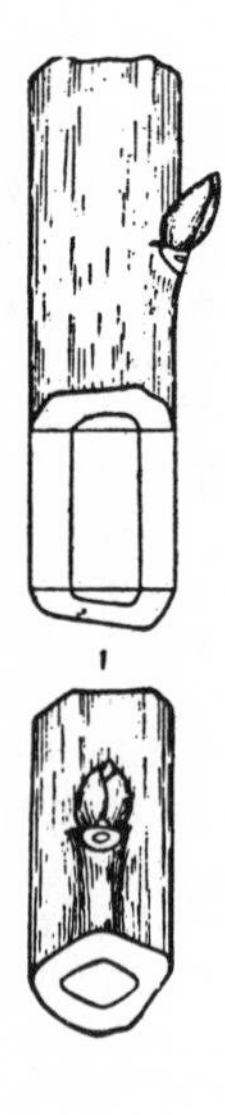

Small shrubs: deciduous. Twigs slender, 5-sided, glabrous: pith relatively large, angular, white, continuous. Buds rather small, solitary or with a small lower one, compressed-ovoid, with about 3 exposed scales. Leaf-scars alternate, minute, half-round, slightly raised: bundle-trace 1: stipules subpersistent at the sides. Most of the upper axils are occupied by scars from which flower- and fruit-clusters have fallen.—Sometimes called *Acidoton.*

Though a number of large and important or interesting trees belonging to the Euphorbiaceae occur in the tropics, and poinsettias, crotons and castor beans are frequent among herbaceous plants grown in temperate regions, *Andrachne* and *Securinega*, which are scarcely more than half-shrubs, are the only woody genera found native or cultivated in the North.

Twigs olive-colored or green. (1). S. ramiflora.
Twigs purple. S. flueggeoides.

Shirasawa gives winter-characters of *Excoecaria japonica*, 245, pl. 4; *Glochidion obovatum*, 253, pl. 6; *Mallotus japonica*, 234, pl. 1; and *Stillingia sebifera*, 244. These genera belong likewise to the Euphorbiaceae.

BUXUS. Box Tree.
(Family Buxaceae).

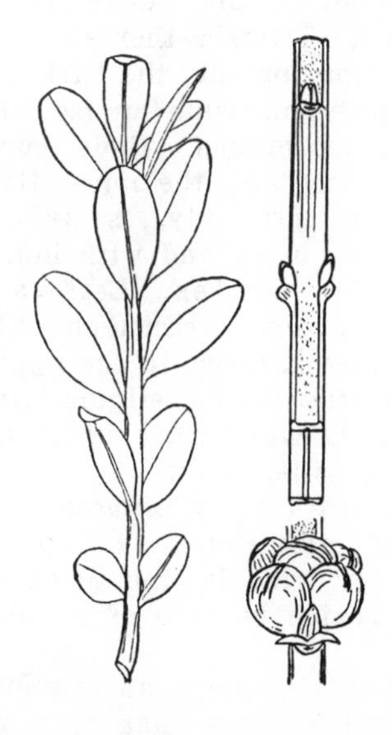

Shrubs or small trees: evergreen. Twigs very slender, green, flat-grooved between each pair of leaves: pith minute, continuous. Buds sessile, solitary, small, ovoid, with 1 or 2 pairs of visible scarcely specialized scales, or the flower-buds quickly globosely enlarged and multiple. Leaf-scars opposite, minute, crescent-shaped, raised: bundle-trace 1: stipule-scars lacking. Leaves small, subelliptical, entire, short-petioled, paler beneath.

Box, like ivy, unfortunately is unable to endure the winter extremes of the North and it is rarely seen, at any rate far from the coast, except as unhappy stragglers or in satisfactorily grown tubbed specimens. It is not commonly known that it is acridly poisonous. As a rule winter-manuals do not concern themselves with evergreens, but *Buxus sempervirens* is included by Bösemann, 38; and Ward, 1:43, f. 65. Goebel, in the Botanische Zeitung for 1880, p. 756, points out that the buds are naked.

Boxwood was used formerly almost exclusively for rulers, and is found yet in the finer draftsman's scales.

1. Twigs puberulent in the grooves. (1). B. sempervirens.
   Twigs glabrous: leaves rather obovate. 2.
2. Bushy. B. japonica.
   Prostrate or small. B. microphylla.

SIMMONDSIA. Jojoba.
(Family Buxaceae).

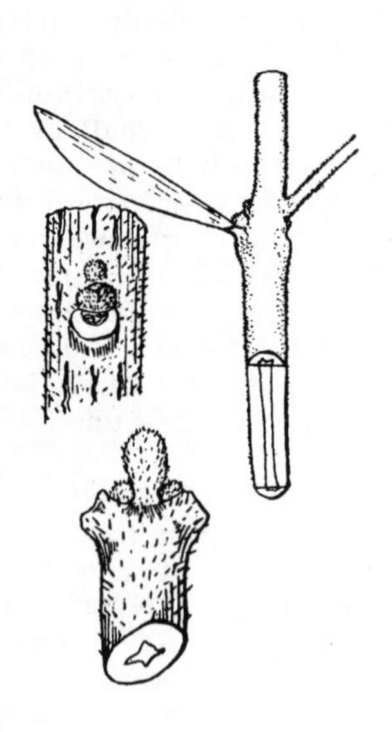

Shrub or small bushy tree: evergreen. Twigs rather slender, terete, often forking, the bark fissured: pith somewhat angled and colored, continuous. Buds commonly superposed, the upper often developing promptly, sessile, round, very hairy and with indistinguishable scales. Leaf-scars opposite, raised, crescent-shaped: bundle-trace 1, large, in the upper part of the scar: stipule-scars lacking. Leaves rather small, elliptical, sessile, entire.

Some years since, *Simmondsia* attracted attention as a plant worthy of trial in the Mediterranean region because of its oily seeds.

Simmondsia affords an example of the misfortunes that may attend the use of names indicating the source or peculiarities of plants. What is called *S. californica*, now, was grown in the botanical garden at Berlin a century ago, supposedly from China. Link, recognizing its now admitted but sometimes questioned relationship to the box, christened it *Buxus chinensis.* The genus *Simmondsia* was described two decades later, when Nuttall found and named its original if not only species *S. californica.* Strict application of the nomenclatorial rule of priority would cause restoration under *Simmondsia* of the totally misleading name *chinensis.*

Appressed-puberulent: leaves thick. S. californica.

COREMA. Broom Crowberry.
(Family Empetraceae).

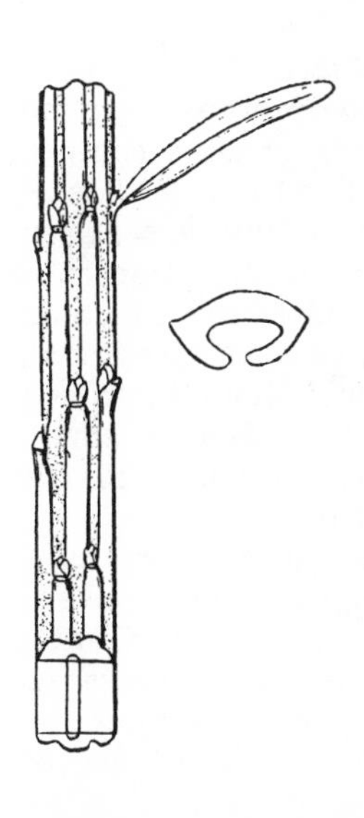

Low spreading shrubs: evergreen. Twigs slender, ridged below the leaf-scars: pith minute, continuous. Buds solitary, sessile, compressed round-ovoid, minute, with 2 or 3 scales. Leaf-scars subverticillate, minute, half-round, somewhat raised: bundle-trace 1, indistinct: stipule-scars lacking. Leaves linear-oblong, revolute to a dorsal slit, microscopically denticulate.

Though very different in technical characters, the Empetraceae are suggestive of Ericaceae in vegetative characters. Anatomical comparisons are made by Gibelli in volume eight of the Nuovo Giornale Botanico Italiano, and by Mori in the same journal for 1877; and an instructive lecture by Miall, in which their inrolled leaves figure, is published in volume 58 of Nature. The leaf-anatomy is discussed comparatively by MacEwan in the Bulletin of the Torrey Botanical Club for 1894.

Corema Conradii has borne the generic names *Tuckermannia*, given it by Klotzsch in 1842, but already in use for another plant, and *Oakesia*, given it by Tuckerman in the same year,—both botanists failing to identify the supposedly new genus with the earlier named *Corema*.

Glabrate on the ridges: bark exfoliating. C. Conradii

EMPETRUM. Crowberry.
(Family Empetraceae).

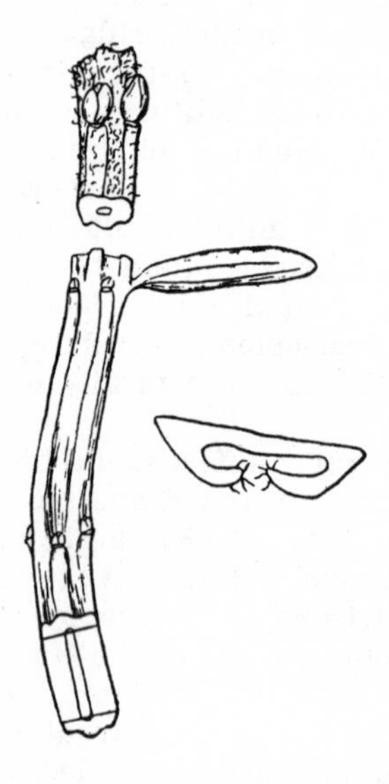

Low spreading shrubs with exfoliating bark: evergreen. Twigs slender, ridged below the leaf-scars: pith minute, continuous. Buds solitary, sessile, compressed round-ovoid, with 2 or 3 exposed scales, very minute except for the flower-buds in the upper axils. Leaf-scars subverticillate, minute, half-round, somewhat raised: bundle-trace 1, indistinct: stipule-scars lacking. Leaves small, elliptical-oblong, revolute to a hairy groove, entire.

The winter-characters of *Empetrum nigrum* are given by Bösemann, 35; and Fant, 53. Solereder figures a cross-section of its leaf in his Systematic Anatomy of the Dicotyledons, 2:800, f. 188.

The type of inrolled leaves that Empetraceae and certain Ericaceae possess has been shown by Gibelli's developmental studies to differ essentially from the usual type of revolute leaves which are merely rolled backward for a distance from the margin. Here, the grooves at either side of the midrib develop in such a manner as to make them morphologically elongated pits rather than merely covered parts of the normal lower leaf surface.

Glabrate. E. nigrum.
Tomentose. E. nigrum andinum.

CERATIOLA.
(Family Empetraceae).

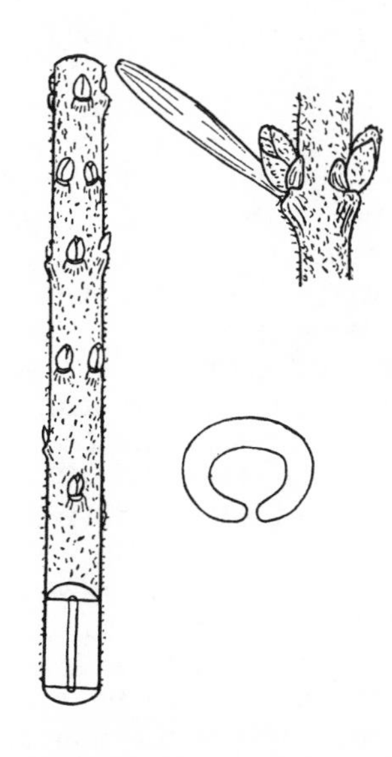

Low tender aromatic shrubs: evergreen. Twigs very slender, terete: pith minute, continuous. Buds sessile, compressed-ovoid, solitary and minute or the flower-buds in the upper axils larger and collaterally multiple, with about 3 exposed scales. Leaf-scars subverticillate, minute, crescent-shaped, elevated: bundle-trace 1: stipule-scars lacking. Leaves linear, revolute to a dorsal slit so as to be almost terete.

Only the genera of Empetraceae here given are known, and there is only one additional species,—a *Corema* in the Mediterranean region. *Ceratiola* is distinctly more southern than our others and occurs from Florida to South Carolina. The cavity formed by its revolute leaves is filled by loose hairs.

The Empetraceae not only resemble heaths in the peculiar type of revolution that their leaves show, but their fruit is comparable with that of the bearberry, and their pollen-grains occur in coherent groups of four as in the Ericaeceae, of which family Dr. Gray has supposed the Empetraceae to be a reduced off-shoot.

Twigs puberulent: bark tardily exfoliating. C. ericoides.

CORIARIA.

(Family Coriariaceae).

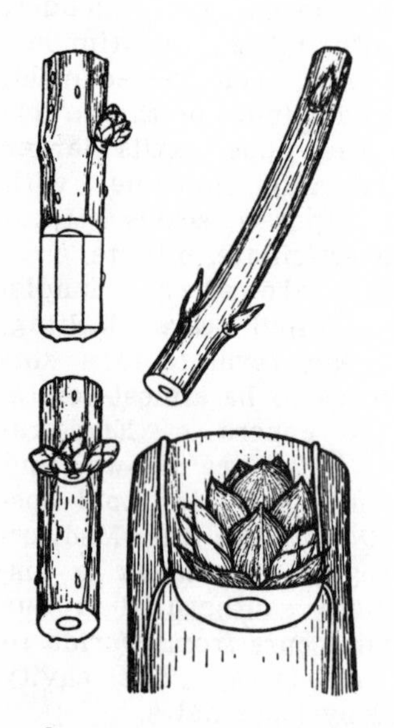

Shrubs, sometimes soft-wooded: deciduous. Twigs terete, or 4-lined below the nodes, stout, with red-scaly short spurs bearing clustered very slender shoots of the season: pith rather large, round, continuous, brownish. Buds at first solitary and with 2 nearly valvate scales but very quickly on the stout twigs becoming multiple by branching, with several scales. Leaf-scars opposite, low, crescent-shaped or the smaller rounded: bundle-trace 1: stipule-scars lacking.

The axillary clustering of slender leafy shoots which suggest compound leaves recalls a somewhat similar appearance in *Zizyphus*, where, however, the slender twigs may bear flowers and fruit, and results in an appearance not unlike that of *Prosopis* and other Leguminosae which produce compound leaves in clusters from dwarf spurs. The winter-characters of *Coriaria myrtifolia* are pictured by Schneider, f. 116.

Twigs glabrous, glossy red-brown: lenticels prominent.
C. japonica.

MANGIFERA. Mango.
(Family Anacardiaceae).

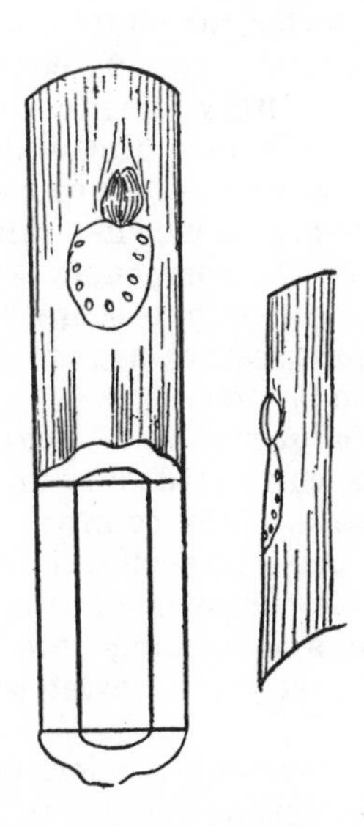

Glabrous trees with milky or gummy sap: evergreen. Twigs moderate, somewhat corrugated: pith relatively large, continuous, brownish. Buds solitary, sessile, depressed-ellipsoid, indistinctly 2-scaled, the terminal conical. Leaf-scars alternate, more crowded near the end of the season's growth, low, half-round to nearly elliptical, somewhat concave at top: bundle-traces about 9: stipule-scars lacking. Leaves simple, entire, petioled.

A striking feature of the mature mango is its long clusters of large fruits. Though a tropical tree, it is coming into considerable cultivation in subtropical parts of the United States, in carefully selected varieties.

The mango is one of the rather few really good exclusively tropical fruits, of most of which, as a lady who had learned to know them through many years of experience once said, it is nearly or quite true that each new kind puts one in mind of a new toilet soap. To millions of persons living within the tropics this fruit is said truthfully to be of greater importance than the apple is to us.

Leaves lance-oblong, large (5 × 20 cm.). M. indica.

PISTACIA. Mastic.
(Family Anacardiaceae).

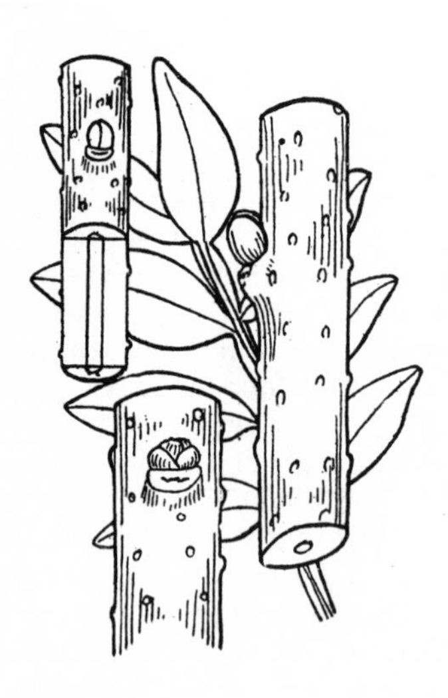

Tender gummy aromatic shrubs or small trees: evergreen or deciduous. Twigs moderate, roundish: pith small, round, continuous. Buds solitary, sessile, ovoid, with several scales, the end-bud lacking. Leaf-scars alternate, crescent-shaped, somewhat raised: bundle-trace 1, compound, or a curved series: stipule-scars lacking. When leaves are present they are odd-pinnate.

Like *Mangifera* and *Schinus*, *Pistacia* is cultivated only in the warmer parts of the country. Besides the mastic species, *P. vera* which yields the pistachio nuts of confectioners is coming into cultivation, in selected varieties, in California.

Another, but very tender, member of the Anacardiaceae, capable of growth only in the extreme subtropical parts of our country, is the small tree *Anacardium occidentale*, that yields the now rather familiar cashew nuts, and, in the tropics, the brilliant red or yellow cashew "apples" which are the enlarged flower-stalks or receptacles. This color contrast recalls strikingly that of sweet peppers, tomatoes, holly-berries, etc., in which a normal brilliant red coloration is replaced by an equally brilliant yellow.

Deciduous, very resinifluous. P. Terebinthus.
Evergreen. (1). P. Lentiscus.

SCHINUS. Pepper Tree.
(Family Anacardiaceae).

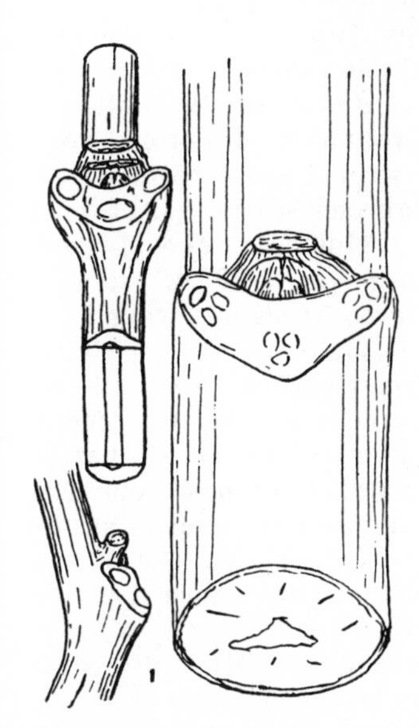

Tender round-topped rather weeping trees, pungently aromatic, glabrous: evergreen. Twigs slender, roundish, zig-zag: pith rather small, more or less 3-angled, continuous, white when fresh. Buds superposed, the upper commonly developing precociously, round, ovoid, or oblong, much flattened, with 2 scales, the end-bud absent. Leaf-scars alternate, often 2-ranked, crescent-shaped, slightly raised: bundle-traces 3, large or often compound: stipule-scars lacking. Leaves petioled, odd-pinnate with pointed leaflets. Fruit glossy round drupes of the size of peas, in rather large panicles or racemed.

Broken leaflets, thrown on water, are a source of interest, the explosive liberation of the volatile oil that they contain causing them to dart forward on the surface.

Leaves of many leaflets: fruit panicled. (1). S. Molle.
Leaves of about 7 leaflets: fruit racemed. S. Terebinthifolius.

COTINUS. Smoke Bush.
(Family Anacardiaceae).

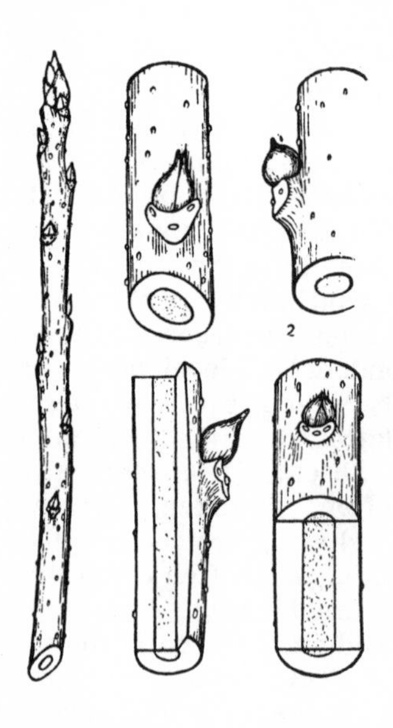

Shrubs or small trees with free-flowing gummy aromatic sap: deciduous. Twigs round, moderate, brown or purplish, with prominent lenticels, glabrate: pith moderate, round, brown, continuous. Buds small, solitary, sessile, round-ovoid, often compressed, with 1 or 2 pairs of exposed glabrous scales. Leaf-scars alternate, clustered above, crescent-shaped or 3-lobed, raised: bundle-traces 3: stipule-scars lacking. (*Rhus*).

The American smoke bush or chittam wood is counted among our very rare or local native plants though it occurs from Alabama to Texas and extends as far north as Forsythe on the White River in Missouri, where it grows along the cliffs.

Buds attenuate: leaf-scars lobed; twigs orange. (1). C. americana.
Buds acute from the front: leaf-scars not lobed.
(2). C. Coggygria.

Winter-character references:—*Cotinus coggygria* (*Rhus Cotinus*). Schneider, f. 79; Willkomm, 41, f. 67. *Rhus canadensis* (*R. aromatica*). Brendel, pl. 3; Hitchcock (3), 12. (4), 135, f. 37-39. *R. copallina*. Blakeslee & Jarvis, 342, 526; Hitchcock (1), 4, f. 7. *R. glabra*. Blakeslee & Jarvis, 342, 526; Brendel, pl. 3; Hitchcock (3), 11; Greene, Ottawa Naturalist, 24:139. *R. javanica* (*R. semialata Osbeckii*). Shirasawa, 236, pl. 2. *R. succedanea*. Shirasawa, 233, pl. 1. *R.*

sylvestris. Shirasawa, 233, pl. 2. *R. Toxicodendron* (including *R. radicans*). Blakeslee & Jarvis, 528; Brendel, pl. 3; Hitchcock (3), 11, (4), f. 135, f. 35-36; Schneider, f. 79; Shirasawa, 259, pl. 1. *R. trichocarpa*. Shirasawa, 233, pl. 1. *R. typhina* (*R. hirta*). Blakeslee & Jarvis, 342, 526, pl.; Bösemann, 55; Greene, Ottawa Naturalist, 24:139; Schneider, f. 79. *R. vernicifera*. Shirasawa, 232, pl. 1. *R. Vernix*. Blakeslee & Jarvis, 333, 334, 528, pl.

RHUS. Sumach.
(Family Anacardiaceae).

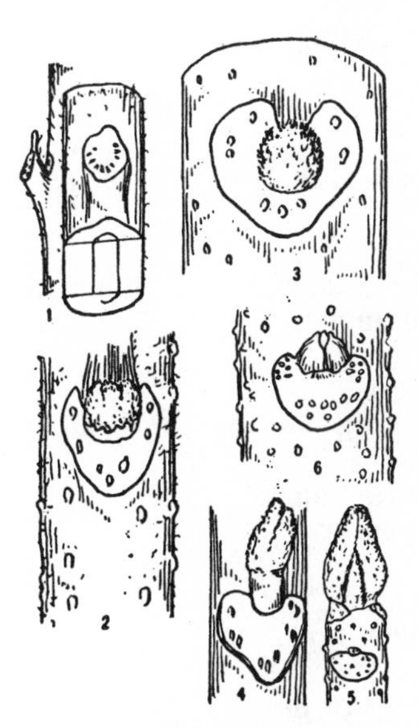

Shrubs, exceptionally climbing by aerial roots or becoming small open trees; with milky sometimes very poisonous sap: deciduous as to our species. Twigs round or bluntly 3-sided, sometimes fluted, slender to very stout: pith rather large, roundish, continuous, often pink or brown. Buds moderate or rather small, solitary, sessile, round-ovoid, hairy and indistinctly scaly or with 3 or 4 evident scales, the end-bud often lacking. Leaf-scars alternate, round or crescent-shaped, or C-shaped and encircling the buds, more or less raised: bundle-traces rather numerous in the lower half of the round leaf-scars but sometimes in 3 more or less evident groups or 3 or 5 to 9 single scars or groups in the narrower leaf-scars: stipule-scars lacking.

The fragrant sumach has a very distinctive type of leaf-fall and the generic name *Schmaltzia* has been used exclusively for it sometimes. The poisonous group, for which the name *Toxicodendron* has been used, but to which the name *Rhus* is most strictly applicable, is equally distinct in leaf-scars from the true sumachs, to which the name *Schmaltzia* is extended. Opinions differ as greatly in the definition of their species as in the limitation of these nominal genera; and Greene, in the eighth volume of Proceedings of the Washington Academy of Sciences, has made no fewer than 29 species of what is here called *R. glabra.*

1. Leaf-scars round, much elevated, covering the small yellow hairy buds: twigs slender.
(Fragrant sumach). (1). R. canadensis.
Leaf-scars C-shaped, nearly encircling the buds: twigs stout. 2.
Leaf-scars U-shaped: twigs terete, puberulent.
(2). R. copallina.
Leaf-scars broadly crescent- or shield-shaped. *Poisonous.* 5.
2. Tall shrubs or small trees. 3.
Very low hairy shrub.
(Southern hairy sumach). R. Michauxii.
3. Twigs glabrous, 3-sided. (Smooth sumach). (3). R. glabra.
Twigs hairy, rounded. 4.
4. Hairs dense, concealing the lenticels.
(Staghorn sumach). R. typhina.
Hairs scanty: lenticels prominent.
(Asiatic sumach). R. javanica.
5. Twigs slender: buds stalked, naked. 6.
Twigs stout: buds sessile. 7.
6. Climbing by aerial roots, or spreading.
(Poison ivy). (4). R. radicans.
Bushy. (Poison oak). R. Toxicodendron.
7. End-buds yellow-pubescent, large (8-10 mm. long).
(Lacquer tree). (5). R. vernicifera.
End-buds glabrate, moderate (scarcely 5 mm.).
(Poison sumach). (6). R. vernix.

CLIFTONIA. Buckwheat Tree.
(Family Cyrillaceae).

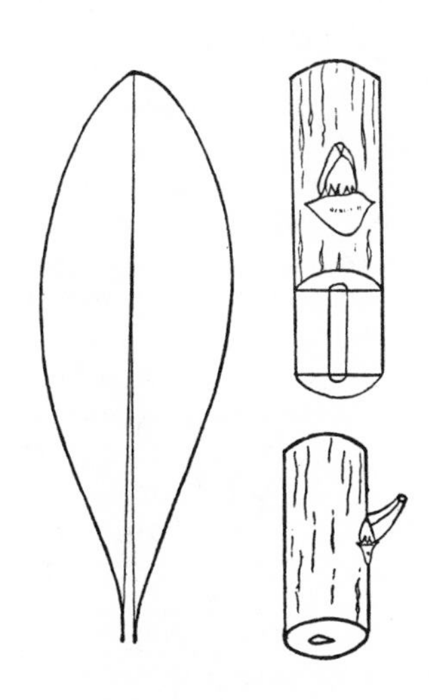

Shrubs: evergreen. Twigs rather slender and 3-sided: pith small, more or less 3-sided, continuous, pink. Buds small, sessile, solitary, ovoid, with about 2 exposed scales. Leaf-scars alternate, shield-shaped, often acutely angled at the sides, fringed at the top: bundle-trace 1, transverse, sometimes broken: stipule-scars lacking. Leaves obovate-oblanceolate, entire, subsessile, thick and nearly veinless.

The single species of *Cliftonia* has been known as *C. nitida* and, more commonly, *C. ligustrina*. The specific name *monophylla* which it bears now has been restored of late years because it was applied to the plant before either of the others, though under another genus, *Ptelea*, to which Lamarck referred the plant because of the winged fruits to which it owes also its common name of buckwheat tree.

Twigs gray, glabrous: leaves puberulent, glaucous.
C. monophylla.

CYRILLA. White ti ti.
(Family Cyrillaceae).

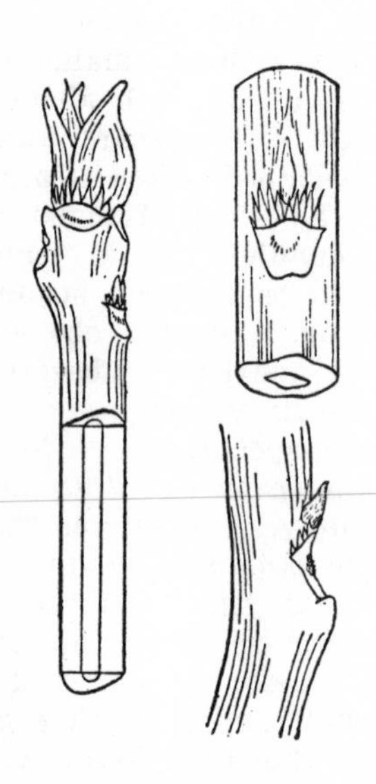

Shrubs or small trees: deciduous or subevergreen. Twigs rather slender and 3-sided: pith small, somewhat 3-sided, continuous. Buds small, sessile, several superposed in an axillary groove, with a few pointed scales. Leaf-scars alternate, low, shield-shaped with acute lateral angles, fringed at top: bundle-trace 1, rather large and curved: stipule-scars lacking. Leaves when present rather thin, very hairy, entire, petioled.

In addition to the two barely differentiable cyrillas of the southern United States, another occurs in the West Indies and still another in Brazil. Even these are so similar to our northern species that for some botanists they constitute only varieties of it.

Twigs straw-colored, glabrous: leaves glabrous, green.

Some leaves 10 cm. long. C. racemiflora.

Leaves under 5 cm. long. C. parvifolia.

ILEX. Holly.
(Family Aquifoliaceae).

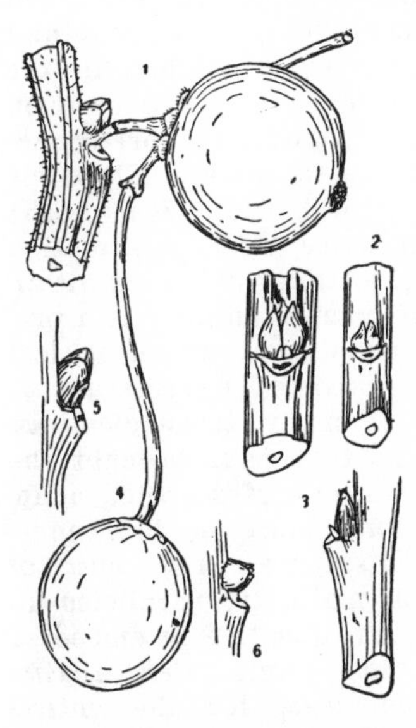

Shrubs or trees: evergreen or deciduous. Twigs usually 3- or 5-sided, rather slender, often developed as spurs with densely crowded leaf-scars: pith small, roundish or angled, subcontinuous. Buds small, commonly superposed, sessile, with 2 or mostly 4 or 6 exposed scales. Leaf-scars alternate, clustered above, crescent-shaped, more or less raised: bundle-trace 1: stipule-scars minute or the minute pointed stipules persistent at the angles of the leaf-scars. Leaves, when persistent, coriaceous and sometimes very pungently toothed. Fruit a berry-like drupe with several nutlets.

Winter-character references:—*Ilex Aquifolium*. Blakeslee & Jarvis, 530; Bösemann, 34; Fant, 48; Ward, 1:144, f. 66. *I. decidua*. Hitchcock (1), 5. *I. geniculata*. Shirasawa, 236, pl. 2. *I. macropoda*. Shirasawa, 265, pl. 9. *I. opaca*. Blakeslee & Jarvis, 329, 530, pl. *I. Sieboldii*. Shirasawa, 235, pl. 2. *I. verticillata*. Brendel, pl. 3; Schneider, f. 116.

The dots or cork-warts which characteristically mark the lower leaf-surface of certain species are figured in section by Solereder in his Systematic Anatomy of the Dicotylendons, 1:210, f. 50.

As Sir John Lubbock points out in his studies of buds and stipules, *Ilex* possesses small stipules. Though they are often so minute as to escape attention unless very carefully looked for they are of diagnostic value as between *Ilex* and *Nemopanthus*.

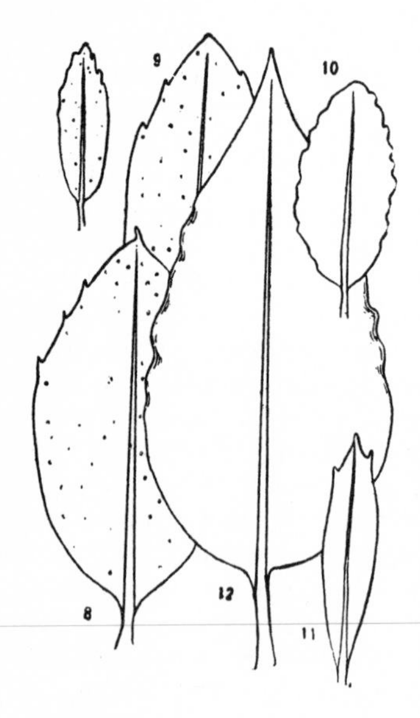

On the large-leaved evergreen hollies some leaves are entire and others pungently toothed in the same species—sometimes even on the same plant, and correspondents of the Gardeners' Chronicle (1853, pp. 630, 646; 1864, p. 25) have discussed this. Assumption that the toothing of leaves within reach of grazing animals is a protective adaptation which is lost when it becomes unnecessary is typical of many teleological assumptions that have brought the entire category of so-called adaptations into more or less undeserved disrepute. The idea of aging or maturity, paralleled in the ivy, as causative is embodied in Gaudin's name, *Ilex Aquifolium senescens*, for the entire-leaved holly of Europe.

1. Deciduous. 2.
   Evergreen. 10.
2. Twigs dingy-tomentulose. (1). I. serrata.
   Twigs at most sparingly puberulent. 3.
3. Often very divaricately twiggy. (2). I. decidua.
   Not stiffly twiggy. 4.
4. Buds appressed, pointed. 5.
   Buds spreading, blunt. 6.
5. Buds 2 mm. long; pedicels short. (3). I. monticola.
   Buds smaller: pedicels very long (15 mm.). (4). I. geniculata
6. Bud-scales obtuse: sepals ciliate. 7.
   Bud-scales: sepals glabrous. 9.

7. Branches spreading. 8.
   Branches upright. I. verticillata fastigiata.
8. Fruit bright red. (Black alder). (5). I. verticillata.
   Fruit yellow. I. verticillata chrysocarpa.
9. Fruit orange-red. (Smooth winterberry). (6). I. laevigata.
   Fruit yellow. I. laevigata Herveyi.
10. Leaves dotted beneath. 11.
    Leaves not dotted. 13.
11. Leaves small (5 × 15 mm.), low-serrate. (7). I. crenata.
    Leaves larger (15 × 30 mm. or more). 12.
12. Leaves entire or sharply low-serrate: dots black. (8). I. lucida.
    Leaves crenately few-toothed above: dots pale. (Inkberry). (9). I. glabra.
13. Leaves small (scarcely 10 × 20 mm.). 14.
    Leaves much larger. 15.
14. Leaves blunt, crenate or low-serrulate. (Yaupon, Cassena). (10, and cover). I. vomitoria.
    Leaves pointed, entire or serrate. (11). I. Cassine myrtifolia.
15. Leaves ovate: petioles long (8-10 mm.). (12). I. pedunculosa.
    Leaves not ovate: petioles short (5-8 mm.). 16.
16. Leaves oblong or oblanceolate-obovate: teeth if any small. 17.
    Leaves elliptical or quadrate, often very pungent. 18.
17. Leaves oblanceolate-obovate, large. (Dahoon). I. Cassine.
    Leaves oblong, scarcely 15 mm. wide. I. Cassine angustifolia.
18. Leaves dull. (American holly). 19.
    Leaves very glossy above. 20.
19. Fruit red. I. opaca.
    Fruit yellow. I. opaca xanthocarpa.
20. Leaves elliptical. (European holly). I. Aquifolium.
    Leaves quadrate with large teeth at the angles. I. cornuta.

NEMOPANTHUS. Mountain Holly.
(Family Aquifoliaceae).

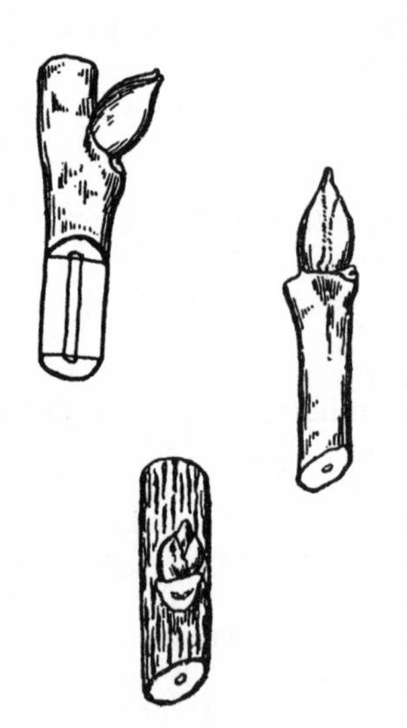

Shrubs: deciduous. Twigs rather slender, often remaining short, glabrous, and more or less glaucous, with finely fissured cortex when old: pith small, continuous. Buds rather small, solitary, sessile, ovoid, usually attenuate at tip, with about 2 ciliate exposed scales. Leaf-scars alternate, clustered at the ends. slightly raised, triangular or crescent-shaped: bundle-trace 1: stipule-scars lacking. (*Ilicioides*).

Winter-characters are pictured by Schneider, f. 127.

The mountain holly differs from the true hollies in lacking the short sepals that are to be found at the base of holly berries, so that when its long-stalked red fruits are present this aids in an otherwise difficult recognition.

Twigs from glaucous purplish becoming gray. N. mucronata.

Like *Prunus*, *Quercus*, *Rhamnus* and other generic names of woody plants, *Evonymus* proves puzzling as to the agreement of its specific names. Following earlier botanists, Linnaeus treated it as masculine and in this he has been followed by most writers though Schneider, as well as Rehder in the Standard Cyclopedia, has considered it to be a feminine fourth-declension noun because some of the species are unquestionably trees. The practice of Linnaeus is followed here, and agreements are made masculine.

EVONYMUS. Burning Bush. Spindle Tree.
(Family Celastraceae).

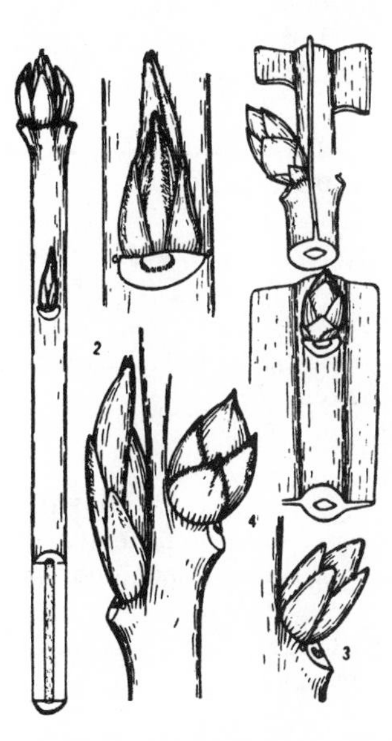

Shrubs or very small trees, exceptionally scrambling or climbing by aerial routes: deciduous or a few species evergreen. Twigs moderate, terete or mostly 4-lined from the nodes, sometimes with warty lenticels or corky wings, characteristically green: pith round, angled or 4-armed, greenish, spongy or finally incompletely excavated. Buds small to rather large, solitary, sessile, with 3 to rarely 5 pairs of at first serrulate scales. Leaf-scars opposite or exceptionally whorled or the pairs broken, half-elliptical, rather small, somewhat elevated: bundle-trace 1, transverse, toward the top of the scar: stipule-scars minute and usually indistinct. (*Evonymus*).

Winter-character references:—*Evonymus alatus*. Shirasawa, 278, pl. 2. *E. atropurpureus*. Brendel, 28, 29, 30, pl. 1; Hitchcock (1), 3, f. 4, (3), 9, (4), 34, f. 15. *E. europaeus*. Bösemann, 65; Fant, 44, f. 48; Schneider, f. 209; Ward, 1:172, f. 85; Willkomm, 51, f. 95; Zuccarini, 12, pl. 7. *E. europaeus Hamiltonianus*. Shirasawa, 278, pl. 12. *E. latifolius*. Schneider, f. 195; Willkomm, 11, 52, f. 96; Zuccarini, 10, pl. 6. *E. nanus*. Schneider, f. 209. *E. oxyphyllus*. Shirasawa, 277, pl. 12. *E. verrucosus*. Bösemann, 65; Schneider, f. 209; Willkomm, 52, f. 97; Zuccarini, 11, pl. 6.

Gibson pictures a very large waahoo tree at p. 499 of his American Forest Trees.

The corky lines or wings which occur on the twig-angles in *E. europaeus*, beside them in *E. americanus*, and between them in *E. alatus*, have been described by Miss Gregory in the Botanical Gazette for 1888, p. 12, and 1889, pp. 7, 10, 39, 43.

1. Deciduous. 2.
   Partly or wholly evergreen. 12.
2. At least the terminal buds long (20 mm.). 3.
   Buds moderate or small. 4.
3. Buds ovoid. E. sanguineus.
   Buds fusiform. E. latifolius.
4. Twigs very warty: buds round-ovoid. E. verrucosus.
   Twigs corky-winged: bud-scales 6-8 pairs. (1). E. alatus.
   Twigs neither warty nor corky-winged. 5.
5. Twigs square: buds oblong, upcurved. 6.
   Twigs terete but often 4-lined. 7.
6. Low and prostrate. E. obovatus.
   Bushy. (Strawberry bush). (2). E. americanus.
7. Buds narrowly oblong, appressed, 2-scaled. E. occidentalis.
   Buds about 6-scaled. 8.
8. Buds rather oblong: scales oblong, loose. 9.
   Buds round-ovoid: scales ovate, appressed, dry-margined. 10.
9. Very dwarf: buds very small. E. nanus.
   Bushy or aborescent. (Waahoo). (3). E. atropurpureus.
10. Bud-scales with long points. 11.
    Scales not long-pointed. (Spindle tree). (4). E. europaeus.
11. Fruit small (10 mm.), bright red. E. lancifolius.
    Fruit larger (12-15 mm.), dull. E. yedoensis.
12. Leaves thin, partly evergreen. E. patens.
    Leaves thick, more persistent. 13.
13. Low and spreading or else climbing. E. radicans.
    Bushy. E. japonicus.

GLOSSOPETALON.
(Family Celastraceae).

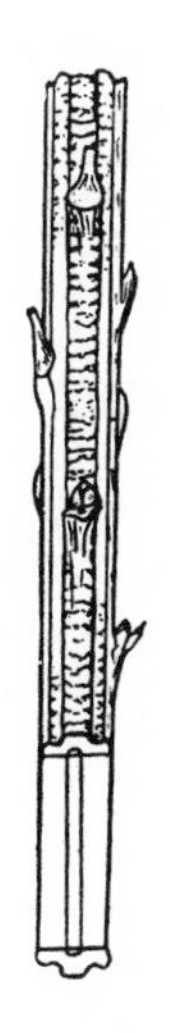

Shrubs: deciduous. Twigs sometimes forming blunt spines, slender, flat-ridged below the leaf-scars: pith small, roundish, white, continuous. Buds solitary, sessile, minute, round-ovoid, appressed, with 2 or 3 exposed scales, the end-bud lacking. Leaf-scars alternate, very narrowly triangular-crescent-shaped or almost linear, slightly elevated, minute, the petioles at first persisting and covering the buds: bundle-trace 1: stipule-scars lacking. (*Forsellesia*).

When Dr. Gray first published this genus he called it *Glossopetalon*, with the characteristic Greek ending, and this form is used here. In an effort to Latinize all generic names, some botanists write it in the form *Glossopetalum*. The plant is a close counterpart, vegetatively, of the rhamnaceous *Adolphia*.

Twigs gray-green, transversely rugulose. G. spinescens.

PACHISTIMA.
(Family Celastraceae).

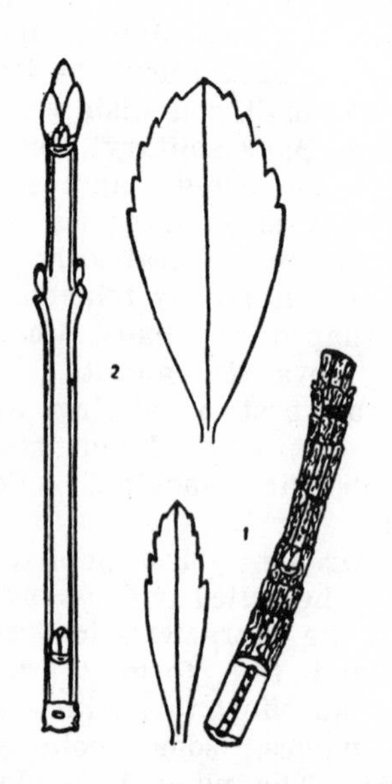

Low shrubs: evergreen. Twigs very slender, somewhat 4-sided, the bark becoming corky-thickened and transversely checked: pith minute, rounded, brownish and spongy. Buds solitary, sessile, ovoid, appressed, very small, with about 2 pairs of exposed scales, the terminal somewhat larger and with more visible scales. Leaf-scars opposite, minute, crescent-shaped, somewhat raised: bundle-trace 1, indistinct: stipule-scars lacking. Leaves small, subsessile, more or less serrate toward the end.

In the Canadian mountains *Pachistima* is called the mountain lover. It is pictured photographically under this name in the Alpine Flora of the Canadian Rocky Mountains by Stewardson Brown and Mrs. Charles Schäffer.

Leaves elliptical-oblong, revolute. 1. P. Canbyi.
Leaves elliptical-oblanceolate, often flat. (2). P. Myrsinites.

CELASTRUS. Bittersweet, Waxwork.
(Family Celastraceae).

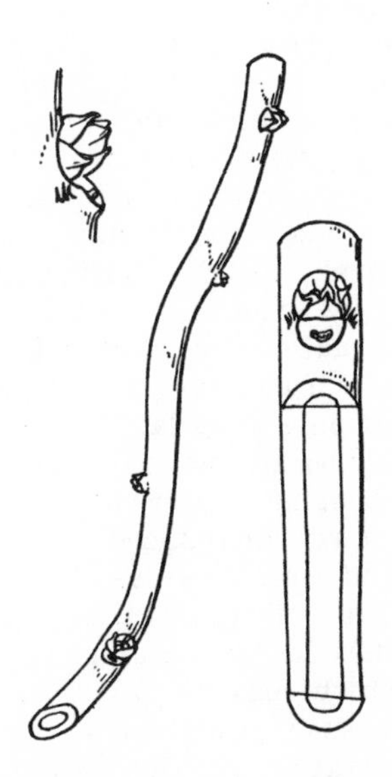

Woody twiners: deciduous. Stems terete, rather slender: pith relatively large, continuous and homogeneous, round, white. Buds small, solitary, sessile, subglobose, with half-a-dozen mucronate scales. Leaf-scars alternate, half-elliptic or broadly crescent-shaped, low: bundle-trace 1, transverse: stipule-scars minute or indistinguishable, or the persistent stipules minute and resembling tufted hairs.

Winter-character references to *Celastrus scandens*:—Brendel, 30, pl. 4; Hitchcock (3), 9, (4), 134, f. 14; Schneider, f. 116.

In two species referred to this genus, Damaskinos and Bourgeois, in volume 5 of the Bulletin de la Société Botanique de France, show that two axillary buds are superposed, the lower developing into a spine or an inflorescence.

Stems and buds glabrous, brownish. C. scandens.

TRIPTERYGIUM.
(Family Celastraceae).

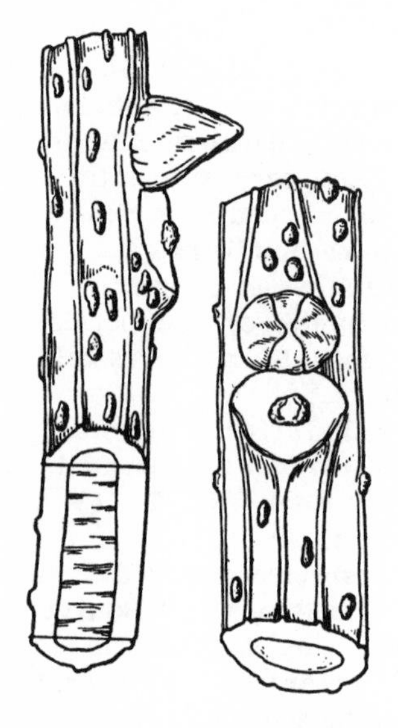

Shrubs: deciduous. Twigs moderate, angled, very warty, somewhat zig-zag: pith round, continuous, with firmer cross-plates at intervals, pale, pinkish. Buds moderate, solitary, sessile, conical, nearly horizontal, with about 2 exposed scales. Leaf-scars alternate, somewhat raised, half-round: bundle-trace 1, C-shaped: stipule-scars lacking.

Few shrubs are so well marked by conspicuous winter-characters as this newly introduced Asiatic species, and Mrs. Vieh has brought these out unmistakably in a few strong lines in the accompanying sketch which may be taken as a model of such illustration. The rusty coloration of the twigs is quite as characteristic as the clean-cut buds, leaf-scars, and surface.

Twigs rust-colored, glabrous. T. Regelii.

STAPHYLEA. Bladdernut.
(Family Staphyleaceae).

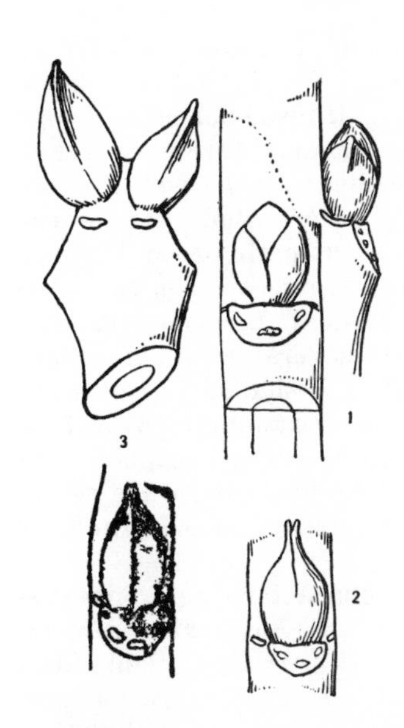

Shrubs or small trees: deciduous. Twigs moderate, rounded, glabrous: pith rather large, rounded, continuous, white. Buds solitary, sessile, ovoid, glabrous, with a single sac or 2 or 4 exposed scales, the end-bud commonly lacking. Leaf-scars opposite, broadly crescent-shaped or half-round, slightly raised: bundle-traces 3, compound, or often 5 or 7 or broken into an elliptical series: stipule-scars half-round or elongated.

Winter-character references:—*Staphylea Bumalda.* Shirasawa, 271, pl. 10. *S. pinnata.* Schneider, f. 193; Willkomm, 51, f. 94; Zuccarini, 29, pl. 16. *S. trifolia.* Brendel, 28, 29, 30, pl. 1; Hitchcock (3), 11, (4), 135, f. 32-34; Schneider, f. 193.

1. Buds with 4 blunt exposed scales. (1). S. trifolia.
   Buds 2-edged, with 2 sometimes connate exposed scales. 2.
2. Buds acute: bundle-traces 5 or 7. S. pinnata.
   Buds acuminate: bundle-traces three or five. 3.
3. Twigs brown: buds long-pointed. (2). S. Bumalda.
   Twigs green: buds short-pointed. (3). S. colchica.

Winter-characters of *Euscaphis japonica*, another member of the Staphyleaceae, are given by Schneider, f. 193; and Shirasawa, 275, pl. 11.

ACER. Maple.
(Family Aceraceae).

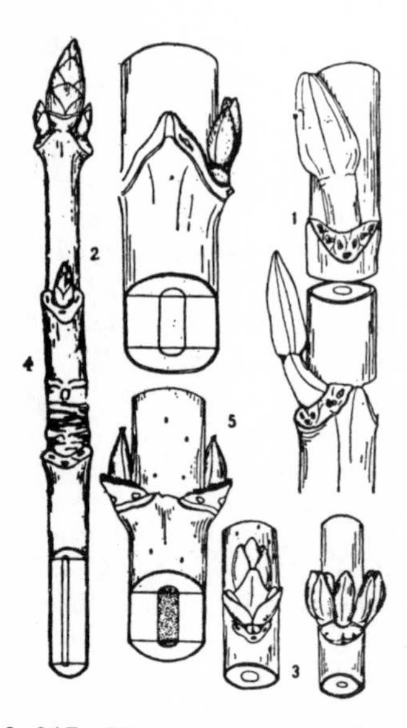

Shrubs or round-topped trees: deciduous. Wood rather hard, brownish, diffused-porous. Twigs moderate, nearly terete or somewhat 6-sided: pith round, continuous, pale. Buds moderate, solitary or sometimes collaterally multiple, ovoid or conical, distinctly stalked in some groups, with 2 or several pairs of scales. Leaf-scars U-shaped: bundle-traces 3 or occasionally 5 or 7 or 9, or multiplied: stipule-scars lacking. The box elders are segregated frequently as *Negundo* or *Rulac*.

Winter-character references:— *Acer argutum*. Shirasawa, 275, pl. 21. *A. californicum*. Schneider, f. 219. *A. campestre*. Bösemann, 63; Fant, 42, f. 41; Schneider, f. 217; Ward, 1:170, f. 84; Zuccarini, 14, pl. 8. *A. carpinifolium*. Shirasawa, 278, pl. 12. *A. circinatum*. Schneider, f. 218; Trelease (2), 101, 103, pl. 14. *A. cissifolium*. Shirasawa, 272, pl. 10. *A. crataegifolium*. Shirasawa, 271, pl. 10. *A. distylum*. Shirasawa, 275, pl. 11. *A. Drummondii*. Trelease, (2), 101, 104, pl. 15. *A. floridanum*. Trelease (2), 102, 105, pl. 16. *A. Ginnala*. Schneider, f. 220; Shirasawa, 279, pl. 12. *A. glabrum*. Trelease (2), 101, 102, pl. 14. *A. grandidentatum*. Trelease (2), 102, 104, pl. 16. *A. japonicum*. Shirasawa, 276, pl. 11. *A. leucoderme*. Trelease (2), 101, 103, pl. 15. *A. monspessulanum*. Bösemann, 63; Schneider, f. 221.

A. Negundo. Blakeslee & Jarvis, 342, 546, pl.; Bösemann, 63; Brendel, 29, pl. 1; Hitchcock (1), 3, (3), 11, (4), 135, f. 26-31; Otis, 192; Schneider, f. 50, 219; Trelease (2) 105,—illustration on cover of separates. *A. nigrum.* Blakeslee & Jarvis, 536; Otis, 182; Trelease (2), 102, 105, pl. 16. *A. nikoense.* Shirasawa, 278, pl. 12. *A. obtusatum.* Schneider, f. 220. *A palmatum.* Schneider, f. 219; Shirasawa, 271, pl. 10. *A. pennsylvanicum.* Blakeslee & Jarvis, 342, 532, pl.; Otis, 176; Schneider, f. 221; Trelease (2), 101, 102, pl. 14. *A. pictum.* Shirasawa, 280, pl. 12. *A. platanoides.* Blakeslee & Jarvis, 342, 542, pl.; Bösemann, 63; Fant, 42, f. 40; Otis, 188; Schneider, f. 51, 217; Ward, 1:154, f. 72; Zuccarini, 16 pl. 9. *A. pseudoplatanus.* Blakeslee & Jarvis 342, 544, pl.; Bösemann, 63; Fant, 42, f. 42; Otis, 190; Schneider, f. 19, 217; Ward, 1:156, f. 73; Willkomm, 4, 9, 53, f. 99; Zuccarini, 15, pl. 8. *A. purpurascens.* Shirasawa, 280, pl. 12. *A. pycnanthum.* Shirasawa, 280, pl. 12. *A. rubrum.* Blakeslee & Jarvis, 324, f. 7, 342, 540, pl.; Otis, 186; Schneider, f. 221; Trelease (2), 101, 104, pl. 15. *A. rufinerve.* Shirasawa, 271, pl. 10. *A. saccharinum.* Blakeslee & Jarvis, 342, 538, pl.; Brendel, 29, pl. 1; Hitchcock (1), 3, f. 8, (3), 11; Otis, 184; Trelease (2), 101, 103, pl. 15. *A. saccharum.* Blakeslee & Jarvis, 342, 536, pl.; Brendel, 29, pl. 1; Hitchcock (1), 3; Otis, 180; Trelease (2), 102, 104, 105, pl. 16. *A. Sieboldianum.* Shirasawa, 276 *A. spicatum.* Blakeslee & Jarvis, 342, 534, pl.; Otis, 178; Trelease (2), 101, 102, pl. 14. *A. tataricum.* Bösemann, 62; Schneider, f. 220.

In their opposite lobed leaves, maples in general are familiar to most people who have even the slightest knowledge of plants, and the characters of flowers and fruit on which their botanical classification rests are distinctive.

A novice is apt to mistake the sweet gum for a maple through failing to observe that its leaves are alternate and not opposite, and comparable leaves occur more confusingly in *Viburnum* and some other genera, certain species of which have been given specific names indicative of their maple-like foliage. Indeed it proves difficult to point unexceptionable vegetative characters by which maples and viburnums may be told apart with certainty, though individual species are recognized readily after they have been learned.

Some few Asiatic maples have elongated leaves that are toothed but not at all lobed, and such a species as that which has been named *Acer carpinifolium* might be mistaken for a hornbeam or some related shrub if attention were not paid to its opposite leaves. Though the box elders appear to us peculiar in their compound leaves, the Rocky Mountain maple is trifololiate, and certain Asiatic species not of the American Negundo group, have conspicuously compound leaves.

1. Scales 2, valvate. 2.
   Scales more than two. 8.
2. Buds short (scarcely 5 mm.). 3.
   Buds large (8 mm. or more). 5.
3. Twigs and buds glabrous.
   (Rocky Mountain maple). A. glabrum.
   Twigs and buds puberulent. 4.
4. Buds rather slender (2×5 mm.).
   (Mountain maple). A. spicatum.
   Buds stouter (2.5×4 mm.). Asiatic. A. argutum.
5. Buds moderate (8 mm.): glabrous. 6.
   Buds long (10 mm. or more), thick and blunt, glabrous. 7.
6. Buds slender, pointed. Asiatic. A. Tschonoskii
   Buds stouter, blunt.
   (Striped maple). (1). A. pennsylvanicum.
7. Twigs olive. A. rufinerve.
   Twigs dull purplish. A. capillipes.
8. End-bud lacking: buds short. 9.
   End-bud characteristically present or scales numerous. 12.
9. Leaf-scars low and narrow: glabrous.
   (Japanese maple). A palmatum.
   Leaf-scars broad or raised in a cup, or ciliate. 10.

10. Leaf-scars with a membranous wing at top. 11.
Leaf-scars not winged: twigs purplish.
(Vine maple). A. circinatum.
11. Scales blunt: buds and twigs usually green. A. japonicum.
Scales mucronate: buds and twigs purplish.
A. Sieboldianum.

12. Exposed scales about four. 13.
Exposed scales six or more. 23.
13. Leaf-scars meeting in a point. 14.
Leaf-scars connected by a transverse line. 20.
14. Buds gray-hairy: leaf-scars with minute red glands above. (Box elder). 15.
Buds glabrate: leaf-scars not glandular. 18.
15. Twigs very glaucous. 16.
Twigs little if at all glaucous, or else puberulent. 17.
16. Twigs green when rubbed. (2). A. Negundo.
Twigs violet when rubbed. A. Negundo violaceum.
17. Twigs olive, puberulent. A. Negundo interius.
Twigs bright green, glabrous. A. Negundo Nuttallii.
18. Twigs moderate (4 mm.): buds large.
(Norway maple). A. platanoides.
Twigs slenderer (3 mm.): buds small. 19.
19. Bud-scales purplish, brown-bordered. A. pictum.
Bud-scales light brown. A. truncatum.
20. Twigs woolly near the end.
(Woolly red maple). A. Drummondii.
Twigs glabrous. 21.
21. Buds collaterally multiple toward spring. 22.
Buds always solitary. 27.
22. Bark of trunk rough but not flaking: twigs not fetid.
(Red maple). (3). A. rubrum.
Bark flaking, leaving brown areas: twigs ill-smelling.
(Silver maple). A. saccharinum.
23. Buds ovoid, usually very blunt. 24.
Buds conical or acute. 29.

24. Twigs stout (4-6 mm.), green.
    (Oregon maple). A. macrophyllum.
  Twigs moderate or slender. 25.
25. End-bud rather long (over 5 mm.).
    (Sycamore maple). A. pseudoplatanus.
  Buds distinctly smaller. 26.
26. Exposed scales about 6: buds as thick as long.
    (Tartarian maples). 27.
  Exposed scales about 8. (Field maples). 28.
27. Buds blackish: twigs dark. A. tataricum.
  Buds red-brown or paler. A. Ginnala.
28. Buds gray-woolly, at least above. A. campestre.
  Buds glabrate, becoming dark. A. monspessulanum.
29. Buds glabrous. 30.
  Buds more or less silky or hairy and dull. 31.
30. Buds stout, prismatic: end-bud often lacking.
    A. carpinifolium.
  Buds fusiform, terete, very acute. A. mandshuricum.
31. Twigs loosely hairy above. A. nikoense.
  Twigs glabrescent. 32.
32. Twigs 3-4 mm. thick: buds 10 mm. long. A. diabolicum.
  Twigs slenderer and buds smaller. 33.
33. Buds moderate (the terminal 5 mm. long). 34.
  Buds small (scarcely 2×3 mm.). 35.
34. Twigs and buds dull straw-color, hairy.
    (Black maple). A. nigrum.
  Twigs glossy buff: buds darkening, glabrate.
    (Sugar maple). (4). A. saccharum.
35. Bark of trunk finally rough. A. floridanum.
  Bark persistently smooth and white. A. leucoderme.

AESCULUS. Horsechestnut. Buckeye.
(Family Hippocastanaceae).

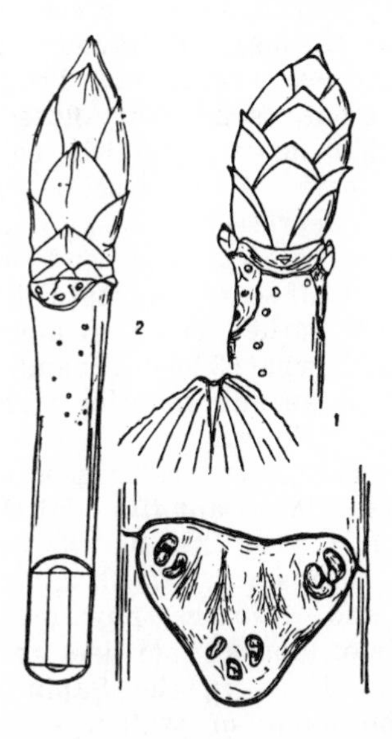

Round-topped trees or exceptionally shrubs: deciduous. Twigs stout, nearly terete: pith large, rather 6-sided, continuous, pale. Buds, especially the uppermost, very large, solitary, ovoid, sessile, with some half-dozen pairs of exposed scales. Leaf-scars opposite, low, shield-shaped or triangular: bundle-traces 3 or in 3 compound groups, exceptionally 7 or 9 in a single series: stipule-scars lacking.—References under *Koelreuteria*.

Meyer reports in volume 7 of Linnaea exceptional superposed buds in horsechestnut. A characteristic feature of the bud-scales is the rudimentary leaf, or its scar, at the tip. As in *Acer* and other genera with terminal inflorescence, the twig may end in an inflorescence-scar.

1. Buds gummy. (§Hippocastanum, the horsechestnuts). 2.
   Buds not gummy. (§Pavia, the buckeyes). 3.
2. Buds persistently gummy. (1). A. Hippocastanum.
   Buds gradually becoming dry. (Hybrid h.). × A. carnea.
3. Trees. 4.
   Shrubs. 5.
4. Bark rough, soft and cork-like. (Ohio b.). (2). A. glabra.
   Bark smooth and firm. (Sweet buckeye). A. octandra.
5. Lowest scale less than half as long as bud. A. Pavia.
   Lowest scale half as long as bud. (Shrubby b.). A. parviflora.

SAPINDUS. Soapberry.
(Family Sapindaceae).

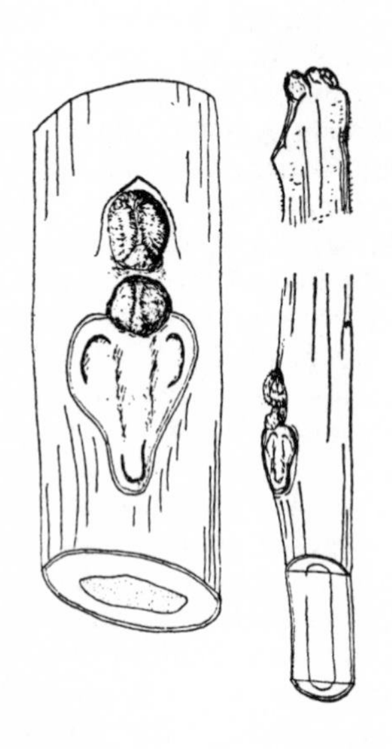

Trees (some species erect or climbing shrubs): deciduous or some species evergreen. Twigs rather stout, somewhat fluted: pith rather large, roundish, continuous, pale. Buds sessile, superposed, depressed-globose, with 2 exposed scales, the end-bud lacking. Leaf-scars alternate, little raised, rather large, triangular or somewhat 3-lobed: bundle-traces 3, large but indistinct: stipule-scars lacking.

Winter-character references:—*Sapindus Drummondii.* Hitchcock (1), 4, f. 6, (3), 10. *S. Mukurosi.* Shirasawa, 237, pl. 2.

Acer and *Aesculus*, now made the basis of distinct families, were formerly placed in the Sapindaceae, the name of which, as of its typical genus *Sapindus*, refers to a saponifying glucoside, saponin, which occurs abundantly in the buckeyes. One case has come to my knowledge in which pollen of *Aesculus glabra* caused a severe inflammation of the eyes that extended to the throat and bronchial tubes and was held to be the predisposing cause of a fatal pneumonia infection.

1. Twigs and buds quite glabrous. S. Saponaria.
   Buds, at least, pubescent. 2.
2. Twigs becoming nearly glabrous.
   (Wild China-tree). (1). S. Drummondii.
   Twigs persistently yellow-tomentose. S. marginatus.

KOELREUTERIA. Varnish Tree.
(Family Sapindaceae).

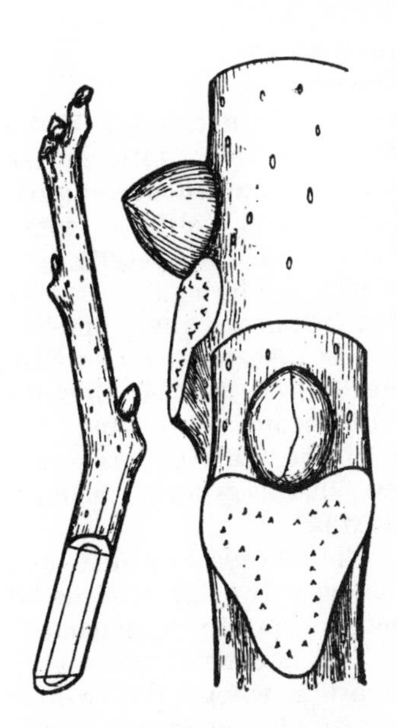

Small or moderate-sized trees: deciduous. Twigs rather stout, very slightly angled: pith rather large, rounded, continuous, white. Buds moderate, solitary, half-ellipsoid, sessile, with 2 exposed scales, the end-bud lacking. Leaf-scars alternate, raised, rather large, shield-shaped: bundle-traces 3 and compound, or forming a singled jagged irregular series: stipule-scars lacking.

Winter-character references:—*Koelreuteria paniculata.* Schneider, f. 47, 215; Shirasawa, 245, pl. 4.

Twigs olive-buff, glabrescent.
K. paniculata.

Winter-character references to *Aesculus*:—× *A. carnea.* Schneider, f. 214. *A. glabra.* Blakeslee & Jarvis, 548; Brendel, 29, pl. 1; Otis, 198; Schneider, f. 214. *A. glabra Buckleyi.* Hitchcock (1), 3, f. 5, (3), 10, (4), 135. f. 24. *A. Hippocastanum.* Blakeslee & Jarvis, 320, f. 4, 330, 548, pl.; Bösemann, 64; Fant, 41, f. 38; Otis, 196; Schneider, f. 213, 214; Ward, 1:15, f. 7-8, 104, f. 57, 118, f. 59, 150, f. 70; Willkomm, 53, f. 98; Zuccarini, 31, pl. 17. *A. humilis.* Schneider, f. 215. *A. octandra.* Blakeslee & Jarvis, 548; Bösemann, 64; Schneider, f. 214. *A. parviflora.* Schneider, f. 215. *A. Pavia.* Bösemann, 64. *A. turbinata.* Shirasawa, 268, pl. 10.

UNGNADIA. Mexican Buckeye.
(Family Sapindaceae).

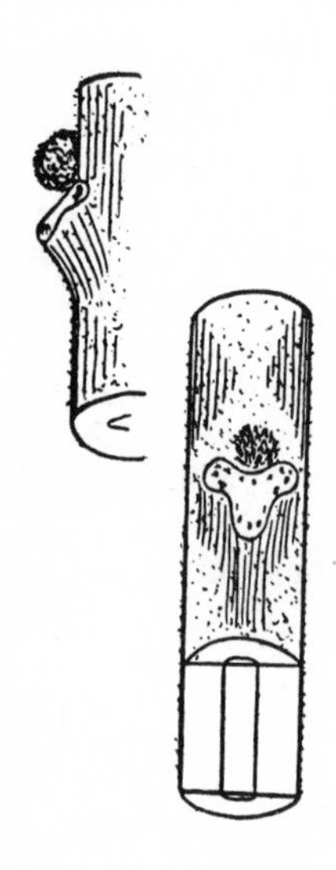

Tender shrub: deciduous. Twigs moderate, subterete: pith moderate, rounded, continuous, slightly brownish. Buds solitary, somewhat above the axil, sessile, globose, very red-hairy and with concealed scales, the end-bud lacking. Leaf-scars alternate, somewhat raised, 3-lobed: bundle-traces numerous, following the contour of the scar, or somewhat clustered in 3 groups: stipule-scars lacking.

Like the horsechestnut and true buckeyes, the large seeds of this species contain a poisonous principle. It is considered worthy of cultivation where the winter temperature is moderate, but rather as a novelty than in competition with many other shrubs. Like the following genus, it has the sapindaceous character of alternate leaves, in contrast with the opposite leaves of Hippocastanaceae.

Twigs densely dingy-tomentulose. U. speciosa.

XANTHOCERAS. Chinese Buckeye.
(Family Sapindaceae).

Tree-like shrub, or small tree: deciduous. Twigs moderate, terete, with coarse lenticels: pith moderate, continuous, slightly brownish. Buds moderate, solitary, sessile, round-ovoid, with about half-a-dozen more or less fringed or lacerate scales. Leaf-scars alternate, half-elliptical, moderate, elevated: bundle-traces 3, large.

Winter-character reference to *Xanthoceras sorbifolia*: — Schneider, f. 127.

Xanthoceras is coming into extensive cultivation on lawns and in shrubbery masses, and is a shapely hardy plant with pleasing compound leaves and conspicuous white flowers which show a change in their striping similar to that of the spotting of horsechestnut flowers, as they change in maturity.

Glabrate: buds chestnut, glossy. X. sorbifolia.

Winter-characters of *Meliosma myriantha*, of the related family Sabiaceae, are pictured by Shirasawa, 234, pl. 1.

ZIZYPHUS. Jujube.
(Family Rhamnaceae).

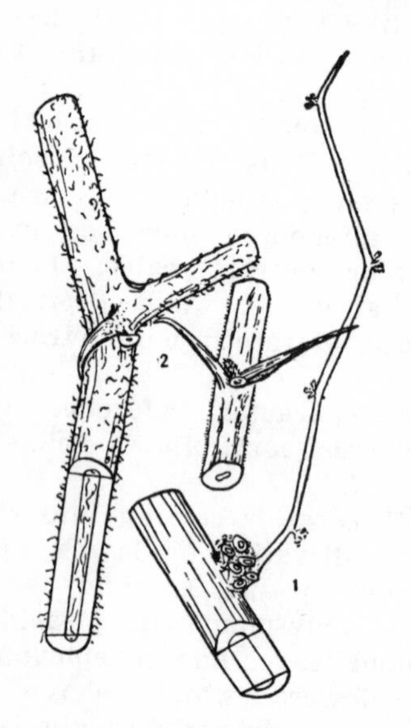

Shrubs or trees, more or less armed with pungent stipules: deciduous in the North. Twigs terete, stout, with spurs bearing clustered scars and very slender zig-zag shoots: pith small and brownish and spongy, or larger and continuous. Buds minute, rounded, very obliquely sessile, solitary, or in some species superposed, with several scarcely distinguishable scales, the end-bud lacking. Leaf-scars alternate, 2-ranked, minute, elliptical or triangular, low: bundle-trace 1 or fragmented, indistinct: stipule-scars small and round, or the stipules forming short spines.

Winter-character references:—*Zizyphus sativa* (*Z. vulgaris*). Schneider f. 69; Shirasawa, 235, pl. 2.—According to the belief of many people the food of the African lotus eaters was the fruit of a species of *Zizyphus*, which, in this belief, botanists have called *Z. Lotus*.

1. Tomentose: spines stout, curved. (2). Z. Jujuba.
   At most puberulent. 2.
2. With slender spines, one straight. Z. sativa.
   Unarmed. (1). Z. sativa inermis.

PALIURUS. Jerusalem Thorn.
(Family Rhamnaceae).

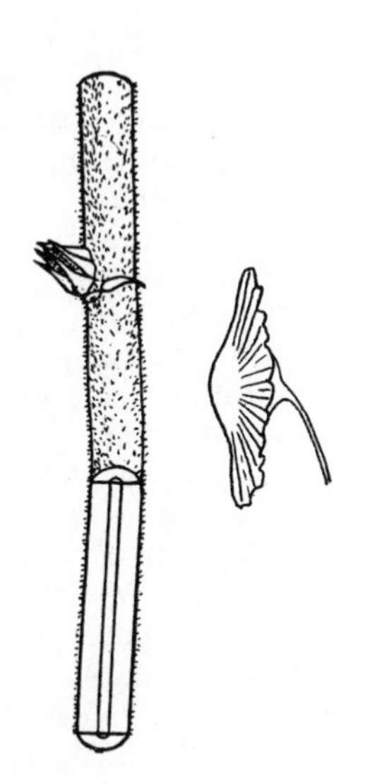

Shrubs or small trees, more or less armed with unequal pungent stipules. Twigs slender, zig-zag, terete: pith small, rounded, pale continuous. Buds solitary, obliquely sessile, ovoid with a half-dozen pointed scales or the smaller indefinitely scaly. Leaf-scars alternate, 2-ranked, minute, half-round, low: bundle-trace 1 or fragmented, indistinct: stipule-scars minute and round or the stipules forming short spines.

Winter-character references:—*Paliurus Aubletia.* Shirasawa, 235, pl. 2. *P. australis.* Lubbock, On Buds and Stipules, 194, f. 313,—with suggestion that the hooked stipule is an aid in scrambling; Schneider, f. 69.

A gray-twigged Oriental jujube, *Zizyphus Spina-Christi*, like this shrub, has been given its specific name because it has been taken to be the plant which was used in making the biblical crown of thorns.

Puberulent: twigs brown. P. Spina-Christi.

COLLETIA.
(Family Rhamnaceae).

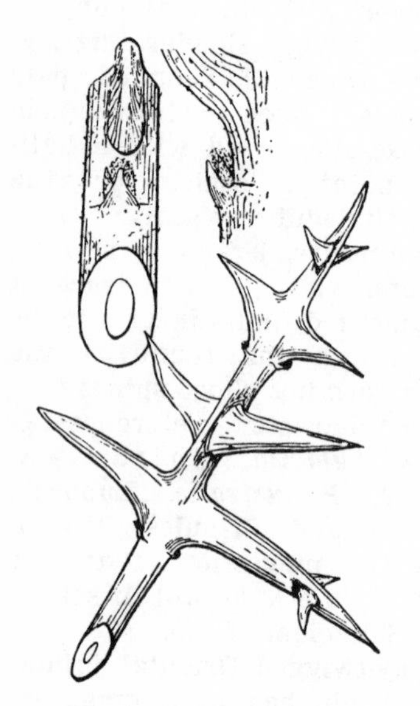

Shrubs, horridly spiny by the decussate branchlets: pith moderate, rounded, white, continuous. Buds superposed, the upper at once developing into a spine-branch, the lower minute with about 2 scales concealed in tomentum. Leaf-scars lacking, the opposite minute scales which represent the true foliage persistent.

Except for a few other species of *Colletia*, which have slenderer or more rounded spines and are seldom if ever seen in this country, *Colletia cruciata*, or *C. horrida* as it is called sometimes, reresembles only the related genus *Adolphia* of the Southwest, and the rather distantly related Mexican *Koeberlinia* which differs from both in having its spines alternately placed and not in the form of a cross.

Gray-tomentulose, leaf-green when denuded. C. cruciata.

CONDALIA.
(Family Rhamnaceae).

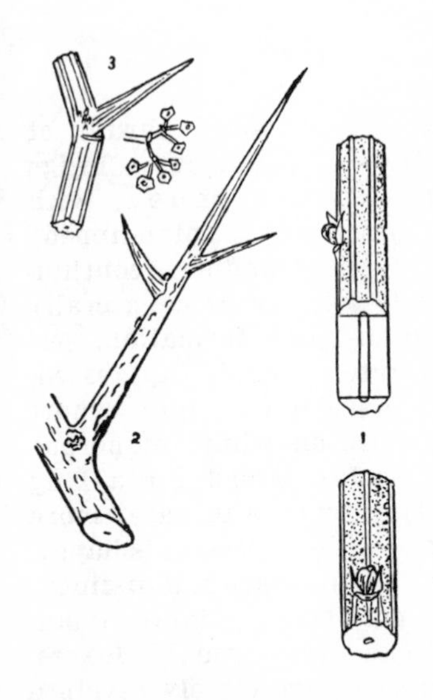

Intricately branched spiny shrubs or small trees of the southwest. Twigs slender, usually obscurely 5-angled, gray; pith small, roundish, continuous. Buds sessile, small, rounded, with about 2 exposed scales, solitary, or collaterally branched in spine formation, more or less developed as short spurs. Leaf-scars alternate, crescent-shaped, minute, somewhat raised: bundle-trace 1, indistinct: stipules persistent beside the bud. The first and last species are frequently treated under *Zizyphus*.

Though the Spanish word chaparral, now familiar in the southwest, properly means a thicket of scrub oak, it has come into general use as the designation of any dense tangle of low stiff shrubs. *Condalia, Ceanothus* and *Lycium* are prominent spiny constituents of such tangles.

1. Tree. (Purple haw). C. obovata.
   Shrubs. 2.
2. Twigs glaucous, with black dots. (1). C. obtusifolia.
   Twigs not glaucous when mature. 3.
3. Twigs terete, with roughening bark. (2). C. spathulata.
   Twigs rather evidently angled. 4.
4. Glabrate. (3). C. lycioides.
   Persistently somewhat white-hairy. C. lycioides canescens.

MICRORHAMNUS.
(Family Rhamnaceae).

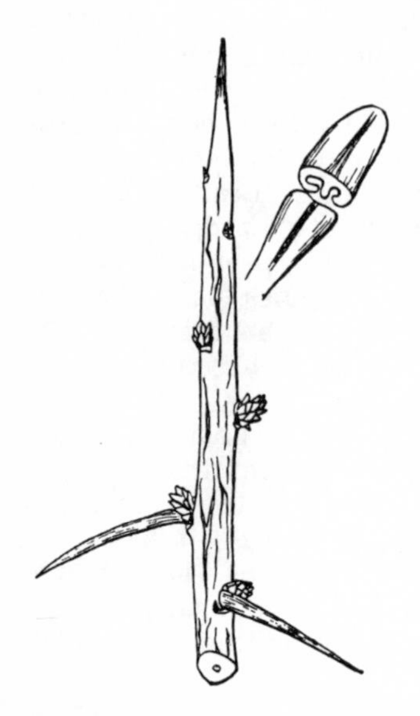

Intricately branched shrubs of the southwest: deciduous. Twigs glabrous, terete, slender, with short internodes, spine-tipped: pith minute, roundish, continuous. Buds solitary or collaterally branched in spine formation, sessile, minute, round, appressed, quickly developing into short foliage spurs on which numerous stipular scales persist for a long time. Leaf-scars alternate, more or less raised, crescent-shaped, minute: bundle-trace 1, indistinct: stipules persistent, minute, triangular. The very small leaves, when present, are closely revolute to the midrib as in *Loiseleuria* and some other Ericaceae and in some Empetraceae.

Like the preceding genus, *Microrhamnus* often forms dense masses of chaparral.

Twigs with light gray splitting epidermis. M. ericoides.

BERCHEMIA. Supple Jack.
(Family Rhamnaceae).

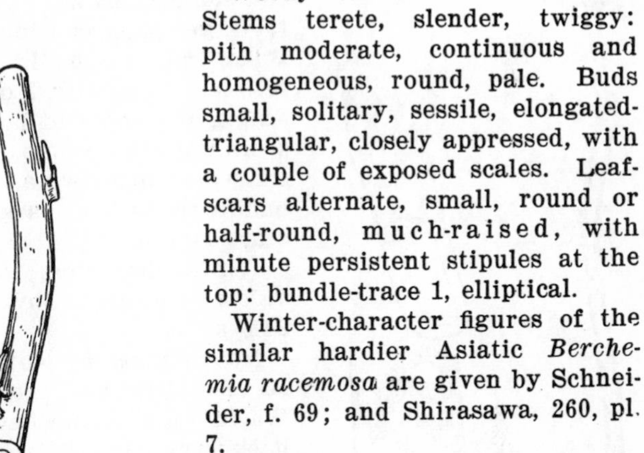

Woody twiners: deciduous. Stems terete, slender, twiggy: pith moderate, continuous and homogeneous, round, pale. Buds small, solitary, sessile, elongated-triangular, closely appressed, with a couple of exposed scales. Leaf-scars alternate, small, round or half-round, much-raised, with minute persistent stipules at the top: bundle-trace 1, elliptical.

Winter-character figures of the similar hardier Asiatic *Berchemia racemosa* are given by Schneider, f. 69; and Shirasawa, 260, pl. 7.

When they can be grown successfully, the berchemias are effective climbers, growing rapidly and producing an abundance of slender branches covered in the open season with rather small and neat leaves. In the South *B. scandens*, or *B. volubilis* as it is called sometimes, often reaches far up into the tops of tall trees.

Glabrous: bud-scales with exfoliating cuticle. B. scandens.

HOVENIA. Honey Tree.
(Family Rhamnaceae).

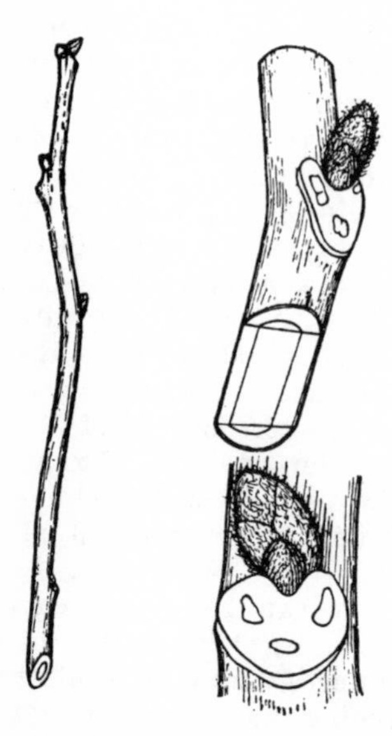

Trees: deciduous. Twigs terete, slender, zig-zag: pith relatively large, pale, continuous, round. Buds rather small, superposed, sessile, ovoid, with 1 or 2 exposed scales, the end bud lacking. Leaf-scars alternate, round-heart-shaped, somewhat elevated: bundle-traces 3, large: stipule-scars lacking.

Winter-characters of *Hovenia dulcis* are given by Shirasawa, 241, pl. 3.

Hovenia dulcis, which is grown successfully as far north as Washington, somewhat suggests a hackberry in its foliage and slender zig-zag twigs. When it becomes old enough to fruit its fleshy edible branching flower-stalks, quite unlike the product of any other northern tree but in a way morphologically comparable with the cashew "apples" of the tropics (*Anacardium*), attract attention, and finally litter the ground, in autumn and winter.

Twigs from villous, glabrescent: buds dark brown, hairy.
H. dulcis.

CEANOTHUS. New Jersey Tea.
(Family Rhamnaceae).

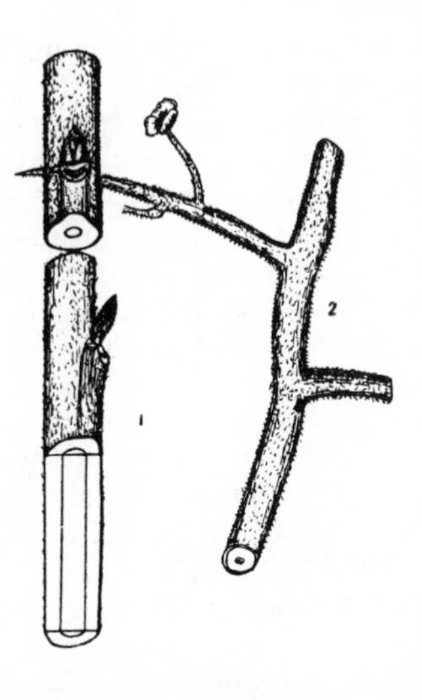

For our purpose low and deciduous shrubs, sometimes with twig-spines. Twigs rounded, rather slender, more or less puberulent, green or brownish: pith relatively large, white, continuous, sessile or often developing the first season, ovoid, with several glabrate stipular scales of which the lowest only are distinct and the leaf-blades are very hairy. Leaf-scars alternate, half-round somewhat raised, small: bundle-trace 1, transverse, more or less evidently compound; sometimes distinctly 3: stipules small, persistent or leaving narrow scars. Bases of the half-inferior clustered capsules usually persist and some tender species have opposite evergreen leaves.—In California known as wild lilac.

Winter-character references: — *Ceanothus americanus.* Hitchcock (4), 134, f. 16-18; Schneider, f. 9. *C. ovatus.* Hitchcock (3), 9.

Except for the short time when they are in flower, the New Jersey tea shrubs of the Northeast are of little interest; but several Mexican and Californian species have been favorites in the milder climate of Europe for many years, and a number of their hybrids are very attractive in English gardens.

Unarmed, low bushy. (1). C. americanus.
Spiny, prostrate: twigs gray-hairy. (2). C. Fendleri.

RHAMNUS. Buckthorn.

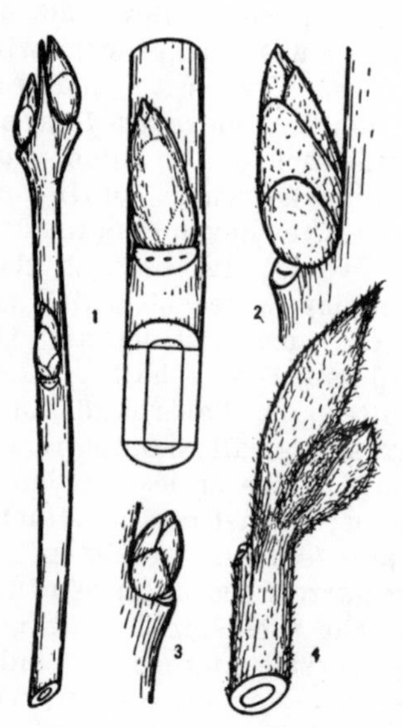

Shrubs or rather small trees: deciduous. Twigs rather slender, rounded: pith moderate, rounded, continuous, white. Buds moderate, solitary, sessile or exceptionally developing the first season, naked (*Frangula*) or with some half-dozen scales (*Rhamnus* proper). Leaf-scars alternate, or in some species opposite or in decussating broken pairs, crescent-shaped or half-elliptical, small, more or less raised: bundle-traces 3 or joined into a transverse series: stipule-scars mostly minute, or stipules small and persistent. References under *Adolphia*, p. 223.

Cascara sagrada is much used in medicine.

1. Buds scaly (*Rhamnus*). 2.
   Buds naked (*Frangula*). 6.
2. Buds chiefly opposite: shoots often spine-tipped. 3.
   Buds alternate: not spiny. 4.
3. Spines scarcely longer than buds. (1). R. cathartica.
   Spines long and very pungent. R. japonica.
4. Buds large (7-8 mm. long). (2.) R. alpina.
   Buds small (under 5 mm. long). 5.
5. Twigs gray, often downy. (3). R. lanceolata.
   Twigs red or brown, glabrous. R. alnifolia.
6. Buds long (8-10 mm.). (Cascara sagrada). R. Purshiana.
   Buds short (scarcely 5 mm.). 7.
7. Fruiting pedicels separate. R. Frangula.
   Fruiting pedicels several in a cluster. (4). R. caroliniana.

ADOLPHIA.
(Family Rhamnaceae).

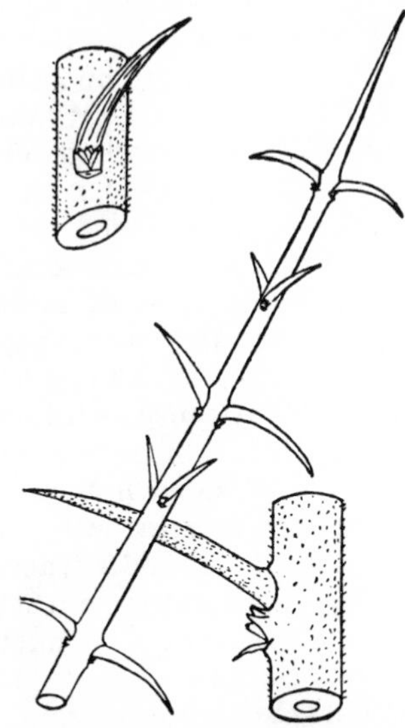

Intricately green-branched shrubs, very spiny by the decussate terete granular and puberulent branchlets; pith moderate, rounded, continuous. Buds superposed, the upper at once developing into a recurving spine-branch, the lower minute, with 2 outer and ultimately several inner blackening scales. Leaf-scars opposite, transverse, minute and indistinct. or lacking, the infra-spinal buds developing as short spurs on which the small spatulate leaves sometimes persist.

In its opposite spines *Adolphia* resembles *Colletia*, to which the genus is not distantly related; and it suggests *Koeberlinia*.

Of Arizona, New Mexico and Mexico. A. infesta.
Of Lower California. (1). A. californica.

Winter-character references to *Rhamnus*:—*R. alpina*. Schneider, f. 169; Willkomm, 40, f. 64. *R. cathartica*. Bösemann, 48; Fant, 41, f. 39; Schneider, f. 169; Ward, 1:46, f. 28, 160, f. 76-77; Willkomm, 4, 45, f. 77. *R. Frangula*. Bösemann, 49; Fant, 40, f. 36; Schneider, f. 101; Ward, 1:215, f. 110; Willkomm, 40, f. 66. *R. japonica*. Shirasawa, 268, pl. 10. *R. lanceolata*. Brendel, 27, pl. 1; Hitchcock (3), 9, *R. pumila*. Schneider, f. 101. *R. saxatilis*. Bösemann, 48; Schneider, f. 169. *R. utilis*. Schneider, f. 169.

AMPELOPSIS.
(Family Vitaceae).

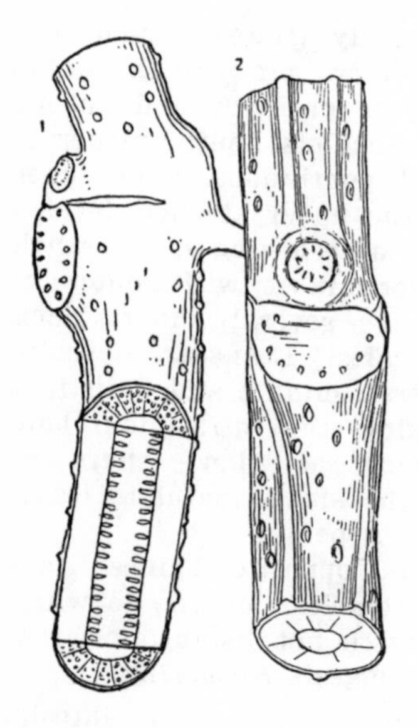

Rather soft-wooded climbers, sometimes with tendrils only on the upper branches, these opposite the leaf-scars when present and not thickened at tip; foliage deciduous. Stems angled or nearly terete, moderate: pith moderate, white, without firmer diaphragms even at the nodes, soon dividing into thin plates by transverse fissures beginning at the periphery. Buds subglobose, solitary though collaterally branched in development, sessile, with 2 or 3 scales. Leaf-scars alternate, 2-ranked, rounded: bundle-traces about a dozen in an ellipse, rather small and indistinct: stipule-scars long and narrow. (*Cissus*).

Winter-character references: — *Ampelopsis cordata* (*Cissus Ampelopsis*). Hitchcock (3), 10, (4), 135, f. 21.

A long time will be required to get uniform usage of the name *Ampelopsis*. Popularly it is applied almost universally to the Virginia creeper and Boston ivy, now called variously *Parthenocissus* or *Psedera* by botanists.

1. Bushy and usually without tendrils. (1). A. cordata.
   Climbing. 2.
2. Stems subterete: tendrils rather few. (Pepper vine). A. arborea.
   Stems angular. (Turquoise berry). (2). A. heterophylla.

CISSUS. Marine Ivy.
(Family Vitaceae).

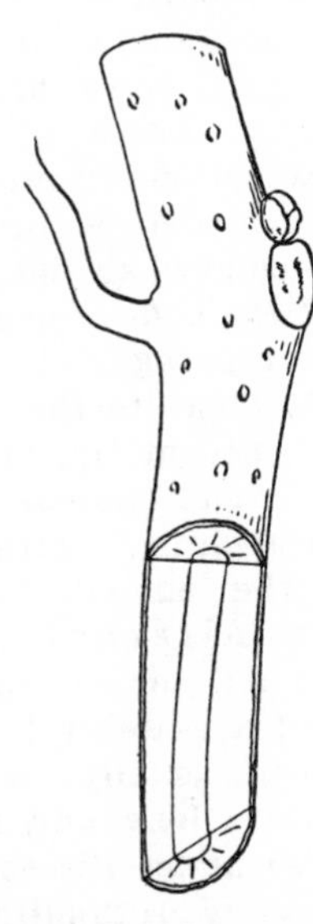

Soft-wooded or rather succulent climbers with simple coiling tendrils opposite the leaf-scars: deciduous. Stems subterete, moderate or rather slender: pith rounded, moderate, white, continuous and without nodal diaphragms. Buds small, collaterally branching, globose, sessile, with 2 scales. Leaf-scars alternate, 2-ranked, rounded: bundle-traces indistinct, in an ellipse: stipule-scars small. Sometimes included in *Ampelopsis* as now defined.

A still tenderer species than *C. incisa* is *C. acida*, which is cultivated in the open sometimes. The beautiful *C. discolor*, sometimes called trailing begonia, is familiar in hot-houses everywhere.

Glabrous or puberulent: internodes short (2-3 cm.). C. incisa.

Winter-character references to *Vitis*—*V. cinerea*. Hitchcock (3), 10. *V. cordifolia*. Engelmann, Bushberg Catalogue, 10, f. 36; Hitchcock (3), 6. *V. flexuosa*. Shirasawa, 260, pl. 7. *V. labrusca*. Engelmann, Bushberg Catalogue, 9. *V. rotundifolia* (*V. vulpina*). Engelmann, Bushberg Catalogue, 10, f. 37. *V. rupestris*. Engelmann, Bushberg Catalogue, 10, f. 35. *V. Thunbergii*. Shirasawa, 261. *V. vinifera*. Schneider, f. 122; Shirasawa, 260, pl. 7. *V. vulpina* (*V. riparia*). Brendel, 27, pl. 4; Engelmann, Bushberg Catalogue, 10, f. 34; Hitchcock (3), 10, (4), 135, f. 19-20.

VITIS. Vine. Grape.
(Family Vitaceae).

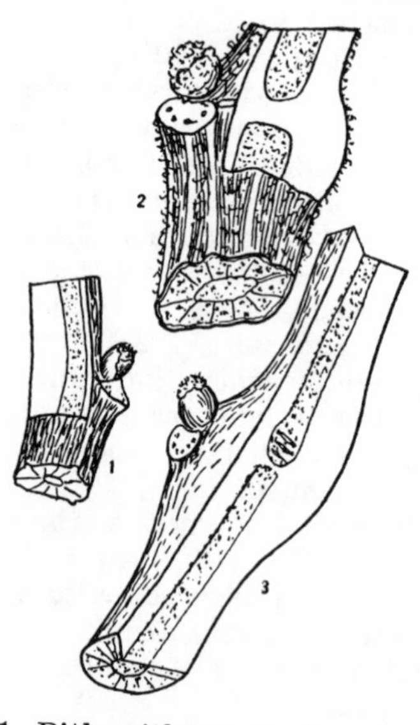

Rather hard-wooded climbers, often very thick-stemmed in the forest, with usually very flaking bark: deciduous. Stems striate, subterete or exceptionally angled, moderate: pith moderate, brown, continuous or somewhat fissured near the swollen nodes, usually with a firmer diaphragm at each node. Tendrils opposite the leaf-scars, not thickened at tip. Buds subglobose, not superposed, but collaterally branching, with 2 broad scales, the end-bud lacking. Leaf-scars alternate, 2-ranked, half-round or crescent-shaped: bundle-traces several in a C-shaped series, usually indistinct: stipule-scars long and narrow. References under *Cissus*.

1. Pith without diaphragms: bark tight. (1). V. rotundifolia.
   Pith firmer at the nodes: bark flaking. 2.
2. Twigs distinctly angled, woolly. (2). V. cinerea.
   Twigs nearly terete. 3.
3. A tendril at each node. (Hybrids of, and) V. labrusca.
   Tendrils lacking from usually each third node. 4.
4. Spreading and rather bushy. V. rupestris.
   Climbing. 5.
5. Nodal diaphragms thin (under 1 mm.) (3). V. vulpina.
   Nodal diaphragms thick (2-4 mm.). 6.
6. Panicle vestiges open and large. V. cordifolia.
   Panicle vestiges compactly branched. V. aestivalis.

PARTHENOCISSUS. Virginia Creeper.
(Family Vitaceae).

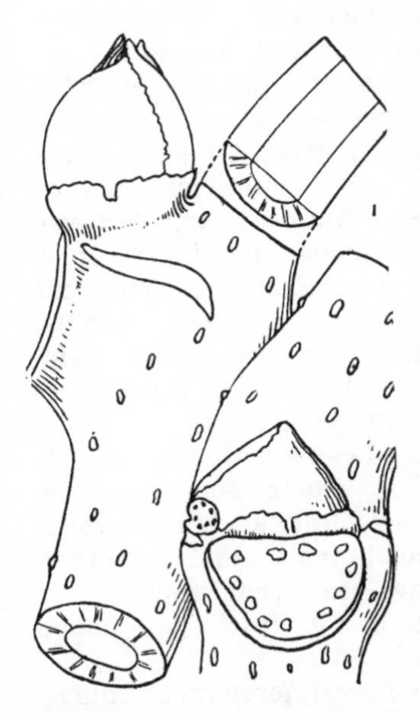

Somewhat fleshy woody climbers: deciduous. Stems terete, moderate or rather slender: pith relatively large, continuous, greenish and large-celled in the internodes, whiter and more compact at the swollen nodes. Buds moderate, not superposed, but frequently collaterally branching in development, sessile, round-conical, with 2 or 3 exposed scales, the end-bud absent. Leaf-scars alternate, half-round or nearly circular: bundle-traces about a dozen, in an ellipse: rather indistinct, in an ellipse: stipule-scars long and narrow. Tendrils opposite the leaf-scars, absent from every third node. (*Ampelopsis; Psedera*).

Winter-character references:— *Parthenocissus quinquefolia* (*Ampelopsis hederacea*). Bösemann, 41; Hitchcock (3), 10; Schneider, f. 122. *P. vitacea* (*A. quinquefolia*). Brendel, 27, pl. 4. *P. tricuspidata*. Schaffner & Tyler, Ohio Naturalist, 1:32.

1. Nearly or quite glabrous. 2.
   Persistently distinctly pubescent. 4.
2. Tendrils rarely with suckers, long. (1). P. vitacea.
   Suckers abundant at ends of the tendrils. 3.
3. Tendrils rather long. P. quinquefolia.
   Tendrils and internodes short. (Boston ivy). P. tricuspidata.
4. Pubescence coarse: not rooting. P. quinquefolia Engelmannii.
   Pubescence downy: rooting. P. quinquefolia Saint-Paulii.

TILIA. Linden. Lime. Basswood.
(Family Tiliaceae).

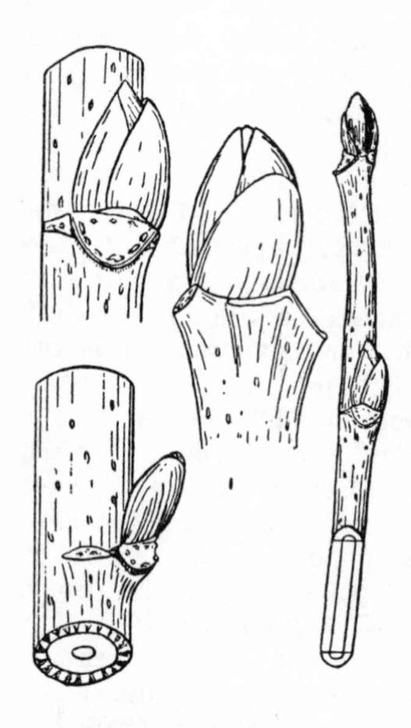

Trees: deciduous. Twigs moderate, zig-zag, with elongated internodes, terete, the cortex with fibrous wedges in section: pith round or squarish, moderate, continuous, pale, sometimes pink or yellowish. Buds solitary or precociously branched in inflorescence, or with lateral inflorescence-scar afterwards obliquely sessile, rather large, inequilaterally ovoid, with 2 mostly green or red glistening-punctate scales, the end-bud lacking. Leaf-scars alternate, 2-ranked on shoots, somewhat elevated, half-elliptical: bundle-traces 3 or mostly compound and then sometimes scattered: stipule-scars unequal, one of each pair much elongated.

The winter-differences of lindens are not very marked. References to them are given under *Grewia*, p. 229.

1. Twigs somewhat loosely hairy. — T. platyphyllos.
   Twigs tomentulose. 2.
   Twigs glabrous. 3.
2. Weeping. — T. petiolaris.
   Not weeping. — T. tomentosa.
3. Twigs slender (2-3 mm.). — T. cordata.
   Twigs moderate (3 mm.). — T. heterophylla.
   Twigs relatively stout (often 4 mm.). — (1). T. americana.

GREWIA.
(Family Tiliaceae).

Shrubs, deciduous. Twigs rounded, somewhat fluted near the tip. rather slender, hispid: pith rather small, roundish, continuous, white with somewhat greenish or browning border. Buds small, solitary, sessile, naked, hairy, the end-bud lacking. Leaf-scars alternate, 2-ranked, somewhat crowded at tip, elliptical or half-round, raised: bundle-trace elliptical, compound: stipules setaceous, hairy, persistent, surpassing the buds.

The winter-characters of *Grewia parviflora* are pictured by Schneider, f. 66.

Twigs olive, with conspicuous lenticels when denuded.
G. parviflora.

Winter-character references to the limes or lindens:—*Tilia americana.* Blakeslee & Jarvis, 550, pl.; Brendel, 27, 29, 30, 31, pl. 4; Hitchcock (1), 3, f. 2, (3), 8, (4), 134, f. 10-11; Otis, 200; Schneider, f. 44, 66. *T. cordata* (*T. parvifolia*). Bösemann 68; Fant, 31, f. 31; Schneider, f. 32, 129; Willkomm, 44, f. 75; Zuccarini, pl. 9. *T. heterophylla* (*T. Michauxii*). Blakeslee & Jarvis, 550. *T. japonica.* Shirasawa, 263, pl. 8 *T. Miqueliana.* Shirasawa, 263, pl. 8. *T. platyphyllos* (*T. grandifolia*). Bösemann, 68; Fant, 31; Schneider, f. 129. *T. tomentosa.* Schneider, f. 43, 129. *T. vulgaris* (*T. europaea*). Blakeslee & Jarvis, 550; Ward, 1:186, f. 93.

HIBISCUS. Rose of Sharon.
(Family Malvaceae).

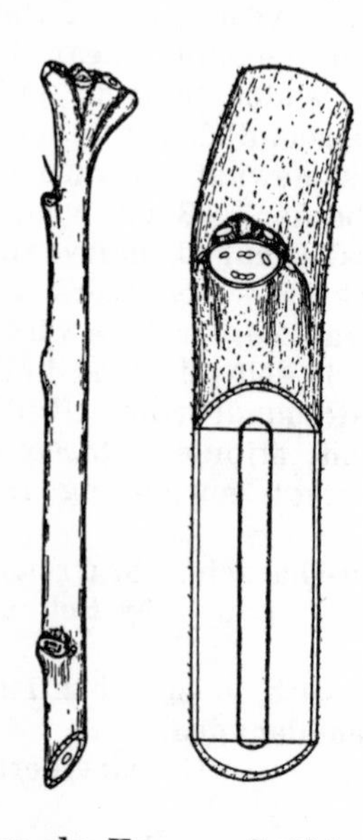

Shrubs or very small trees: deciduous. Twigs rounded, fluted near the dilated tip, rather slender, glabrescent: pith rather small, continuous, white with green border. Buds not evident, their position usually occupied by the scars of fallen inflorescences or branch-vestiges. Leaf-scars alternate, crowded at tip, half-round or transversely elliptical, raised, shortly decurrent in more or less evident ridges: bundle-traces about 4, compoundly irregular and indefinite: stipule-scars small, elliptical.

Winter-character references to *H. syriacus*:—Schneider, f. 66; Shirasawa, 236.

Damaskinos and Bourgeois, in the Bulletin de la Société Botanique de France, 5:604, indicates the position of the inflorescence below the rudiments of the vegetative bud; and the literature of the subject is given by Russell in the botanical section of the Annales des Sciences Naturelles for 1892.

Though it is a stiff shrub out of harmony with most of its associates, the shrubbery Althea as it is often called is one of the most universally planted shrubs, and in its better varieties affords an abundance of bright color through the summer. The tender *H. Rosa-sinensis* is used frequently in bedding.

Twigs gray: flower-scars abundant. H. syriacus.

THEOBROMA. Cacao.
(Family Sterculiaceae).

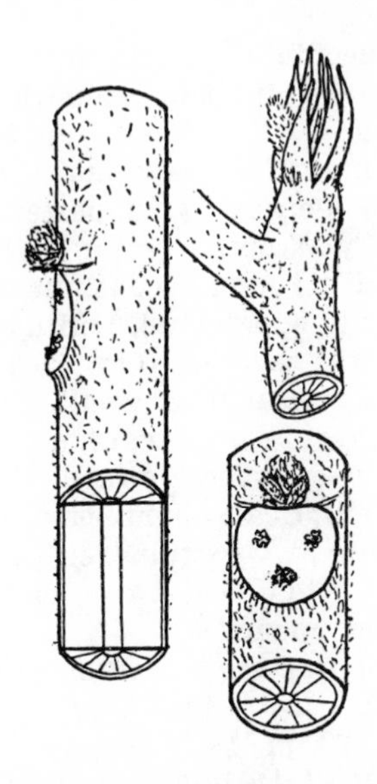

Tender small trees, flowering and fruiting on spurs from the trunk: evergreen. Twigs moderate, terete: pith small, round, continuous, white. Buds small, solitary, sessile, subglobose, not evidently scaly except for the stipules of their leaves, the end-bud oblong with a number of protruding slender stipules. Leaf-scars alternate, 2-ranked, very slightly raised at the bottom, half-round to nearly round: bundle-traces 3, rather large: stipule-scars somewhat elongated. Leaves simple, entire, petioled.

Cauliflory, as flowering and fruiting from the trunk or spurs on it instead of from ordinary branches is called, is considered in detail by Huth in volume 30 of the Ablandlungen of the Botanischer Verein der Provinz Brandenburg.

Cacao, or cocoa as English-speaking people too often call it, like coffee and tea produces a stimulating alkaloid, which in this case is theobromin while in the others it is caffein. It has been esteemed for untold centuries, and was so common in South America in the time of the Incas that its seeds are said to have been strung like cash or wampum shells and used in place of money,—which in this instance possessed intrinsic value.

Twigs brown, puberulent or glabrescent. T. Cacao.

STERCULIA.
(Family Sterculiaceae).

Trees: deciduous. Bark smooth, gray. Wood soft, pale, somewhat ring-porous, with small ducts, moderate medullary rays and tangential wood-parenchyma pattern. Twigs very stout, terete: pith very large, round, continuous, white. Buds subglobose, solitary, sessile, with several very hairy scales; the lateral buds small, the terminal large. Leaf-scars alternate, more crowded toward the tip, low, elliptical: bundle-traces about 10, in an irregular ellipse, compound: stipule-scars elongated, often upcurved.

Winter-characters of *Sterculia platanifolia* are indicated by Shirasawa, 23, pl. 13.

Sterculia platanifolia is probably the most striking tree that can be cultivated in the near-North, because of its very large leaves, deeply palmately lobed with rounded sinuses and acuminate segments. In winter its thick green twigs with strongly contrasting reddish hairy buds and large leaf-scars mark it almost as distinctly in comparison with anything else grown in the Botanical Garden at Washington, where it is to be seen.

Twigs green: buds dark red-brown. S. platanifolia.

COLA. Cola.
(Family Sterculiaceae).

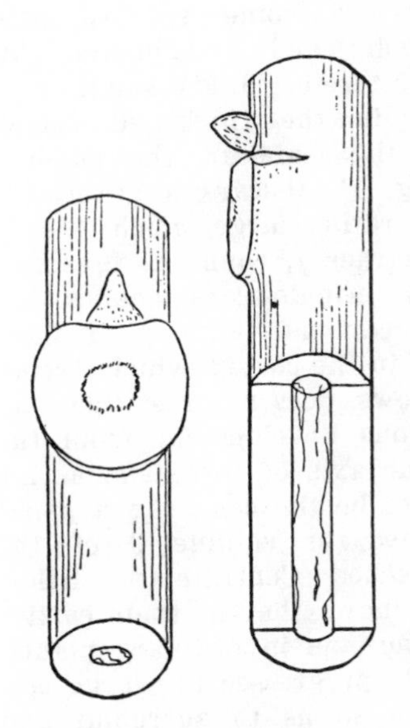

Trees: subdeciduous. Twigs moderate, terete: pith relatively large, rounded, spongily excavated, orange. Buds solitary, sessile, conical, divergent, with stipular scales only. Leaf-scars alternate, nearly round, abruptly raised, large for the size of the twig: bundle-trace 1, round, large but indistinct: stipule-scars elongated. Leaves, if present, simple, oblanceolate, acuminate, on a petiole nearly as long as the blade. Sometimes spelled *Kola.*

Few words of recent introduction are in such common popular use as the name of this tropical African tree, because of the extent to which the active stimulant contained in its fruit is used or supposed to be used in summer beverages. Like the maté or Paraguay tea of South America, it enjoys the repute of enabling men to sustain long periods of exertion with little or no food.

Twigs brown, stellate-scurfy when very young. C. acuminata.

ACTINIDIA.
(Family Dilleniaceae).

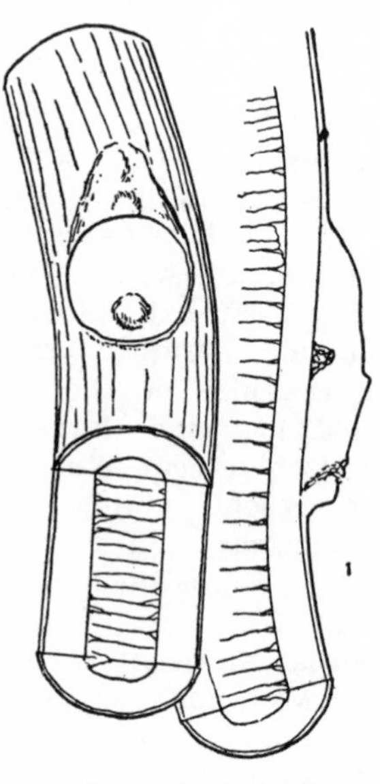

Woody twiners: deciduous. Stems moderate, terete, brown: pith moderate, white and continuous in some species, pale brownish and chambered in others, terete. Buds small, concealed in the thickened cortex above the leaf-scar, the end-bud lacking. Leaf-scars alternate, round, rather large, much raised: bundle-trace 1, round or crescent-shaped: stipule-scars lacking.

The curious anomaly of buds buried in the cortex, which *Actinidia* shows, does not rest upon adventitious development from the vascular axis of the stem, as appears to be the case. In a paper published in volume 3 of the Botanisches Centralblatt, Hildebrand shows that in their earlier stages these buds are at the surface, as in ordinary plants, but as the development of the node progresses the large cortical cushion about them thickens so as to surround and finally overtop them.

Winter-character references:—*A. arguta.* Shirasawa, 259, pl. 7. *A. polygama.* Schneider, f. 93; Shirasawa, 259, pl. 7.

1. Pith white, continuous. (Cat vine). A. polygama.
   Pith brownish, chambered. 2.
2. Twigs glabrous. (1). A. arguta.
   Twigs hairy. A. chinensis.

STEWARTIA. Wild Camellia. (Family Ternstroemiaceae).

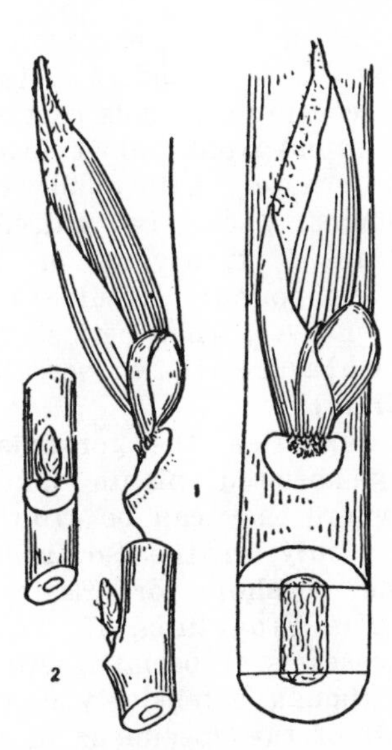

Shrubs or small trees with shredding barks: deciduous. Twigs moderate or slender, subterete: pith rounded, somewhat spongy Buds moderate or small, solitary or superposed, sessile, compressed-fusiform, with 2 or 3 exposed scales. Leaf-scars alternate, half-round, little raised: bundle-trace 1, large, round, at the top of the scar: stipule-scars lacking. (*Stuartia*).

Winter-character references:—*Stewartia monadelpha.* Shirasawa, 262, pl. 8. *S. pseudocamellia.* Shirasawa, 262, pl. 8.

The stewartias are tender except in the south or near the coast. Where they can be grown they vie with Camellias, which they resemble somewhat in flower, Cape jessamines, flowering dogwoods, and magnolias among the large-flowered shrubs.

Many botanists use the name Theaceae for the family to which this and the next two genera belong.

1. Buds silvery, rather small (scarcely 7 mm. long). 2.
   Buds brown, large (fully 10 mm.). (1). S. Pseudo-Camellia.
2. Buds moderate (fully 5 mm. long. silvery). S. pentagyna.
   Buds small (2 mm. long). (2). S. Malachodendron.

GORDONIA.
(Family Ternstroemiaceae).

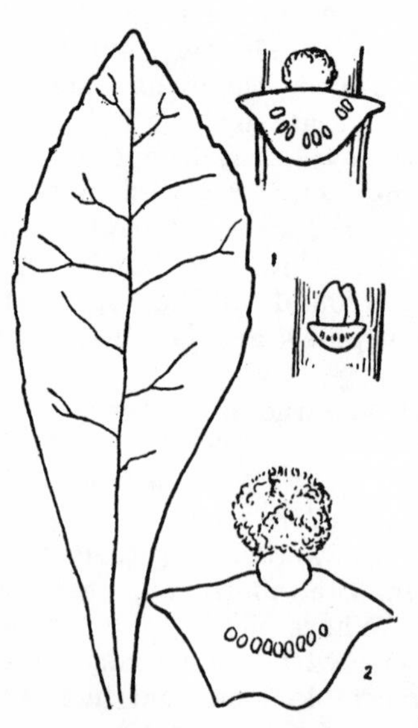

Trees or shrubs: evergreen or deciduous. Twigs moderate, terete: pith continuous. Buds usually solitary, round-ovoid, naked. Leaf-scars alternate, half-round or shield-shaped, scarcely raised: bundle-trace 1, transverse or V-shaped, compound: stipule-scars lacking. Leaves, when persistent, sessile, oblanceolate, serrate. (*Franklinia*).

Like stewartias, the gordonias are large-flowered plants much prized where they can be grown, which is only in the South or near the seashore or Eastern lakes. The Franklinia, *G. Altamaha*, possesses a special interest in that, though extensively cultivated, all of the specimens of it have been propagated directly or indirectly from a single tree cultivated by Bartram near Philadelphia. Notwithstanding its conspicuous flowers, it is not refound in the wild state, even in the locality from which Bartram's specimen came, though repeated search has been made for it.

Leaves evergreen, tomentulose beneath. (1). G. Lasianthus.
Leaves deciduous: pith rather large, coffee-colored.
(2). G. Altamaha.

THEA. Tea. Camellia.
(Family Ternstroemiaceae).

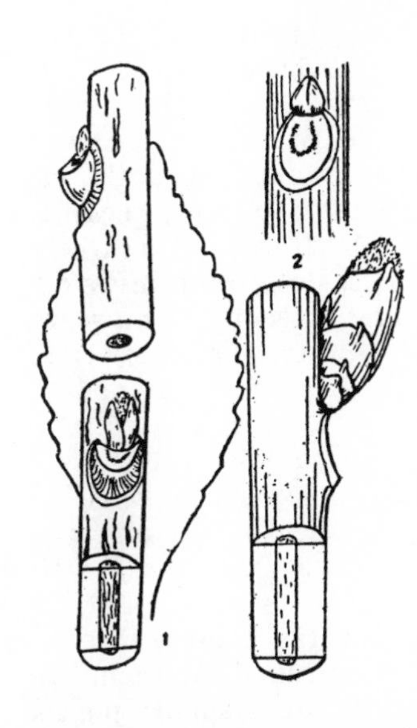

Shrubs: evergreen. Twigs moderate or slender, terete: pith round, more or less spongy. Buds rather small, solitary, sessile, ovoid, with 2 scales, or the flower-buds enlarged and exposing some eight 2-ranked scales. Leaf-scars alternate, crescent-shaped to nearly elliptical, more or less raised from a somewhat shrunken area: bundle-trace 1, compound, crescent- or C-shaped: stipule-scars lacking. Leaves moderate, short-stalked, crenately serrate, (Includes *Camellia*).

Tea (*Thea*) and coffee (*Coffea*) are entirely unrelated plants which produce what is regarded as an identical alkaloid, caffein, which gets its name from the latter but is prepared commercially in large quantities from tea-leaves. The Paraguay tea (*Ilex*) owes its stimulating properties to the same substance, as does the guarana (*Paullinia*), one of the Sapindaceae. Chocolate or cacao contains a closely related alkaloid, theobromin.

1. Twigs glabrous. 2.
   Twigs somewhat loose-hairy. T. Sasanqua.
2. Twigs slender: leaf-scars crescent-shaped. (Tea). (1). T. sinensis.
   Twigs stouter: leaf-scars subelliptical. (Camellia). (2). T. japonica.

ASCYRUM. St. Peter's Wort.
(Family Guttiferae).

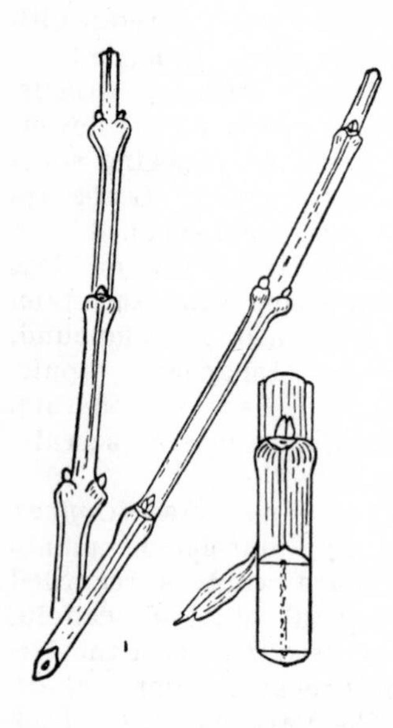

Small dense but flexible shrubs: deciduous. Twigs very slender, 2-winged beneath the leaf-scars, with red quickly exfoliating bark: pith brown, minute, spongily excavated. Buds solitary, sessile, minute, with 2 exposed scarcely specialized scales, often developing the first season. Leaf-scars opposite, minute, triangular, raised by the enlarged nodes: bundle-trace 1, scarcely distinguishable: stipule-scars lacking.

American botanists have been unwilling to merge this and the following genus into the Guttiferae, as is done here, and in local Manuals the family Hypericaceae is maintained for them. As a rule they are small plants scarcely more than half-shrubby, and in comparison with most of the popularly selected shrubbery plants they are without marked value. Like species of *Cistus*, however, they are bright when in flower, and St. Peter's Wort, especially, forms compact masses that fit well into certain situations.

Very low and slender (twigs 1 mm. thick).
(St. Andrew's cross). (1). A. hypericoides.
Somewhat larger and stouter (twigs 1.5-2 mm. thick).
(St. Peter's wort). A. stans.

HYPERICUM. St. John's Wort.
(Family Guttiferae).

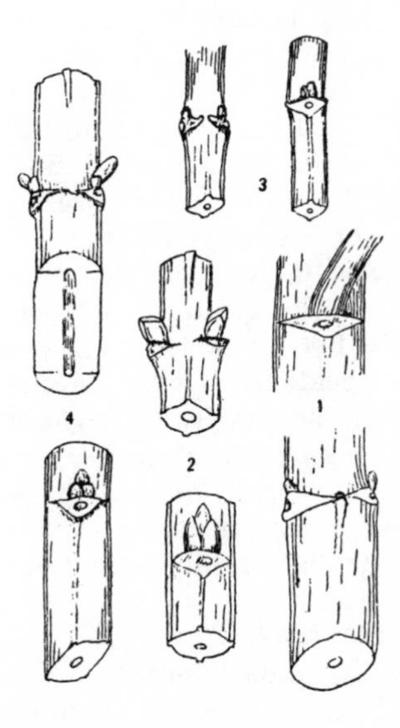

Small shrubs (or most species herbaceous), with exfoliating bark: deciduous. Twigs slender, usually small, angled at least below the nodes: pith small, green or brown, spongy and finally excavated. Buds solitary, sessile, minute, with 2 or several scarcely specialized scales, often developing the first season and sometimes forming short axillary branches covered by scars. Leaf-scars opposite, small, triangularly lens-shaped, little raised. bundle-trace 1: stipule-scars lacking.

Very little attention has been paid to the winter-characters of Hypericaceae. Löfling, in his Gemmae Arborum, p. 198, described the buds of *Hypericum Androsaemum; H. calycinum* is pictured by Schneider, f. 119; and Meigen considers the winter condition *H. elodes* and *H. perforatum* in a paper on the vegetative organs of various perennials.

1. Twigs very evanescently angled. (1). H. prolificum.
   Twigs rather persistently 4-angled. 2.
2. Buds distinctly scaly. (2). H. calycinum.
   Buds scarcely with specialized scales. 3.
3. Openly bushy. (3). H. Kalmianum.
   Round-topped. (4). H. aureum.

TAMARIX. Tamarisk.
(Family Tamaricaceae).

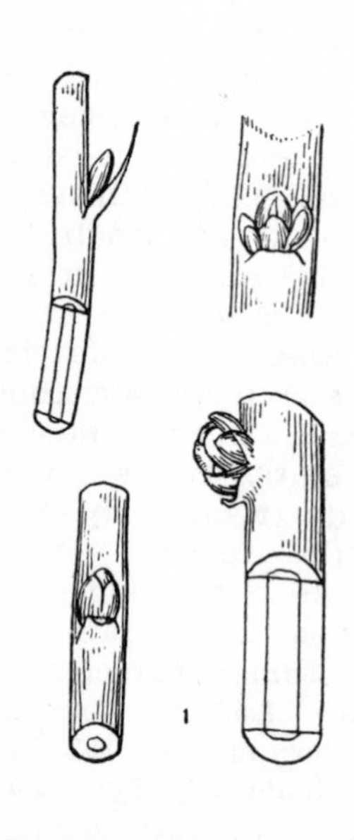

Shrubs or small trees: deciduous through the fall of their very slender branched foliar shoots. Twigs slender, elongated, rounded: pith small, rounded, continuous, not central. Buds small, sessile, rounded, compressed against the twig, solitary or quickly becoming concentrically multiple, with about 3 exposed scales. Leaf-scars lacking. Leaves alternate, scale-like with persistent dilated base, without evident bundle-traces or stipules.

Winter-character references to *T. gallica* — Schaffner & Tyler, Ohio Naturalist, 1:31; Schneider, f. 118.

1. Quite glabrous. 2.
   Leaf-scales puberulent. T. hispida
2. Twigs and buds green or pinkish and glaucescent. T. odessana.
   Twigs and buds red-brown, not glaucous. (1). T. gallica.

MYRICARIA.
(Family Tamaricaceae).

Winter-characters of *Tamarix*, except that the pith is larger and more central. The single species is *M. germanica*, the winter-characters of which are indicated by Fant, 27; and Schneider, f. 119.

FOUQUIERIA. Ocotillo.
(Family Fouquieriaceae).

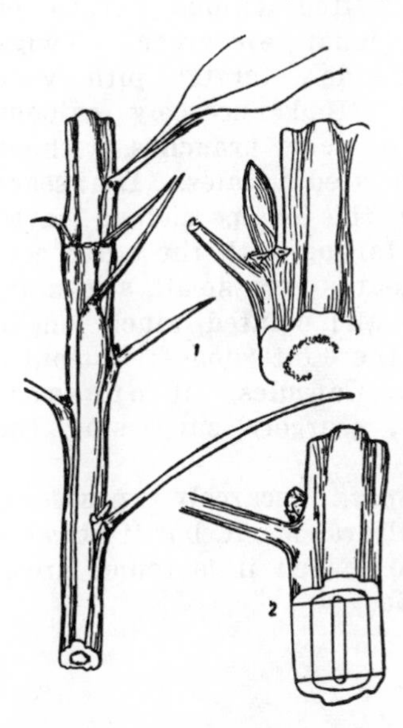

Shrubs, rather few- and arcuately-branched from near the ground, with very sharp slightly curved spines below the buds: deciduous. Twigs moderate or slender, rather fleshy, broadly ridged below the nodes: pith angular, continuous, (or becoming chambered according to Solereder). Buds small, spindle-shaped, quickly developing into short axillary leaf-clusters. Leaf-scars found only on the axillary spurs or at the annual junctures, minute, half-round, raised: bundle-trace 1, minute: stipule-scars lacking. Each spine represents the dorsal part of the petiole of a fallen foliage leaf.

The second species, of Lower California, forming a tapering columnar trunk covered with slender ungrooved branches, and with globose buds, is sometimes separated under the generic name *Idria*. Incidentally, a grove of this is shown on plate 29 of the twenty-second Report of the Missouri Botanical Garden, in a photograph by Mr. E. A. Goldman of the superb agave subsequently named after him.

Shrub: twigs flat-ridged below the spines. (1). F. splendens.
Tree: twigs terete: buds globose. (2). F. columnaris.

HUDSONIA. False Heather.
(Family Cistaceae).

Low tufted villous shrubs of dry regions: evergreen. Twigs very slender, terete: pith very minute. Buds scarcely evident except as short branches, without differentiated scales. Leaf-scars lacking, the long-persistent leaves finally falling with the outer cortex. Leaves very small, alternate, narrow and pointed, much longer than the internodes: stipules lacking. Capsules, if present, narrow, scarcely surpassing the sepals.

Hudsonia scarcely possesses horticultural merit, but it attracts attention when it is found growing wild.

1. Leaves short (2 mm.), appressed. (1). H. tomentosa.
   Leaves larger (3-6 mm.): fruit distinctly stalked. 2.
2. Leaves moderate, rather gray, ascending. (2). H. ericoides.
   Leaves long, more spreading, green. (3). M. montana.

Winter-characters are given for the related genus *Helianthemum* as follows: *H. amabile.* Schneider, f. 119. *H. oelandicum.* Bösemann, 35. *H. vulgare.* Bösemann, 35.

KOEBERLINIA. All Thorn.
(Family Koeberliniaceae).

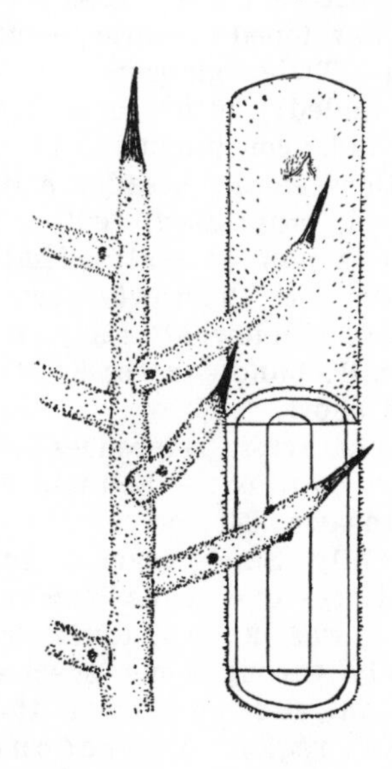

Shrubs, horridly spiny by the ascending or horizontally spreading terete branchlets which taper somewhat acuminately into very sharp black spines: pith moderate, round, continuous. Buds solitary, sessile, not evidently scaly, very minute. Leaf-scars lacking, the minute scales which represent the leaves drying on the twig. The branching is sometimes alternate and very irregular, and sometimes decussately opposite, as is the disposition of flower buds.

Koeberlinia presents very much the appearance of some of the spiny Rhamnaceae, but differs from them in technical characters. Only the one species is known.

Velvety and minutely scabrous. K. spinosa.

Winter-characters of *Idesia polycarpa*, of the family Flacourtiaceae, are given by Schneider, f. 84; and Shirasawa, 283, pl. 13.

STACHYURUS.
(Family Stachyuraceae).

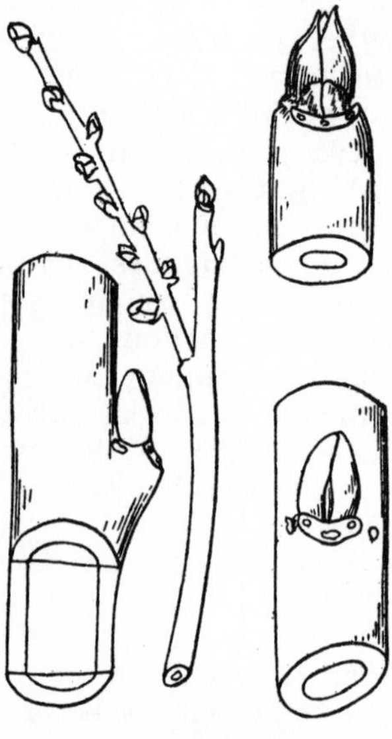

Shrubs, with some inflorescence-branches developed the first year: deciduous. Twigs glabrous, moderate, rounded: pith relatively large, round, continuous, white. Buds rather small, sessile, solitary, ovoid, appressed, with 2 more or less pointed scales. Leaf-scars alternate, narrowly crescent-shaped, somewhat raised, rather small: bundle-traces 3: stipule-scars short.

Winter-character references to *Stachyurus praecox*: — Schneider, f. 7; Shirasawa, 242, pl. 3.

The family Stachyuraceae includes only the one genus, *Stachyurus*, and was known until recently only through one species from Japan and one from the Himalayan region. Of recent years, several Chinese species have been discovered. Those that have been brought into cultivation, like *Forsythia*, some of the bush honeysuckles, and the Asiatic magnolias, are prized because they flower early, before their foliage expands.

Twigs and buds rather glossy brown: Japan. S. praecox.
Twigs green or dull brown: China. S. chinensis.

CARICA. Papaya. True Papaw.
(Family Caricaceae).

Soft-wooded glabrous tender usually unbranched small trees with thin milky sap and smooth bark on which the enlarging leaf-scars persist for years: evergreen at the crown: pith 5-sided, at length hollow in the center, like the petioles. Buds small, round, essentially naked though the outermost leaves do not enlarge greatly, usually abortive except as they collaterally branch and produce inflorescence shoots. Leaf-scars alternate, broadly shield-shaped or shallowly 3-lobed, slightly raised at base: bundle-traces many, small, in an open series, quickly effaced: stipule-scars lacking. Leaves simple, long-stalked.

The papaya is the tropical representative of the muskmelon as a table fruit, and somewhat resembles an under-flavored melon in taste as it does in appearance. It is grown often in plant houses and fruits not infrequently under such conditions. Plants that have reached the flowering age prove to be essentially dioecious, the staminate flowers borne in elongated clusters and the pistillate close to the stem.—though an occasional fruit forms on an otherwise sterile inflorescence. The latex of *Carica* contains the digestive ferment papain.

Leaves palmately 7-divided. (1). C. Papaya.
Leaves oak-like, shallowly 3-lobed. C. quercifolia.

DAPHNE. Mezereon.
(Family Thymelaeaceae).

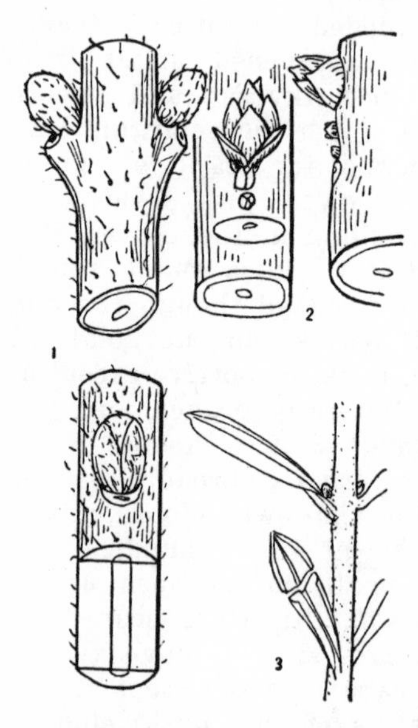

Small shrubs: evergreen or deciduous. Twigs moderate, rounded or somewhat 4-sided: pith small roundish, continuous. Buds sessile, usually solitary but sometimes superposed or collaterally branched, ovoid, with 4 or some half-dozen exposed scales. Leaf-scars opposite or the pairs widely separated in 4 ranks, crescent-shaped, small, exceptionally elevated: bundle-trace 1: stipule-scars lacking.

Winter-character references:— *Daphne alpinum*. Schneider, f. 118, *D. Mezereum*. Bösemann, 75; Schneider, f. 118; Willkomm, 29, f. 36; Zuccarini, 26, pl. 14.

A peculiar white-dotting of the lower surface of the leaf in some of the species is shown to be caused by groups of granular cells surrounding the stomata.

1. Leaf-scars raised: twigs pubescent. (1). D. Genkwa.
   Leaf-scars low: twigs glabrate, or habit low. 2.
2. Deciduous. 3.
   Evergreen. 5.
3. Twigs staring-pubescent and glandular. (2). D. alpina.
   Twigs glabrate. 4.
4. Twigs buff-olive. D. Mezereum.
   Twigs red, quite glabrous. D. altaica.
5. Leaves large (2 × 8 cm.): bushy. D. Laureola.
   Leaves small (.5 × 2 cm.): spreading or prostrate. 6.
6. Glabrous: somewhat bushy. D. Blagayana.
   Twigs crisp-puberulent: trailing. (3). D. Cneorum.

DIRCA. Leatherwood.
(Family Thymelaeaceae).

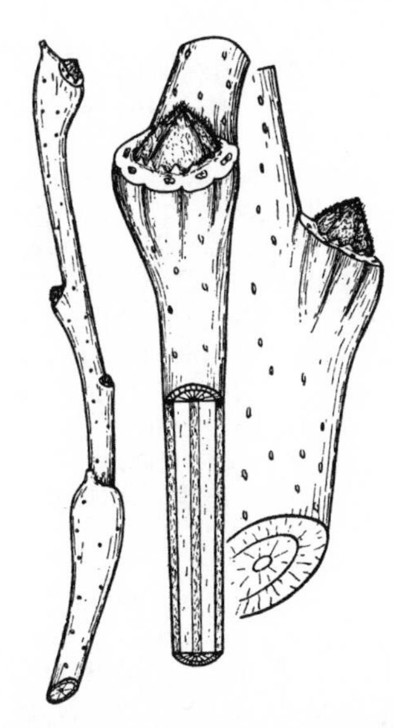

Small rounded shrubs with soft wood but very tough bark: deciduous. Twigs terete, moderately slender, glabrous, light brown becoming olive or darker, with conspicuous small white lenticels, gradually enlarged upwards through the season's growth: pith small, roundish, spongy. Buds small, solitary, sessile, short-conical, with about 4 indistinct dark-silky scales, the end-bud lacking. Leaf-scars alternate, 2-ranked, nearly annular and almost encircling the bud, elevated at the swollen nodes: bundle-traces 5, indistinct: stipule-scars lacking.

Winter-characters of *Dirca palustris* are given by Brendel, 27, pl. 3; and Schneider, f. 98.

Though during the winter the bud-scales are small and closely covered by hairs, the structure of the bud becomes very evident during its unfolding period in the spring, when the scales elongate greatly. A developing bud is pictured in volume 7 of Nature Notes, pp. 171-2.

Twigs often forking, glossy. D. palustris.

The curious lace-bark tree of Jamaica, *Lagetta*, possesses the structural winter-characters of leatherwood, to which it is closely related.

HIPPOPHÄE. Sea Buckthorn.
(Family Elaeagnaceae).

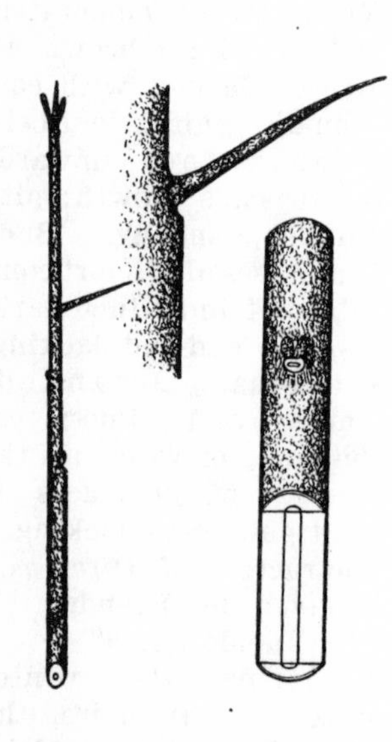

Shrubs, commonly with terminal and axillary twig-spines, stellately pubescent and with silvery or browning small peltate scales: deciduous. Twigs very slender, subterete: pith small, brown, round, continuous. Buds minute, solitary or collaterally branched in spine formation, sessile, round, or heart-shaped from the parting of the 2-scales, the end-bud lacking. Leaf-scars alternate, half-round or transversely elliptical, minute, low: bundle-trace 1: stipule-scars lacking.

Winter-character references to *Hippophäe rhamnoides*: — Bösemann, 49; Fant, 31, f. 33; Schneider, f. 132; Ward, 1: 118, f. 59, 191, f. 95; Willkomm, 4, 30, f. 37; Zuccarini, 30, pl. 16.

Hippophäe is tender and much less frequently seen in America than *Elaeagnus*, from which it scarcely differs in vegetative characters except in having none of its shoots ending in a developed bud, and in its more delicate twigs.

Twigs for a time silvery: buds brown-scurfy. H. rhamnoides.

ELAEAGNUS. Oleaster.
(Family Elaeagnaceae).

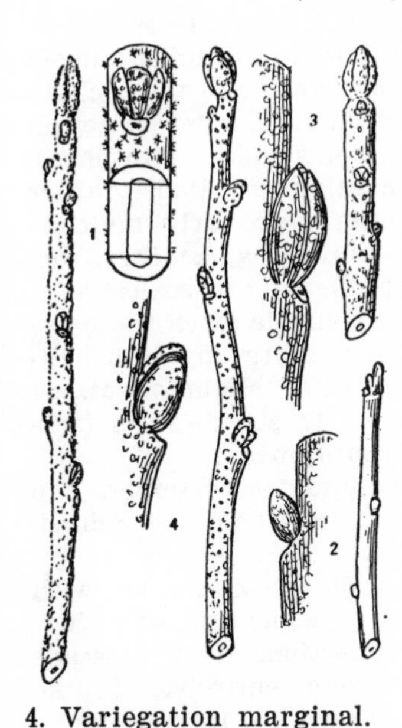

Shrubs or small trees, often twig-spiny, stellate-hairy or with often silvery or glistening-brown peltate scales: mostly deciduous. Twigs terete, rather slender: pith small, round, continuous. Buds small, solitary or collaterally branched in spine-formation or exceptionally superposed, sessile, round, conical or oblong, with about 4 exposed scales. Leaf-scars alternate, half-round, minute, more or less raised: bundle-trace 1: stipule-scars lacking.—References under *Shepherdia*, p. 250.

1. Evergreen. 2.
   Deciduous. 6.
2. Silvery. E. macrophylla.
   Twigs brown-scaly. 3.
3. Not variegated. E. pungens.
   Leaves variegated, crisped. 4.
4. Variegation marginal. E. pungens variegata.
   Variegation median. 5.
5. Center yellow. E. pungens Frederici.
   Blotched with yellow. E. pungens maculata.
   Marked with yellow and red. E. pungens Simoni variegata.
6. Twigs and buds silvery or olivaceous. 7.
   Twigs and buds brown-scaly. 9.
7. Without any brown scales. (1). E. angustifolia.
   Some scales brown. 8.
8. End-bud elongated: twigs very slender. (2). E. umbellata.
   End-bud conical-ovoid. (3). E. argentea.
9. Buds rather silvery and conical. E. argentea.
   Buds dark red-brown, subglobose. (4). E. multiflora.

SHEPHERDIA. Buffalo Berry.
(Family Elaeagnaceae).

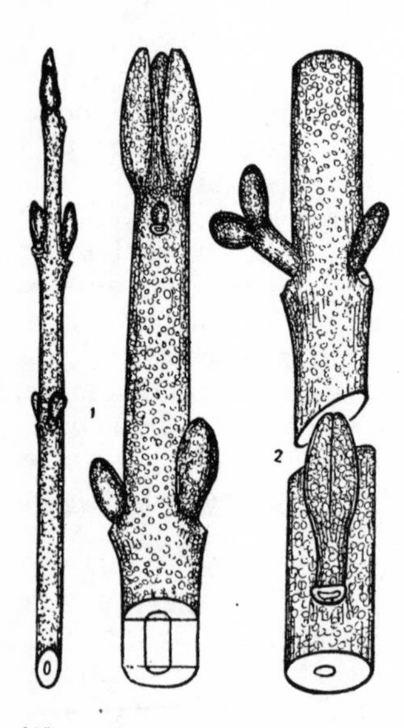

Shrubs or small trees, often twig-spiny, with glistening fringed silvery or red-brown peltate scales: deciduous. Twigs nearly terete, rather slender: pith small, round, continuous. Buds rather small, solitary or early multiple through branching, stalked, oblong, with 2 valvate scales or a second pair visible when these are parted. Leaf-scars opposite, half-round, minute, slightly raised: bundle-trace 1: stipule-scars lacking. (*Lepargyraea*).

Winter-character reference to *Shepherdia argentea*: — Schneider, f. 132.

Shepherdia is confused with *Elaeagnus* frequently, and herbarium collections do not escape this confusion entirely. Unlike either *Elaeagnus* or *Hippophäe*, it has opposite leaves. Meyer, in Linnaea, volume 7, p. 443, speaks of its buds being super posed,—a condition resulting from branching, probably, if the record does not rest on error.

Scurf silvery. . (1). S. argentea.
Scurf red-brown. (2). S. canadensis.

Winter-character references to *Elaeagnus*:—*E. angustifolia*. Bösemann, 49; Schneider, f. 132. *E. argentea*. Bösemann, 49. *E. multiflora* (*E. longipes*). Shirasawa, 235, pl. 2. *E. umbellata*. Shirasawa, 234, pl. 2.

LAGERSTROEMIA. Crape Myrtle.
(Family Lythraceae).

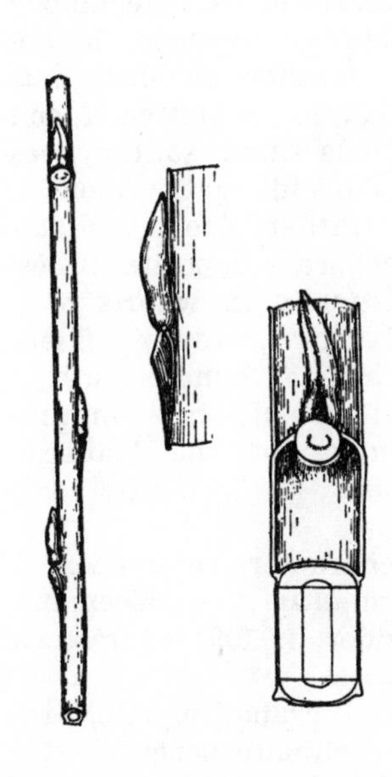

Small trees or large shrubs with flaking bark: deciduous. Twigs rather slender, angled: pith small, roundish, at length spongy. Buds moderately small, solitary, sessile, oblong, somewhat elbowed above the base, closely appressed, with 2 acute ciliate scales. Leaf-scars 4-ranked, separated, or approximated in pairs, or opposite, nearly round, slightly raised and decurrent from the sides but concave: bundle-trace 1, composite, crescent-shaped, sunken: stipule-scars lacking or glandular.

Winter-characters of *Lagerstroemia indica* are figured by Shirasawa, 244, pl. 4.

Like the oleander, the crape myrtle is very popular in the south, where it thrives, and it is rather frequently grown as a tubbed plant north of this,—say a line reaching from Washington to Cairo, Illinois.

Twigs glabrous, 4-winged. L. indica.

PUNICA. Pomegranate.
(Family Punicaceae).

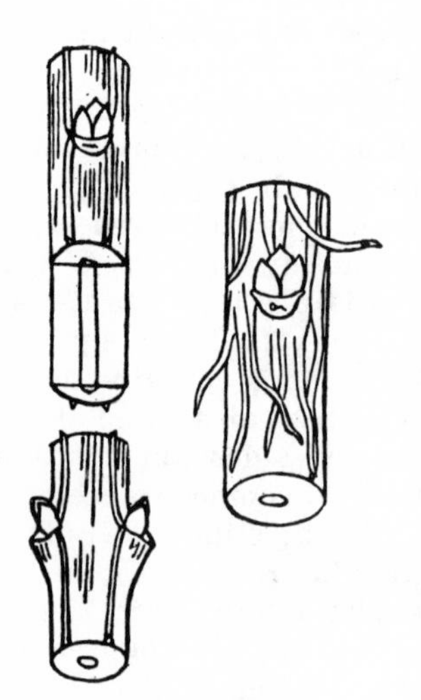

Glabrous shrubs or small trees with flaking cortex: deciduous. Twigs narrowly 4-winged, becoming terete, rather slender: pith minute, roundish or flattened, continuous. Buds small, solitary, sessile, round-ovoid, with about 2 pairs of rather loose pointed scales. Leaf-scars opposite or less characteristically in whorls of 3, half-round or narrowly shield-shaped, raised: bundle-trace 1, transverse: stipule-scars minute, at the angles of the leaf-scar. Often referred to the family Lythraceae.

Winter-character references to *Punica Granatum*: — Bösemann, 49; Schneider, f. 109; Shirasawa, 268, pl. 10.

Like the crape myrtle, the pomegranate is much grown where the climate permits,—and about to the same northern limit; and it is a favorite in cool greenhouses. The dwarf form has come into considerable use for temporary summer bedding effects.

Tall and often arborescent. P. Granatum.
Dwarf. P. Granatum nanum.

RHIZOPHORA. Mangrove.
(Family Rhizophoraceae).

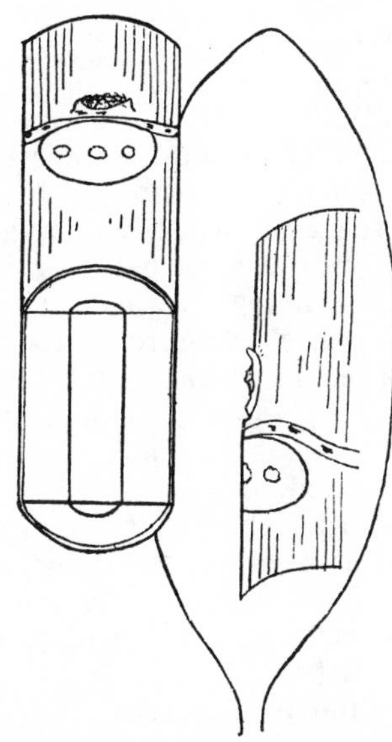

Semi-aquatic shrubs or small trees of the tropical seaside, lifted above the water on outcurving roots: evergreen. Twigs rather stout, round: pith large, round, continuous, brown. Buds solitary, sessile, small, indefinite, with a stipular scale: their position often marked by a flower-scar. Leaf-scars low, half-round or very perfectly transversely elliptical, crowded toward the end of the season's growth: bundle-traces 3, round, becoming indistinct: stipule-scars encircling the stem. Leaves simple, entire, petioled. Fruit commonly germinating on the plant, the dart-like seedlings later falling into the mud.

The common mangrove, *Rhizophora Mangle*, a salt-loving plant, forms one of the most striking and characteristic features of tropical shores, where it occupies lagoons behind the beach or follows the coral formation to the extreme depth of water in which it can exist. The stilted roots on which it stands and its rather fine branching and deep green color produce an appearance of delicate finish quite in contrast with the shores from which it is absent. Figures of the mangrove are published by S. M. Coulter in the Report of the Missouri Botanical Garden, vol. 15, pl. 22-23. Its precocious germination has been the subject of many observations by travelers and naturalists. It forms clearly marked annual rings in its wood.

Glabrous: leaves elliptical, coriaceous. R. Mangle.

MYRTUS. Myrtle.
(Family Myrtaceae).

Aromatic shrub: evergreen. Twigs slender, terete: pith very minute, somewhat spongy. Buds sessile, solitary, small, ovoid, appressed, with 1 or 2 pairs of exposed gray-hairy scales. Leaf-scars opposite, minute, raised. bundle-trace 1: stipule-scars lacking. Leaves small, lanceolate, very acute at both ends, entire, pellucid-dotted.

Myrtle, like the rather similar laurel, was used in an emblematic way by the Greeks, with whom it was a particular badge of judicial authority.

To an inexpert person, myrtle is rather like box in its general effect, and in Azorean gardens a similar suggestion is found in the quite unrelated genus *Myrsine*. The name running myrtle is sometimes given to the periwinkle, *Vinca minor*, for a like reason.

Twigs puberulent, with flaking cortex. M. communis.

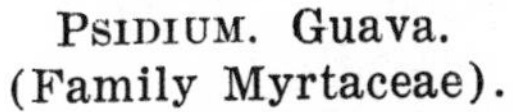

PSIDIUM. Guava.
(Family Myrtaceae).

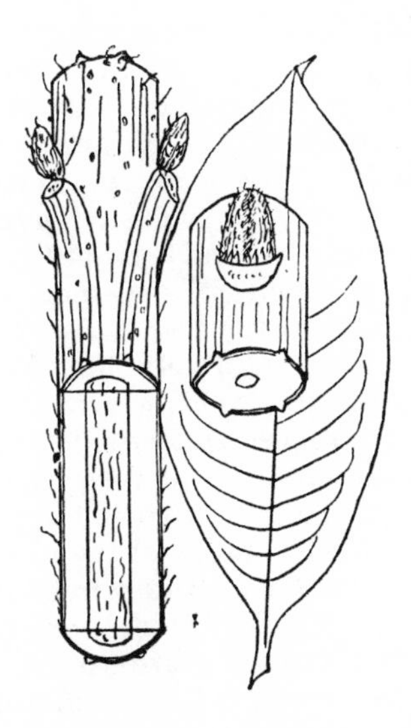

Tender trees: evergreen. Twigs moderate, terete, or 4-ribbed or even winged below the nodes: pith moderate, compressed, 4-sided, spongy, brown. Buds solitary, sometimes developing promptly, naked. Leaf-scars opposite, broadly crescent-shaped, raised, black-ciliate at top: bundle-trace 1, crescent-shaped: stipule-scars lacking. Leaves simple, entire, pellucid-punctate, with looping veins.

Guavas scarcely possess any decorative value, but they are grown in most tropical gardens for their small rather peculiarly flavored seedy fruits, — most favorably known in the West Indian guava jelly which is justly esteemed one of the best of confections.

Twigs angled, hairy. (Guava). (1). P. Guayava
Twigs terete, glabrous. (Strawberry guava). P. Cattleyanum.

FEIJOA. Pineapple Guava.
(Family Myrtaceae).

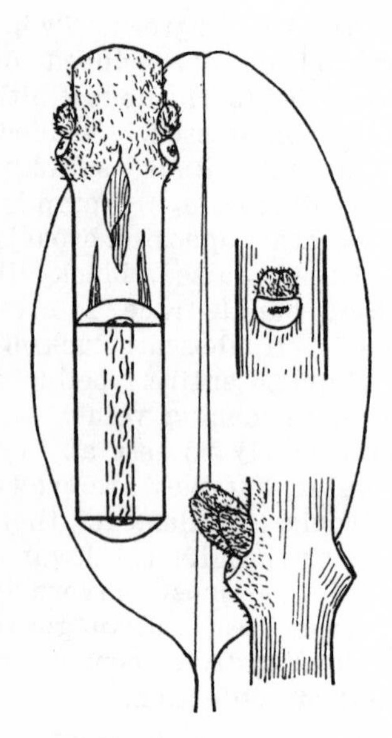

Somewhat aromatic shrubs with shredding bark: evergreen. Twigs moderate, nearly terete: pith roundish or somewhat flattened, spongy, brown. Buds solitary, sessile, globose becoming ellipsoid, naked. Leaf-scars opposite, half-round, somewhat raised: bundle-trace 1, transverse or C-shaped: stipule-scars lacking. Leaves simple, entire, minutely punctate with black. (*Fejoa*).

Feijoa is a close relative, botanically, of the true guavas. Its white-woolly leaves give it an attractive silvery appearance when they are turned by the wind. It apears to be coming into extensive cultivation in southern California, as along the Riviera, for its pleasantly flavored fruit.

At first gray-tomentose: twigs brown. F. Sellowiana.

PIMENTA. Allspice.
(Family Myrtaceae).

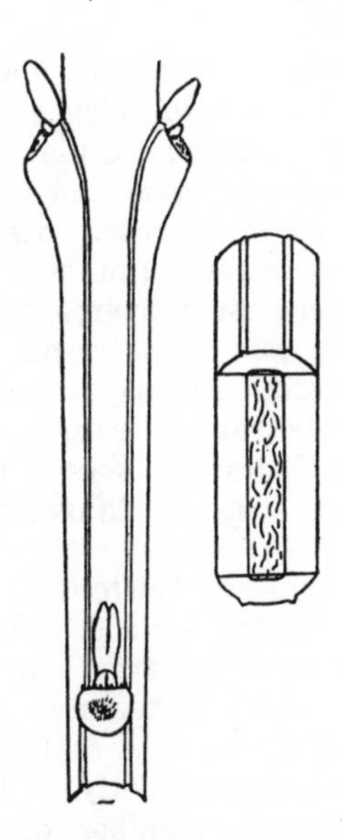

Aromatic trees: evergreen. Twigs moderate, decussately compressed and lined, or even winged, from the nodes: pith compressed, spongy, brown. Buds usually superposed, sessile or the upper becoming stalked, naked. Leaf-scars opposite, half-round or broader, minutely black-fringed at top, not raised except as the nodes are dilated: bundle-trace 1, large but indefinite: stipule-scars lacking. Leaves simple, entire, pellucid-punctate.

Some botanists place allspice in the genus *Eugenia*, the flower-buds of which constitute the cloves of commerce. Both *Pimenta* and *Eugenia* exemplify well the aromatic property which forms one of the myrtaceous characters.

Glabrous: twigs green, glandular-punctulate. P. officinalis.

TRISTANIA. Brisbane Box.
(Family Myrtaceae).

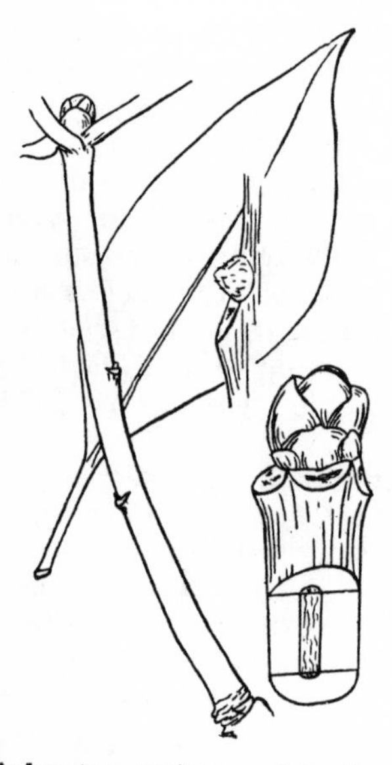

Large trees: evergreen. Twigs rather slender, terete: pith small, round, pale, spongy. Buds solitary, sessile, subglobose, the lateral small with 2 exposed scales. Leaf-scars alternate and narrow but the uppermost subverticillately crowded and half-round or broadly crescent-shaped, slightly raised: bundle-trace 1, transverse: stipule-scars lacking. Leaves pellucid-punctate, rather lanceolate, petioled.

Like *Eucalyptus*, *Tristania* is a tree which produces good timber and becomes very large. It is said to be a favorite avenue tree in Australia, where it is at home, and it rather unusually tolerant of cold for a member of its family.

Glabrate: twigs and buds green. T. conferta.

EUCALYPTUS.
(Family Myrtaceae).

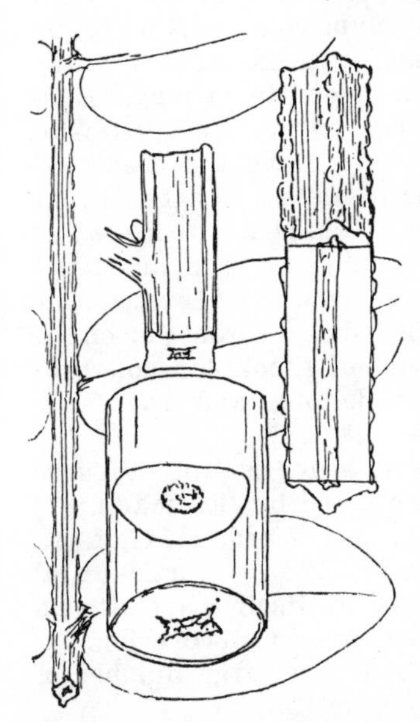

Tender aromatic trees, often of large size: evergreen. Twigs at first slender and 4 angled or ribbed, becoming terete and stout: pith small, more or less angular and flattened, spongy. Buds naked, very small and insignificant, or the lateral like the end-bud elongated as filiform often deciduous branches. Leaf-scars alternate or on young wood opposite, even then sometimes 2-ranked by torsion of the twig, half-round, little raised: bundle-trace 1, large and round: stipule-scars lacking. Leaves simple, entire, pellucid-punctate, those of mature branches often sickle-shaped and standing vertically.

Eucalyptus shares with the coniferous genus *Sequoia* the distinction of producing the tallest trees known. Like many Australian trees, it is given to producing leaves which hang with their edges vertical so that their surfaces are not exposed to the full glare of the sun. *E. globulus*, which produces an excellent timber, is one of the most rapid growing of trees, and its trunk, even when of large size, is willowy and yielding under the force of a gale.

Outer bark loosely shredding: slender twigs warty.
(Blue gum). (1). E. globulus.

HEDERA. Ivy.
(Family Araliaceae).

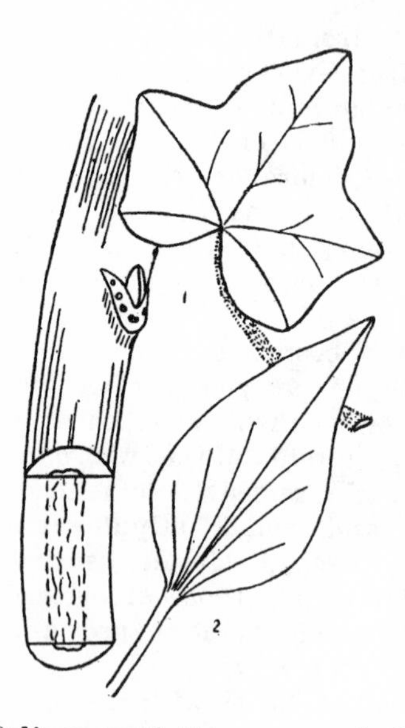

Woody plants, typically climbing by numerous aerial roots: evergreen. Stems moderate, terete: pith moderate, spongy. Buds small, conical, solitary, sessile. naked or with about 2 fleshy unspecialized scales. Leaf-scars alternate, U-shaped, somewhat raised: bundle-traces 5 or 7: stipule-scars lacking. Leaves palmately lobed and cordate or on the older pendent shoots lanceolate, or ovate or deltoid, and round- or acute-based.

Winter-characters of *Hedera Helix* are noted by Bösemann, 37; Fant, 48; and Ward, 1:147, f. 67-68. The ivy is in a horticultural class quite by itself where it can be grown as a wall-covering. It occurs in a very large number of foliage varieties, some of them very beautiful.

Climbing. (1). H. Helix.
Bushy or grafted as a standard. (2). H. Helix arborescens.

Winter-character references to *Acanthopanax*:—*A. pentaphyllum* (*A. spinosum*). Schneider, f. 111; Shirasawa, 250. *A. ricinifolium*. Schneider, f. 111; Shirasawa, 248, pl. 5. *A. sciadophylloides*. Shirasawa, 248, pl. 5. *A. senticosum*. Schneider, f. 124. *A. sessiliflorum*. Schneider, f. 111.

Two species of a related deciduous araliaceous genus, *Fatsia*, with large palmately lobed leaves, are more or less hardy,—*F. japonica* and *F. papyrifera*. The pith of the latter, sliced into thin sheets, constitutes the Chinese rice-paper.

ACANTHOPANAX.
(Family Araliaceae).

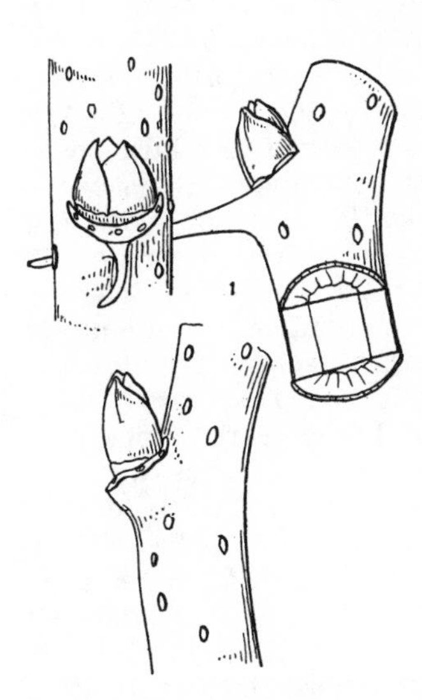

Shrubs or exceptionally trees, usually armed with 1 to 3 prickles beneath each narrow leaf-scar and so likely to be mistaken for leaf-spines: deciduous. Twigs moderate, terete; somewhat zig-zag, often forming spurs: pith moderate, rounded, continuous, white. Buds solitary, sessile, conical-ovoid, with about 3 exposed thin scales. Leaf-scars alternate, narrowly crescent-shaped or U-shaped, somewhat raised: bundle-traces 5, small: stipule-scars lacking. *Panax* and its compounds, following Linnaeus, are treated usually as neuter—for no classical reason.

1. Scrambling or climbing. A. trifoliatum.
   Bushy or arboreous. 2.
2. Trees: prickly between nodes. (*Kalopanax*). A. ricinifolium.
   Loosely branched shrubs. 3.
3. One or two prickles at each node. (1). A. pentaphyllum.
   Essentially unarmed. A. sessiliflorum.
   Prickly between the nodes. 4.
4. Prickles slender, numerous. (*Eleutherococcus*). A. senticosum.
   Prickles stout and strong, fewer. 5.
5. Glabrous and smooth. A. Simonii.
   Twigs pubescent or scabrous. A. Henryi.

ARALIA. Angelica Tree.
(Family Araliaceae).

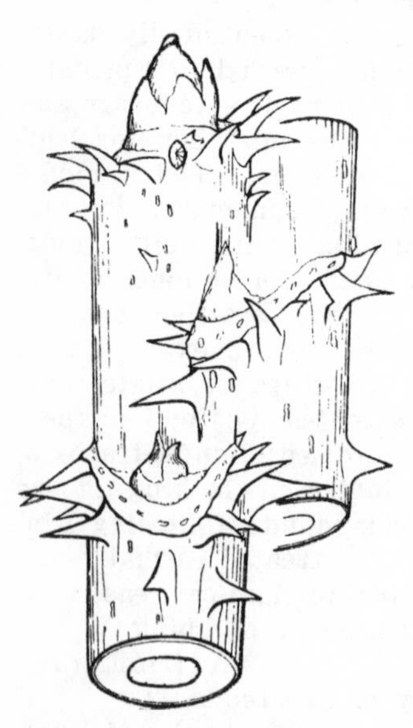

Small few-branched trees or arborescent shrubs with strong cortical prickles—or other species herbaceous: deciduous. Twigs very stout, terete: pith large, pale roundish, continuous. Buds ovoid-conical, solitary, sessile, with few scales. Leaf-scars alternate, U-shaped, fully half-encircling the stem, low: bundle-traces about 15 in a single series: stipule-scars lacking. (*Dimorphanthus*).

Winter-character references: — *Aralia sinensis*. Shirasawa, 248, pl. 4. *A. spinosa*. Schneider, f. 11.

The angelica tree, Hercules' Club, tear-blanket, or monkey tree, as it is variously called, is one of the most tropical-looking of hardy woody plants because of its enormous twice- or thrice-pinnate leaves. If well grown it forms dense masses from the ground, and when it is killed back by an unusually severe winter this habit of growth is intensified.

Few plants present equally good leaf-scars for ready understanding, and few present equally good examples of unmistakable prickles,—representing neither modified leaves nor twigs, but outgrowths of the cortex. As with the devil's club of the Northwest (*Echinopanax horridum*), the prickles are believed popularly to be poisonous.

Branches gray-straw colored, glabrous. A. spinosa.

HELWINGIA.
(Family Cornaceae).

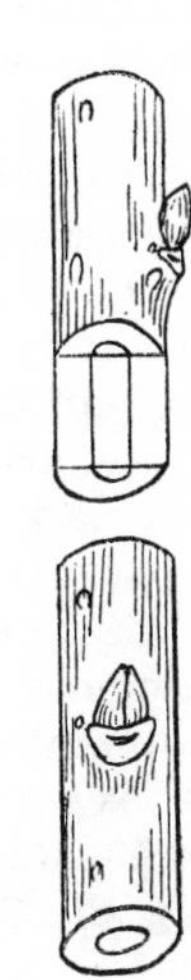

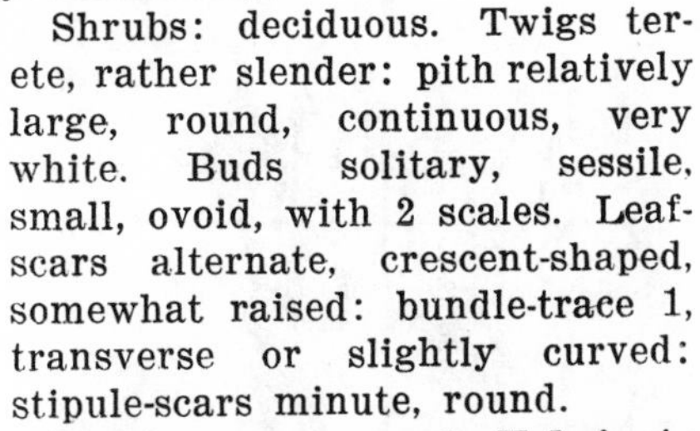

Shrubs: deciduous. Twigs terete, rather slender: pith relatively large, round, continuous, very white. Buds solitary, sessile, small, ovoid, with 2 scales. Leaf-scars alternate, crescent-shaped, somewhat raised: bundle-trace 1, transverse or slightly curved: stipule-scars minute, round.

By common consent, *Helwingia* is now placed in the Cornaceae, but the Standard Cyclopedia follows the usually excellent judgment of Bentham and Hooker in placing it in the related family Araliaceae.

Winter-character references to *Helwingia japonica*: — Schneider, f. 124; Shirasawa, 242, 250, pl. 5.

The specific name *ruscifolia*, which is a synonym of *japonica*, indicates a peculiarity recalling the genus *Ruscus* of the Liliaceae; for the flowers of *Helwingia* are clustered on the surface of its leaves. There is this important difference, though, that in *Helwingia* what are called leaves are really leaves, while in *Ruscus* they are leaf-like branches of the stem, developed in the axils of small scales which are morphologically the true leaves. The inflorescence of *Helwingia* is comparable with that of *Tilia* with its adnate bract,— except that here the really axillary flower-cluster has grown into attachment to a foliage leaf, while in *Tilia* the leaf is reduced to a bract.

Glabrous, with occasional rather large lenticels. H. japonica.

CORNUS. Dogwood. Cornel.
(Family Cornaceae).

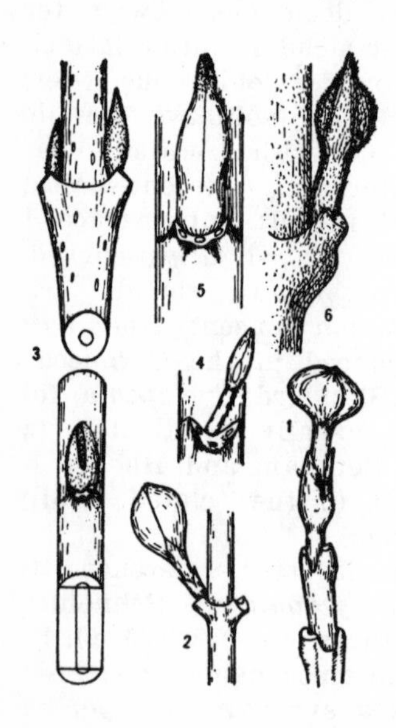

Shrubs or occasionally small trees: deciduous. Twigs moderate or rather slender, often bright-colored, round or more or less 6-sided: pith moderate, round or more or less compressed or angled, white and continuous or somewhat colored and spongy. Buds solitary or exceptionally superposed, stalked, characteristically oblong, with a pair of nearly or quite valvate scales consisting of more or less developed leaves or less commonly of petioles with blade-rudiments at top. Leaf-scars opposite except in one species, crescent- or U-shaped, commonly raised during the first winter on petiole-bases that are later deciduous at the level of the twig: bundle-traces 3: stipule-scars lacking, but the leaf-scars meet or are transversely joined. (*Cynoxylon*, *Svida*).

Winter-character references:—*Cornus alba*. Bösemann, 58; Brendel, pl. 3; Schneider, f. 195. *C. alternifolia*. Blakeslee & Jarvis, 333, 552; Otis, 206; Schneider, f. 195. *C. Amomum* (*C. sericea*). Hitchcock (3), 15. *C. asperifolia*. Hitchcock (3), 15, (4), 137, f. 75-76. *C. circinata*. Schneider, f. 194. *C. florida*. Blakeslee & Jarvis, 329, 552, pl.; Hitchcock (1), 3; Otis, 204. *C. ignorata*. Shirasawa, 269, pl. 10. *C. Kousa*. Shirasawa, 272, pl. 10. *C. macrophylla*. Shirasawa, 283, pl. 13. *C. mas* (*C. mascula*). Bösemann, 57; Schneider, f. 194; Willkomm, 56, f. 92; Zuccarini, 21, pl. 12. *C. officinalis*. Shirasawa, 272, pl. 10, 11. *C. racemosa* (*C. candidissima; C. paniculata*). Brendel, pl. 1. *C. sanguinea.* Bösemann, 58; Fant, 44, f. 46; Schneider, f. 194; Ward, 1:170, f. 83; Willkomm, 9, 50, f. 91; Zuccarini, 22, pl. 12.

1. Leaf-scars alternate: aborescent. C. alternifolia.
   Leaf-scars opposite. 2.
2. Leaf-scars raised through the first winter and covering the buds: flower-buds biscuit-shaped: aborescent. 3.
   Buds not concealed even if the leaf-scars are elevated. 4.
3. Leaf-axils brown-hairy. C. Kousa.
   Leaf-axils not brown-hairy. (Flowering d.). (1). C. florida.
4. Flower-buds enlarged, subglobose. 5.
   Flower-buds not enlarged. 6.
5. Lateral buds very divergent.
   (Cornelian cherry). (2). C. mas
   Lateral buds suberect. C. officinalis.
6. Branching twiggy: often somewhat silky. 7.
   Branching loose and osier-like. 8.
7. Twigs pinkish-gray. (Panicled dogwood). (3). C. racemosa.
   Twigs reddish or purplish.
   (Rough-leaved dogwood). C. asperifolia.
8. Twigs bright yellow in winter. C. alba flaviramea.
   Twigs very bright red. (4). C. alba sibirica.
   Twigs black-purple, not rooting. C. alba Kesselringii.
   Twigs purple, rooting at tip. (Red osier). C. stolonifera.
   Twigs green, becoming pink or purple: not stoloniferous. 9.
9. Buds long-stalked or developing the first year. C. alba.
   Buds nearly sessile. 10.
10. Twigs and buds glabrate. C. femina.
    More or less pubescent. 11.
11. Pubescence woolly. (Kinnikinnik). C. Amomum.
    Pubescence closely appressed. 12.
12. Buds hairy only at tip: twigs rather pink. (5). C. rugosa.
    Buds hairy throughout: twigs often green.
    (6). C. sanguinea.

AUCUBA.
(Family Cornaceae).

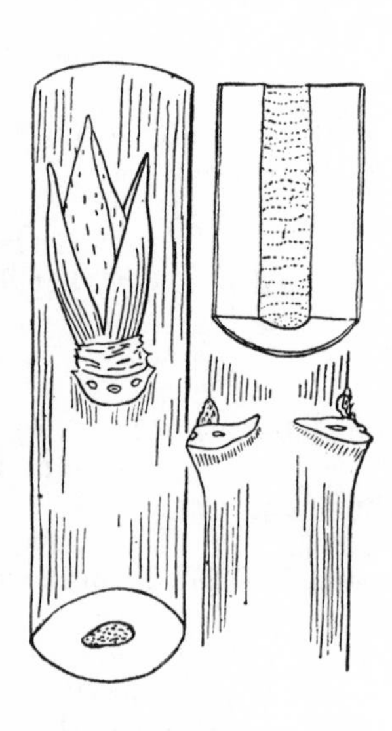

Shrubs: evergreen. Twigs rather stout and succulent, rounded: pith moderate, rounded, continuous when fresh, but becoming chambered with granular septa when dry. Buds minute or becoming rather large and somewhat stalked, with several pointed rather hairy scales. Leaf-scars opposite, slightly raised, relatively large, crescent-shaped: bundle-traces 3. Leaves broadly lanceolate, stalked, toothed and somewhat acuminate.

Like other plants grown chiefly for their foliage, *Aucuba japonica* occurs in a multiplicity of forms which are not classified readily.

1. Dwarf, unvariegated. A. japonica pygmaea.
   Rather tall shrubs. 2.
2. Leaves lanceolate, narrow. A. japonica angustifolia.
   Leaves broadly lance-elliptical or ovate. 3.
3. Leaves sinuately toothed. A. japonica ovata.
   Leaves slightly dentate, large. A. japonica macrophylla.
   Leaves coarsely serrate or dentate. 4.
4. Leaves green. A. japonica.
   Variegated with yellow. 5.
5. With yellow margin. A. japonica limbata.
   With scattered small spots. A. japonica variegata.
   With a larger central blotch. 6.
6. With smaller yellow spots. A. japonica latimaculata.
   Without smaller spots. A. japonica bicolor.

NYSSA. Tupelo.
(Family Nyssaceae).

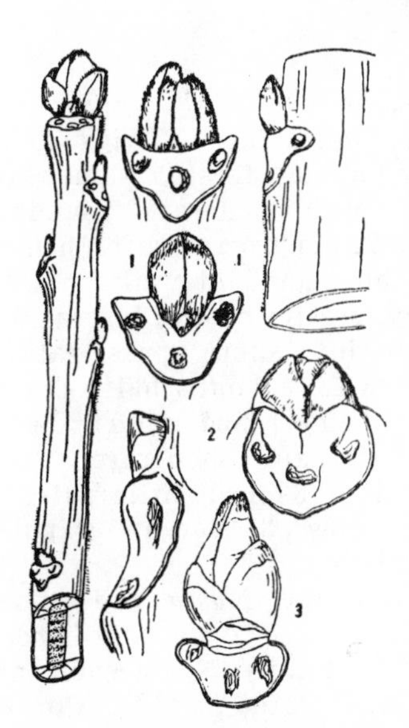

Trees: deciduous. Twigs moderate or rather stout, terete: pith moderate, white, rounded, continuous, but with firmed diaphragms at intervals. Buds moderate, sessile or slightly stalked and superposed or solitary, ovoid, with about 4 exposed scales, the end-bud somewhat larger. Leaf-scars alternate, broadly crescent-shaped or deltoid, sometimes becoming broadly U-shaped by rupture of an articular membrane, low: bundle-traces 3: stipule-scars lacking.

Winter-character references:— *Nyssa sylvatica* (*N. multiflora*). Blakeslee & Jarvis, 331, 554, pl.; Brendel, pl. 3; Otis, 208; Schneider, f. 45, 124.

The firmer cross-plates in the pith of *Nyssa* afford a ready means of identification in the summer when the alternate simple leaves are the only obvious characters in evidence, as is true of staminate trees when out of flower, or pistillate trees when without flowers or fruit.

Nyssa uniflora, growing in deep swamps, is particularly characterized by the enormously swollen base of its trunk,— well figured by S. M. Coulter in the Report of the Missouri Botanical Garden, vol. 15, pl. 18, 19.

1. Twigs densely velvety. (Ogeeche lime). (1). N. capitata.
   Twigs and buds glabrescent or glabrous. 2.
2. Buds depressed. (Cotton gum). (2). N. uniflora.
   Buds ovoid. (Pepperidge). (3). N. sylvatica.

DAVIDIA.
(Family Nyssaceae).

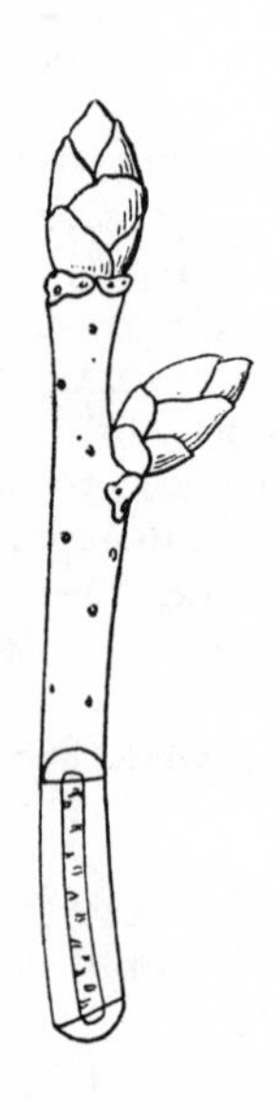

Tree: deciduous. Twigs moderately stout, terete, somewhat zig-zag: pith moderate, rounded, pale, continuous with firmer plates at short intervals. Buds solitary, sessile or the lateral developing into short spurs, rather large, with about half-a-dozen blunt pale-margined scales. Leaf-scars alternate, moderate, half-elliptical or 3-lobed, little raised: bundle-traces 3, large: stipule-scars lacking.

Davidia and *Nyssa* are sometimes separated from the Cornaceae in a family Nyssaceae, and sometimes treated as of the Cornaceae. Baillon, who named the genus and its one known species, was a versatile writer whose Histoire Naturelle des Plantes, and Dictionnaire de Botanique are illustrated with the particular care for detail and artistic touch that characterize the best French work.

Twigs and buds glabrous. D. involucrata.

GARRYA.
(Family Garryaceae).

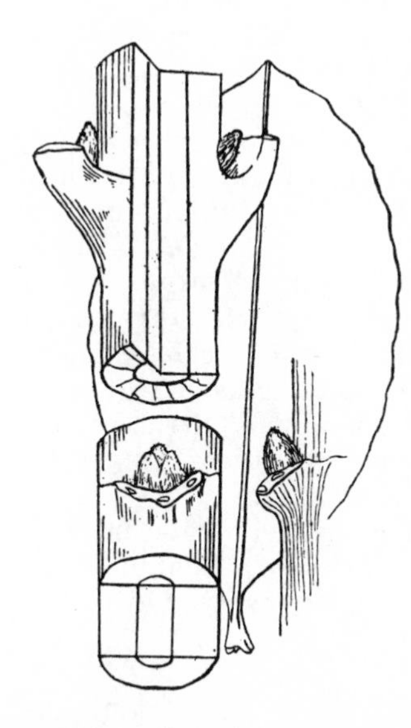

Shrubs, sometimes grown in espalier: evergreen. Twigs moderate, terete, for a time tomentulose: pith moderate, round, continuous. Buds solitary, sessile, ovoid, with 1 or 2 pairs of exposed scales. Leaf-scars opposite, at first elevated but low after the fall of the deciduous base, angularly U-shaped: bundle-traces 3: stipule-scars lacking. Leaves simple, entire, very short-petioled.

This has been made the type of a distinct family, Garryaceae, which some botanists do not consider at all closely related to the Cornaceae, in which others place it.

Most garryas are of the Pacific North American region. A single West Indian species has been separated under the name *Fadyenia;* but the closeness of its relationship to the others is shown by the fact that it has been hybridized with *G. elliptica.*

Leaves elliptical, crisped, tomentulose beneath. G. elliptica.

Winter-characters of *Marlea platanifolia*, of the Cornaceae, are given by Shirasawa, 238, pl. 2.

CLETHRA. Pepper Bush.
(Family Clethraceae).

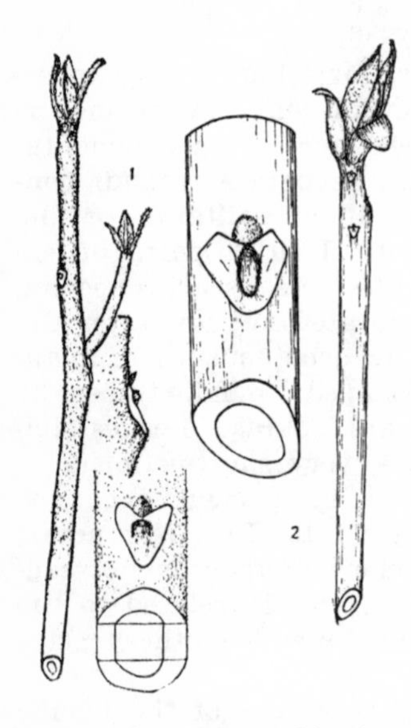

Shrubs or small trees, mostly scurfy- or tussocky-tomentulose when young: commonly deciduous. Twigs rounded or obscurely 3-sided: pith relatively large, white, or browning when cut, continuous, reticulated with firmer strands. Buds solitary, sessile or frequently developing in the first season, the lateral small and obscure, the terminal larger, ovoid, rosy, very sharp, with three caducous tomentulose scales. Leaf-scars alternate, clustered toward the tip, triangular, little raised: bundle-trace 1, protruding: stipule-scars lacking.

Winter-character references:—*Clethra alnifolia.* Schneider, f. 95, *C. barbinervis.* Shirasawa, 283, pl. 13.

Twigs slender: end-bud 3 × 5 mm.
(White alder). (1). C. alnifolia.
Twigs stouter: end-bud large (5×10 mm.). (2). C. barbinervis.

Clethra is unusual among its relatives in possessing a type of pubescence which appears much like that in which the hairs are spoken of as stellate, or several-armed from a common stalk: here the appearance results from the occurrence of unbranched hairs in closely set clusters or tufts.

Not infrequently, this genus is included in the family Ericaceae.

ELLIOTTIA.
(Family Eriacaceae).

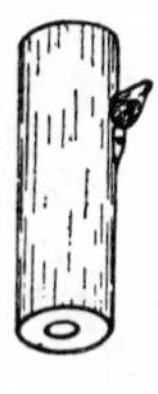

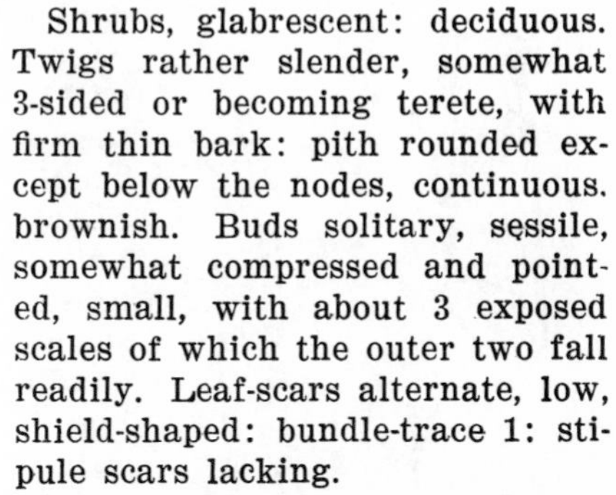

Shrubs, glabrescent: deciduous. Twigs rather slender, somewhat 3-sided or becoming terete, with firm thin bark: pith rounded except below the nodes, continuous. brownish. Buds solitary, sessile, somewhat compressed and pointed, small, with about 3 exposed scales of which the outer two fall readily. Leaf-scars alternate, low, shield-shaped: bundle-trace 1: stipule scars lacking.

Elliottia, like *Gordonia*, is one of the particularly localized plants of the southeastern United States, rare in cultivation; and though several localities have been found for it, it has disappeared from each in succession or at any rate has eluded subsequent search. An interesting note on it is to be found in the Journal of the New York Botanical Garden for August, 1901.

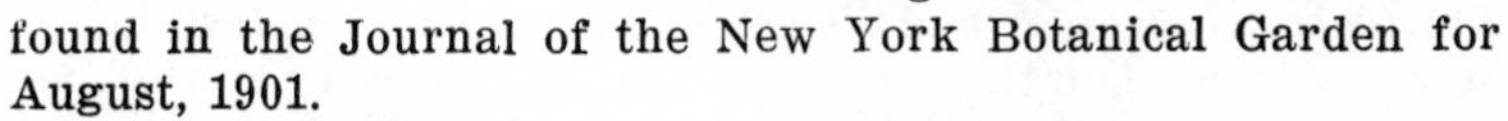

Twigs brown, becoming gray: slightly glaucous. E. racemosa.

ZENOBIA.
(Family Ericaceae).

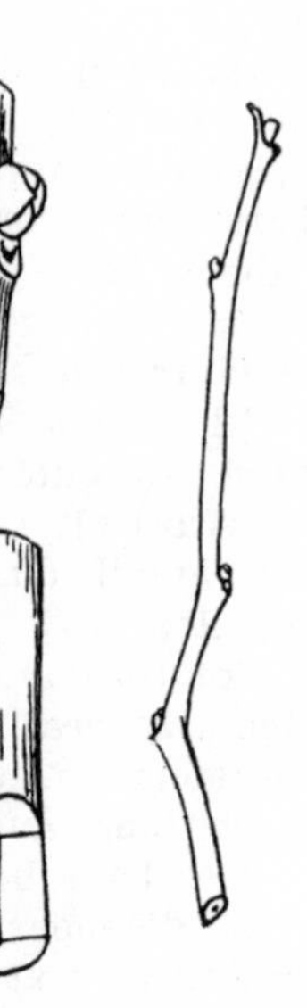

Shrubs: deciduous. Twigs slender, roundish: pith small, more or less 3-sided, continuous but with firmer strands here and there. Buds solitary, sessile, small, conical or somewhat 2-edged and pointed becoming globose and blunt, with 2 or 3 exposed scales. Leaf-scars minute, somewhat raised rather 3-sided: bundle-trace 1: stipule-scars lacking. If fruit is present it consists of small depressed-globose 5-celled capsules.

Like the Rosaceae, the family Ericaceae comprises a number of genera which are readily separable on the technical characters afforded by flowers and fruit, but do not present readily seized winter-differences unless they chance to be evergreen. *Elliottia*, *Enkianthus*, *Leucothöe*, *Lyonia*, *Menziesia*, *Oxydendrum*, *Pieris* and *Zenobia* are certain to afford puzzles: but the fact that they are ericaceous will become the more evident because of this.

Glabrous: twigs reddish becoming buff, smooth.
Z. pulverulenta.

LEDUM. Labrador Tea.
(Family Ericaceae).

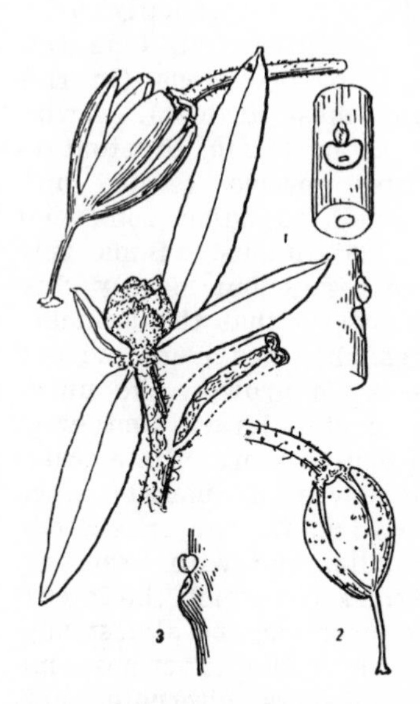

Bog shrubs: evergreen. Twigs rather slender, rounded: pith small, somewhat 3-sided, spongy, brownish. Buds solitary, sessile, somewhat compressed, small, with about 3 exposed scales; the terminal inflorescence buds large, round or ovoid, with some 10 broad mucronate glandular-dotted scales. Leaf-scars alternate, mostly low, half-elliptical or bluntly cordate, the lowest transversely linear: bundle-trace 1: stipule-scars lacking. Leaves simple, entire, elliptitcal to narrowly oblong. The small ovoid or conical-oblong, 5-celled capsules, dehiscing from the base, may be present in winter.

Winter-character references to *Ledum palustre*. Bösemann, 35; Fant, 51. Unlike most of the Ericaceae, but agreeing with *Gaultheria*, *Ledum* possesses a distinctly spongy pith. A suggestion of this condition, however, is seen when the twig of some blueberries is split.

1. Leaves very rusty-woolly beneath, revolute. 2.
   Leaves glabrous, but glandular-dotted beneath. 3.
2. Leaves broad: capsules oblong. (1). L. groenlandicum.
   Leaves narrow: capsules ellipsoid, glandular. (2). L. palustre.
3. Leaves long (4 cm.), much whitened and obscurely glandular beneath. L. columbianum.
   Leaves small (2 cm.), less whitened but more glandular beneath. (3). L. glandulosum.

RHODODENDRON.
(Family Ericaceae).

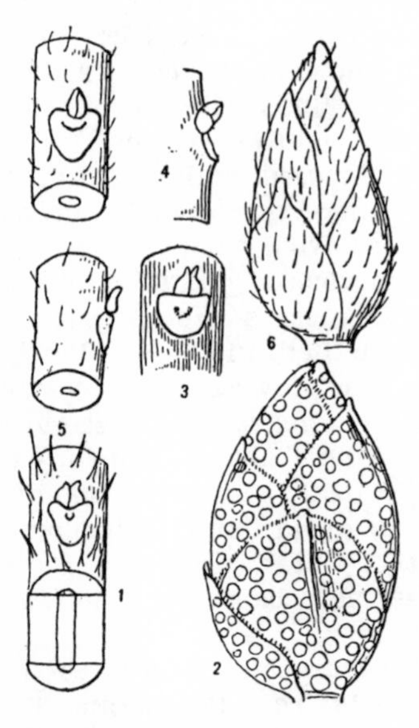

Shrubs or exceptionally arborescent: evergreen (in true rhododendrons) or deciduous (in rhodora and most azaleas). Twigs slender or moderate, or stout in the larger species, terete: pith rather small, roundish, somewhat colored, continuous. Buds solitary and sessile but usually clustered above so that the branches are often clustered from the end of a season's growth, the upper usually ovoid, larger and with half-a-dozen or more ciliate scales and the flower-bud usually much enlarged, but the lower successively smaller and with fewer exposed scales (of which the lateral or lowermost may be almost suppressed) and the lowermost minute. Leaf-scars alternate, low, shield-shaped and often notched at top or the lowest linear: bundle-trace 1, round or crescent-shaped: stipule-scars lacking. Fruit often persistent, as oblong 5-valved capsules. (Includes *Azalea* and *Rhodora*).

A number of the Ericaceae contain glucosides or other poisonous substances and are counted among the dangerous stock poisons. In some cases persons have been made ill by eating the flesh of birds or other animals that have fed on these plants without themselves being injured. The honey of others is reputed to be poisonous, including *Rhododendron*, one species of which possesses a classic reputation.

Winter-character references—*Rhododendron* (*Rhodora*) *canadensie.* Arnoldi pictures a cross-section of the winter bud in Flora, 87:466, f. 27. *R. dahuricum.* Schneider, f. 126. *R. dilatatum.* Shirasawa, 284, pl. 13. *R. ferrugineum.* Arnoldi, Flora, 87:450, f. 8,—bud-section. *R. flavum.* Schneider, f. 95. *R.* (*Azalea*) *procumbens.* Fant, 52. *R. Schlippenbachii.* Shirasawa, 284, pl. 13. *R. sinense.* Shirasawa, 284, pl 13.

1. Twigs with slender flat chaff-like scales rather than hairs. 2.
   Without chaff: sometimes pubescent or glandular-dotted. 6.
2. Evergreen or partly evergreen. 3.
   Deciduous: rather tall. R. Kaempferi.
3. Leaves glossy above: low and compact. R. indicum.
   Leaves dull. 4.
4. Leaves moderate (2.5-5 cm. long), acute. R. indicum.
   Leaves rather small (usually under 2.5 cm.). 5.
5. Leaves acute: rather tall. R. Simsii.
   Leaves typically obtuse: low, compact. (1). R. obtusum.
6. Evergreen. 7.
   Deciduous. 17.
7. Leaves with large glandular dots beneath. 8.
   Leaves glandless and glabrous beneath. 16.
8. Loosely long-hairy: leaves small (1 × 2 cm.). R. hirsutum.
   Twigs velvety. R. micranthum.
   Glabrate except for the glandular scurf. 9.
9. Leaves with scattered glands, green beneath. 10.
   Leaves brown beneath from the glandular scurf. 11.
10. Leaves rather obtuse, smooth-margined. R. dahuricum.
    Leaves very acute, crisped. (2). R. mucronulatum
11. Leaves small (about 1 cm. long): low. R. lapponicum.
    Leaves much larger. 12.
12. Leaves lanceolate, relatively narrow. 13.
    Leaves ovate- or elliptical-lanceolate. 14.

13. Leaves small (1 × 4 cm.), mucronate. R. ferrugineum.
    Leaves larger (1.5 × 5 cm.), acute. × R. arbutifolium.
14. Twigs red-brown. R. minus.
    Twigs green or reddish. 15.
15. Leaves obscurely crisped or crenulate. × R. myrtifolium.
    Leaves quite entire. R. carolinianum.
16. Young growth viscid. R. maximum.
    Not viscid-glandular. R. catawbiense.
17. Buds glabrous except for occasional stalked glands. 18.
    Buds glandular-dotted. 22.
    Buds puberulous. 23.
    Buds with long appressed hairs. 27.
18. Leaf-scars raised, scarcely notched. (3). R. Vaseyi.
    Leaf-scars not raised. 19.
19. Pedicels tomentulose and with glands. R. japonicum.
    Pedicels glabrous except for long glands. 20.
20. Twigs entirely glabrous. R. arborescens.
    Twigs usually sparsely long-hairy. 21.
21. Buds brown. R. calendulaceum.
    Buds rosy. R. nudiflorum.
22. Twigs red-orange. R. dahuricum.
    Twigs buff-orange. (2). R. mucronulatum.
23. Leaf-scars slightly raised. (4). R. canadense.
    Leaf-scars not raised. 24.
24. Twigs reddish. R. luteum.
    Twigs buff or gray. 25.
25. Twigs tomentulose, at least near the tip. R. canescens.
    Twigs glabrate or with stalked glands. 26.
26. Capsules with spreading glands. R. viscosum.
    Capsules with ascending hairs. (5). R. nudiflorum.
27. Leaf-scars distinctly raised. R. albiflorum.
    Leaf-scars not raised. (6). R. rhombicum.

MENZIESIA.
(Family Ericaceae).

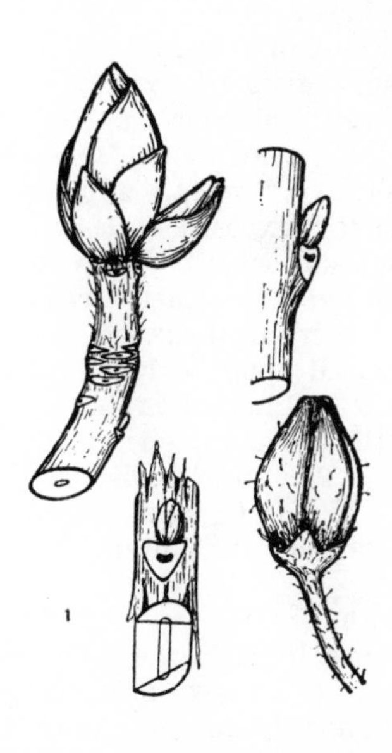

Shrubs: deciduous. Twigs slender, roundish, with shredding bark: pith small, rounded, continuous. Buds solitary, sessile, ovoid, small, with about 2 exposed scales or the terminal or subterminal flower-buds larger and with some half-dozen scales. Leaf-scars crowded toward the tips of the sometimes dwarfed and sometimes greatly elongated twigs, small, low, 3-sided or the lower transversely linear: bundle-trace 1: stipule-scars lacking. The ovoid capsules may be present in winter.

Winter-character reference to *Menziesia pilosa*:—Schneider, f. 123.

In contrast with *Gaultheria*, and in agreement with the larger number of Ericaceae as one ordinarily views them, *Menziesia* has a compact homogeneous pith. Comparative studies of the pith are given by Gris in a memoir on the pith of woody plants published in full in volume six of the Nouvelles Archives du Muséum d'Histoire Naturelle of Paris, and in an abridgement of this in volume 14 of the fifth series of the Annales des Sciences Naturelles. Plate 13 of the former is devoted to Ericaceae.

Capsules bristly-glandular. (1). M. pilosa.
Capsules glabrate. M. glabella.

LEIOPHYLLUM. Sand Myrtle.
(Family Ericaceae).

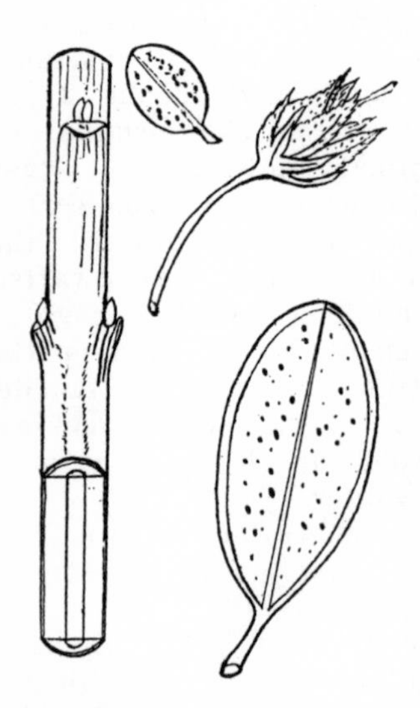

Small slow-growing densely branched shrubs: evergreen. Twigs very slender, subterete: pith minute, continuous. Buds sessile, solitary, ovoid, appressed, with about 2 exposed scales. Leaf-scars opposite or the pairs more or less broken and then 4-ranked, minute, crescent-shaped or 3-sided, raised: bundle-trace 1: stipule-scars lacking. Leaves small, subelliptical, entire, distinctly petioled. The minute-beaked 5-valved clustered pale capsules may be present in winter. (*Dendrium*).

The sand myrtle, which finds its northern limit in the pine barrens of New Jersey, is pictured photographically in an amply illustrated volume on the plants of southern New Jersey by Witmer Stone, constituting the Report of the New Jersey State Museum for 1910.

The typical coastwise sand myrtle reappears in the higher Appalachian mountains in sometimes segregated forms. Stems as thick as ones thumb but scarcely a foot high may show growth-rings covering half a century.

Glabrous: leaves obscurely dotted beneath. L. buxifolium.

LOISELEURIA. Trailing Azalea.
(Family Ericaceae).

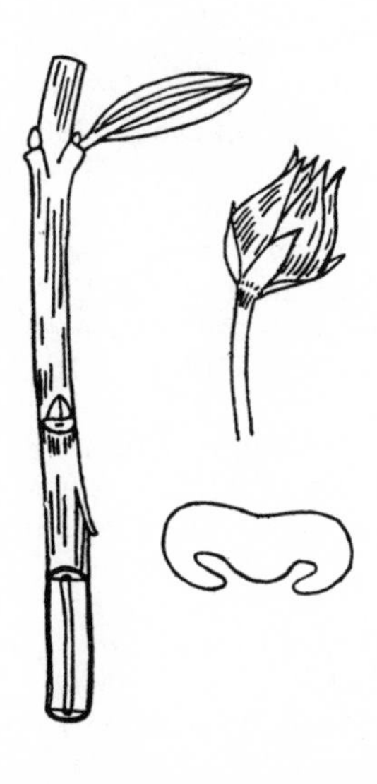

Small matted shrubs: evergreen. Twigs very slender, subterete: pith minute, continuous. Buds sessile, solitary, ovoid, appressed, with about 2 scales. Leaf-scares opposite, minute, crescent-shaped, elevated: bundle-trace 1: stipule-scars lacking. Leaves very small, subelliptical, very revolute, entire, petioled. The small beaked 5-valved red capsules may be present in winter. (*Chamaecistus*).

The trailing or alpine azalea is one of a number of plants which occur only on the higher mountains in our latitude, but have a wide distribution even at sea-level farther north. Sometimes, as in the present instance, they not only extend entirely across the American continent but are found in Europe and Asia in very similar if not identical forms.

Glabrous: leaves revolute to the midrib. L. procumbens.

KALMIA. American Laurel. Ivy.
(Family Ericaceae).

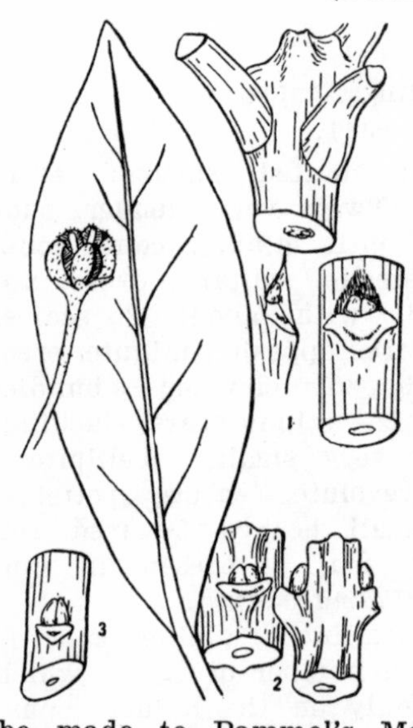

Small trees or mostly shrubs: evergreen. Twigs moderate or slender: pith small, rounded, continuous. Buds minute, naked or with 2 small green scales, solitary, sessile, the end-bud abortive. Leaf-scars clustered at end of the season's growth or in whorls of 3, half-round or shield-shaped, sometimes raised for a time by a finally deciduous base, or sunken: bundle-trace a transverse line: stipule-scars lacking. The small subglobose 5-celled capsules are persistent in winter. (Includes *Kalmiella*).

Kalmia is reputed among the most poisonous of the Ericaceae. For an analysis of the subject, with bibliography, reference may be made to Pammel's Manual of Poisonous Plants. The woody genera listed there as containing poisonous or medicinal properties are *Andromeda*, *Arctostaphylos*, *Calluna*, *Epigaea*, *Erica*, *Gaultheria*, *Kalmia*, *Ledum*, *Lecothöe*, *Lyonia*, *Rhododendron* and *Vaccinium*.

1. Large shrubs or small trees: leaves large. (1). K. latifolia.
   Small shrubs: buds with 2 scales. 2.
2. Twigs 2-edged: leaves opposite. (2). K. polifolia.
   Twigs terete. 3.
3. Leaves mostly in whorls of 2 or 3. (3). K. angustifolia.
   Leaves alternate. 4.
4. Twigs glandular-hairy. (*Kalmiella*). K. hirsuta.
   Twigs hisute, not glandular. K. cuneata.

PHYLLODOCE. Mountain Heath.
(Family Ericaceae).

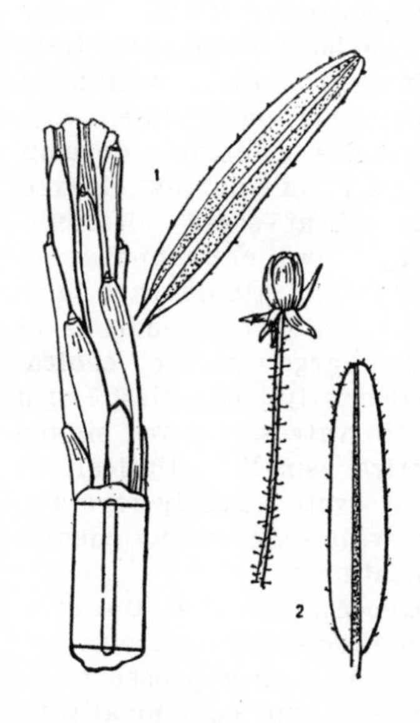

Low matted shrubs: evergreen. Twigs slender, ridged below the leaf-scars: pith minute, continuous. Buds minute, solitary, sessile, of scarcely evident structure. Leaf-scars alternate, minute, crescent-shaped, raised: bundle-trace 1, scarcely distinguishable: stipule-scars lacking. Leaves small, oblong, minutely serrulate. The small ellipsoid capsules, erect on long slender glandular stalks, are evident in winter. Sometimes placed in *Bryanthus*.

Winter-characters of *Phyllodoce caerulea* are given by Fant, 51.

The phyllodoces afford another example of the occurrence of identical or equivalent species in high latitudes on both continents, with extension away from the pole at increased altitudes.

Midrib glabrous: fruit-stalks not bristly. (1). P. Breweri.
Midrib puberulent beneath: pedicels bristly. (2). P. caerulea.

DABOECIA. St. Dabeoc's Heath.
(Family Ericaceae).

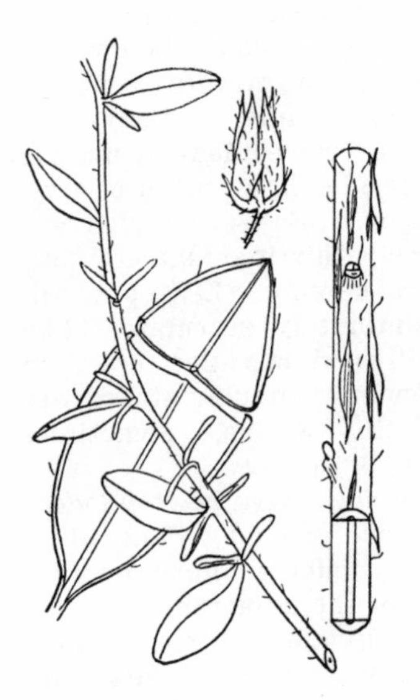

Compact small heath-like shrubs: evergreen. Twigs slender, round, the bark soon shredding: pith minute, roundish, continuous. Buds solitary, subglobose, with about 2 scales, commonly developing a pair of narrow leaves, promptly. Leaf-scars alternate, minute, low crescent-shaped: bundle-trace 1; stipule-scars lacking. The fruit, if present, is of relatively large rather conical glandular-bristly capsules with very acute valves. Leaves simple and entire, small, elliptical or somewhat ovate, slightly revolute, densely white- or rusty-tomentulose beneath.

St. Dabeoc's heath, as the common name indicates, occurs in Ireland and has been supposed to be peculiar to the Emerald Isle; but it is found occasionally as far south as the Mediterranean, and on the oceanic Azores.

Twigs transiently puberulent and sparsely hairy. D. polifolia.

ENKIANTHUS.
(Family Ericaceae).

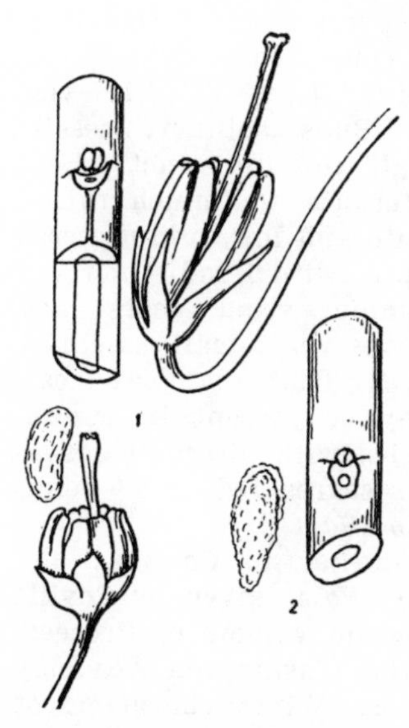

Shrubs: deciduous. Twigs subverticillate, slender, 3-sided or rounded, often reddish: pith rather small, roundish, continuous. Buds minute, sunken and in the notch of the leaf-scar, solitary, sessile, indistinctly scaly, the terminal flower-buds large, ovoid and with some half-dozen mucronate scales. Leaf-scars minute, crescent-shaped or triangular, low: bundle-trace 1, minute, round: stipule-scars lacking. The small oblong or ovoid 5-celled few-seeded capsules are present in winter.

Winter-characters of *Enkianthus japonicus* are given by Shirasawa, 284, pl. 13.

Like many of our common native Ericaceae, among them the dwarf blueberries which cover barren hills in the Eastern States, these Asiatic species color brilliantly in autumn.

Pedicels straight: capsules subglobose: sepals ovate.
(1). E. subsessilis.

Pedicels bent: capsules oblong: sepals elongated.
(2). E. campanulatus.

CASSIOPE.
(Family Ericaceae).

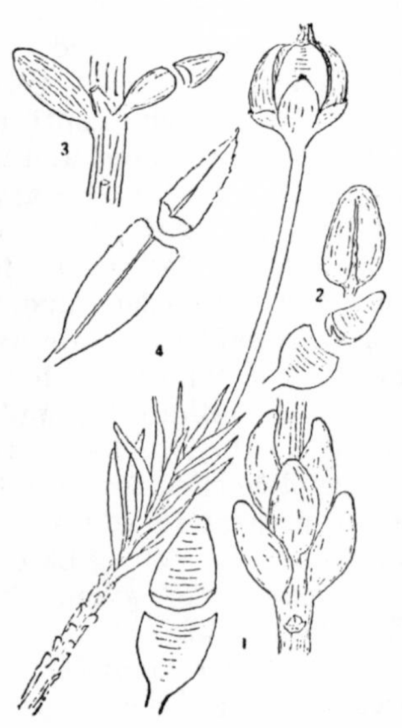

Small tufted and trailing shrubs: evergreen. Twigs very slender, concealed above by the overlapping leaves: pith very minute. Buds solitary, sessile, very small and indistinct. Leaf-scars alternate and much raised, or opposite and low, minute, crescent-shaped, with 1 indistinct vascular bundle: stipule-scars lacking. Leaves very small, essentially entire. The suglobose capsules may be present in winter. The species with alternate leaves have been segregated as the genus *Harrimaniella.*

A foliage-key to *Cassiope* and *Harrimaniella* is given by Coville in the second volume of Proceedings of the Washington Academy of Sciences. Winter-characters of *C. hypnoides* are given by Fant, 50.

1. Leaves opposite, closely imbricated, broad. 2.
   Leaves alternate. 3.
2. Leaves not grooved on the back. (1). C. Mertensiana.
   Leaves with a groove on the back. (2). C. tetragona.
3. Leaves widely spreading, broad, blunt. (3). C. Stelleriana.
   Leaves closely imbricated, narrow, acute. (4). C. hypnoides.

LEUCOTHÖE. Fetter Bush.
(Family Ericaceae).

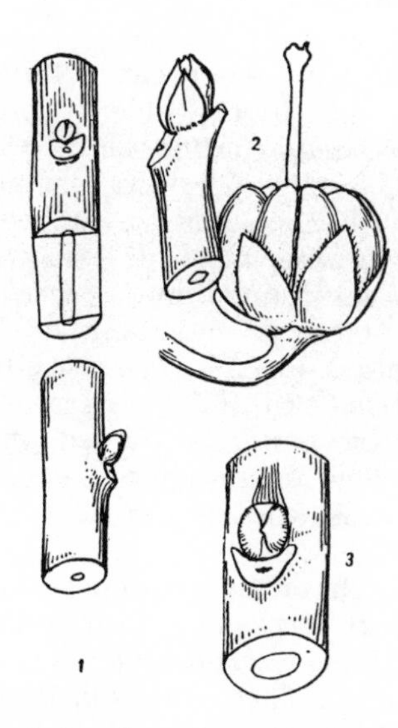

Shrubs: evergreen or deciduous. Twigs rather slender, finally subterete: pith roundish or somewhat 3-sided, continuous. Buds small, solitary, sessile, globose or ovoid, with 3 or 4 exposed scales, the end-bud lacking. Leaf scars alternate, small, crescent-shaped or half-round, little elevated: bundle-trace 1: stipule-scars lacking. Leaves, when present, simple, serrulate. The small depressed-globose capsules are often present in winter.

Winter-character reference to *Leucothöe racemosa*: — Schneider, f. 123.

The flowers of *Leucothöe* sometimes are intensely fragrant and a plant that is quite concealed in surrounding shrubbery may be located often by its fragrance. Unfortunately the genus is poisonous to stock.

1. Deciduous. 2.
   Evergreen. ("Hemlock;" dog hobble). 3.
2. Capsules scarcely lobed: racemes straight. (1). L. racemosa.
   Capsules deeply lobed: racemes curved. (2). L. recurva.
3. Leaves small (4 cm. long), ovate, very obtuse. L. Davisiae.
   Leaves larger, pointed. 4.
4. Leaves lanceolate, acute. L. axillaris.
   Leaves ovate-lanceolate, acuminate. (3). L. Catesbaei.

ANDROMEDIA. Bog Rosemary.
(Family Ericaceae).

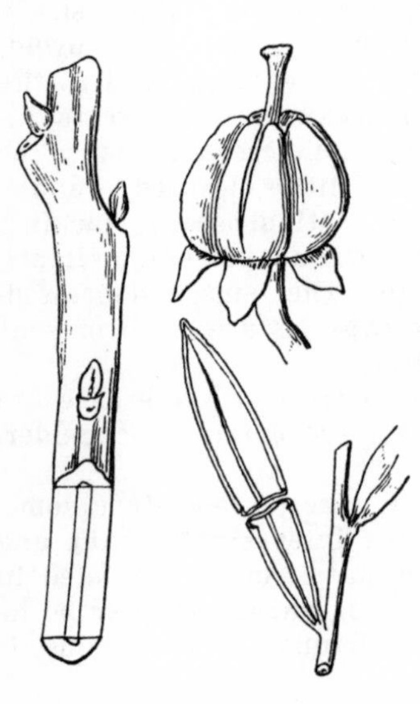

Bog shrubs: evergreen. Twigs slender, at first 3-sided: pith small, 3-sided, continuous. Buds solitary, sessile, compressed, small, ovoid, with 2 exposed scales. Leaf scars alternate, more or less elevated, half-round or crescent-shaped, minute: bundle-trace 1: stipule-scars lacking. Leaves simple, entire, elliptical to narrowly oblong, revolute, whitened beneath. The small short-ovoid 5-celled capsules are present in winter.

Winter-character references: — *Andromeda cernua.* Shirasawa, 284, pl. 13. *A. ovalifolia.* Shirasawa, 242, pl. 3. *A. polifolia.* Bösemann, 35; Fant, 50.

Like *Kalmia*, *Pieris*, *Leucothöe*, *Chamaedaphne* and *Rhododendron*, this genus is reputed to be poisonous.

Leaves glabrous: capsules brown. (1). A. polifolia.
Leaves tomentulose beneath: capsules glaucous.
A. glaucophylla.

CHAMAEDAPHNE. Cassandra.
(Family Ericaceae).

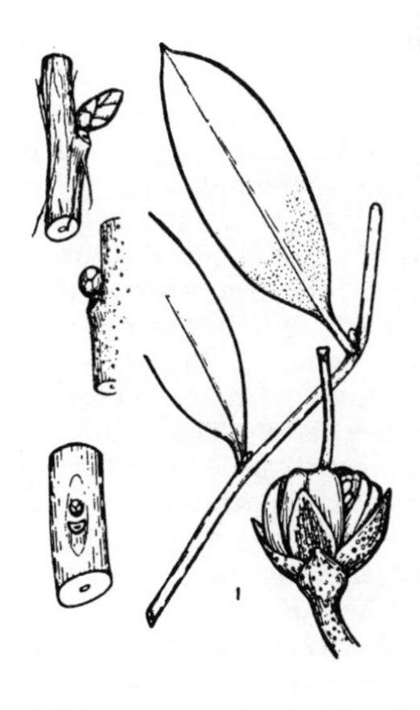

Bog shrubs: evergreen. Twigs slender, roundish, at first puberulent and scurfy, then with shredding gray bark, and finally smooth and deep red-brown: pith small, roundish, continuous. Buds solitary, sessile, small, globose and with about 3 exposed scales or becoming oblong in expansion. Leaf-scars alternate, minute, low, crescent-shaped: bundle-trace 1: stipule-scars lacking. Leaves simple, subentire, scurfy beneath. The small depressed-globose 5-celled capsules, with persistent scurfy calyx and 2-bracted at base, are present in winter.

A peculiar interest attaches to many bog plants in that although they grow with their roots in water they have leaves that are woolly beneath as in *Ledum*, or of firm structure or scurfy as in *Chamaedaphne*, or very glaucous beneath as in *Vaccinium Oxycoccus*, or with their stomata in grooves between the midrib and the revolute margin. These are characters usually connected with plants that scarcely obtain enough water; and, in fact, these bog plants really cannot absorb a sufficiency of water and so experience the condition of physiological if not of actual physical drought.

Leaves relatively broad, flat. (Leather leaf). (1). C. calyculata.
Leaves narrow, crisped. C. calyculata angustifolia.

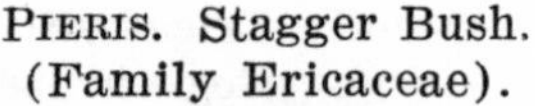

PIERIS. Stagger Bush.
(Family Ericaceae).

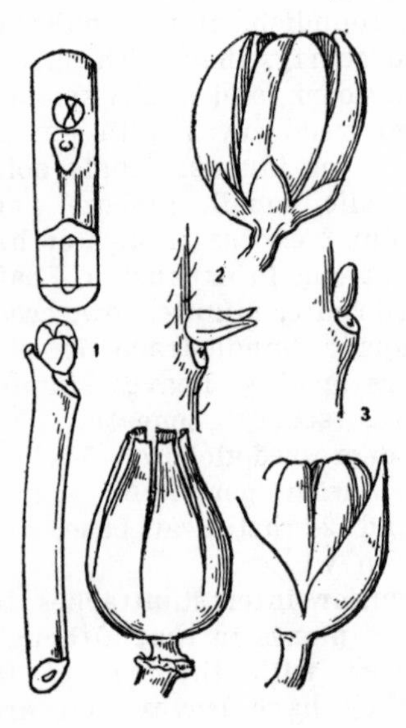

Shrubs: evergreen or deciduous. Twigs rather slender, 3-sided or finally terete: pith somewhat 3-sided, continuous. Buds small, subglobose to conical, with 2-5 exposed scales; the end-bud lacking. Leaf-scars alternate, small, half-round or triangular, somewhat raised: bundle-trace 1: stipule-scars lacking. Leaves, when present, simple, entire and revolute or serrulate. The small globose or urn-shaped capsules are often present in winter.

As its common name indicates, the stagger bush is poisonous to stock, like *Kalmia*, etc. The species of *Pieris* have been placed in the genus *Andromeda* frequently; and they are placed under *Lyonia* by some botanists; as they have been placed by others in *Leucothöe*.

1. Deciduous: buds round-ovoid: capsules urceolate. (1). P. Mariana.
   Evergreen: buds compressed. 2.
2. Pubescent: sepals much shorter than capsules. (2). P. floribunda.
   Glabrous: sepals equaling the capsules. (3). P. nitida.

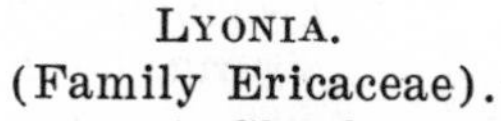

LYONIA.
(Family Ericaceae).

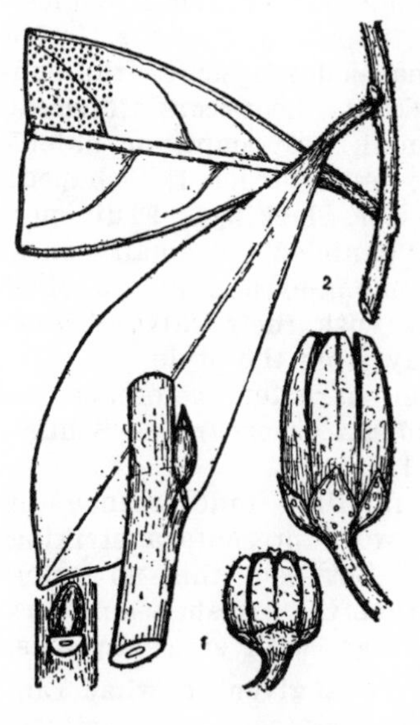

Shrubs or sometimes subarborescent: evergreen or deciduous. Twigs slender, somewhat 3-sided, becoming terete. Buds solitary, sessile, small, oblong, more or less flattened against the stem, with 2 exposed scales. Leaf-scars alternate, minute, low, half-round or crescent-shaped: bundle-trace 1: stipule-scars lacking. Leaves, when persistent, simple, entire or obscurely serrulate, and scurfy beneath.

As with *Pieris*, *Lyonia* was formerly merged in *Andromeda*, and the generic name *Xolisma* has been used for its species, which occur in a number of variants which have been thought by some botanists to represent distinct species.

1. Deciduous: capsules very small, subglobose. (1). L. ligustrina.
   Evergreen: capsules oblong. 2.
2. Leaves without prominent veinlets: tall. (2). L. ferruginea.
   Leaves raised-reticulate beneath: dwarf. L. fruticosa.

OXYDENDRUM. Sourwood.
(Family Ericaceae).

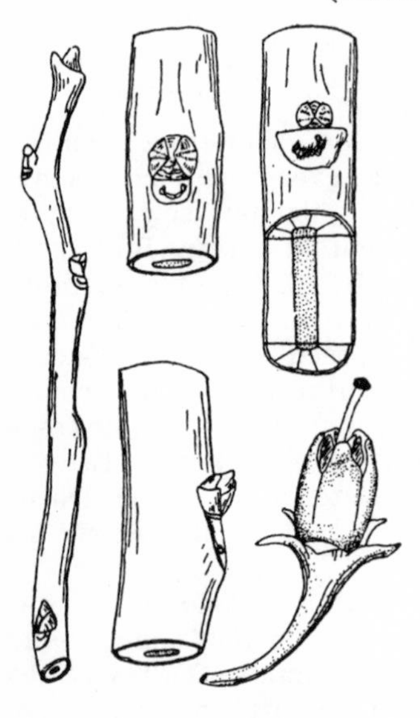

Small or moderate-sized tree: deciduous. Twigs rather slender, zig-zag, terete: pith pale, continuous. Buds rather small, conical-globose, solitary, sessile, with about half-a-dozen scales, the end-bud lacking. Leaf-scars alternate, low, small, half-round or shield-shaped: bundle-trace 1, C-shaped: stipule-scars lacking. Fruit persistent, panicled, as small canescent oblong-pyramidal 5-celled capsules with their valves breaking away from the style.

Winter-character reference to *Oxydendrum arboreum*: —Schneider, f. 123.

The fan-like inflorescence of the sourwood presents a striking contrast between the flowering stage, when the urn-shaped flowers hang downward, and the fruiting stage, with erect capsules.

The generic name *Oxydendrum* was given to what Linnaeus had called *Andromeda arborea*, because of its acidity. Though a pure Greek derivative, its author Latinized the name by changing the ending *on* of the Greek into *um* in accord with a general effort to Latinize all plant names, of whatever derivation,—and a correction of this kind has been made in many though not all cases where the author of a name did not do this himself. Curiously, the established Latinized name of this tree is sometimes written in *on*.

Twigs glabrous, olive or bright pink. O. arboreum.

EPIGAEA. Trailing Arbutus.
(Family Ericaceae).

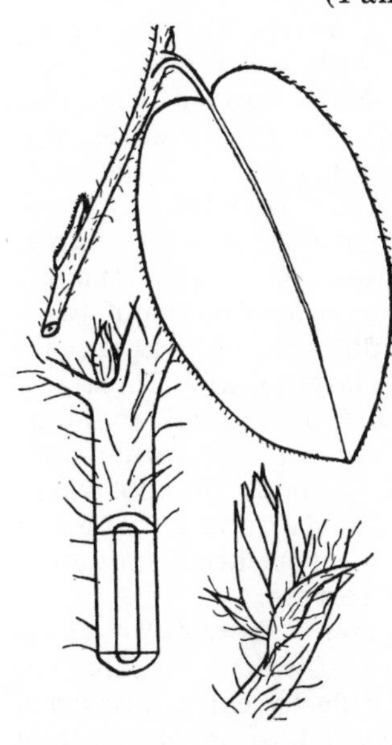

Prostrate and rooting small shrubs with finally exfoliating bark: evergreen. Twigs slender, terete: pith moderate, rounded, continuous, brown. Buds solitary, or the inflorescence-buds quickly multiple and conical-ovoid with 2 hairy outer scales and a number of smooth very acute inner scales. Leaf-scars linear when cataphyls have fallen, or usually lacking, the leaves falling only with the cortex: stipule-scars lacking. Leaves elliptical-ovate, often cordate, entire but usually ciliate.

Like blueberries and rhododendrons, the popular fragrant-flowered May-flower or trailing arbutus requires a certain acidity of the soil for its successful cultivation; but, as Coville has shown, it is capable of successful growth as a compact full-flowered potted plant if given the proper soil conditions.

This sensitiveness of Ericaceae to the condition of the soil has been shown to be connected with the fact that their roots grow in a sort of mutually helpful parasitic relationship with certain fungi, which themselves are prevented from thriving unless the soil is too acid for the growth of most bacteria. An interesting discussion of the question is given by Coville in Bulletin 193 of the Bureau of Plant Industry at Washington.

Twigs very red-bristly. E. repens.

GAULTHERIA. Wintergreen.
(Family Ericaceae).

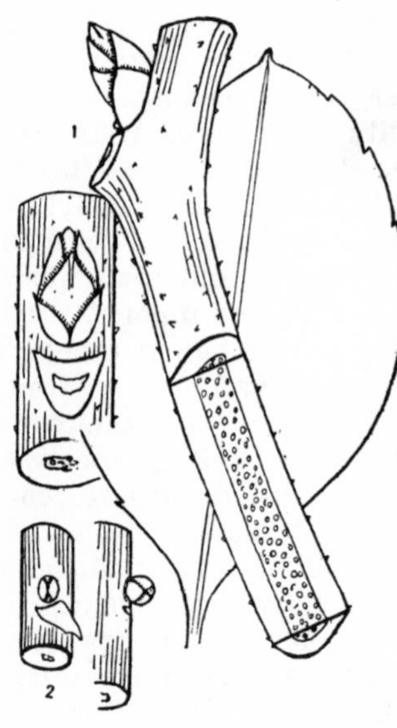

Aromatic small shrubs, either bushy or with short erect shoots that are leafy toward the top: evergreen. Twigs moderate, zigzag and 3-sided in the large type, slender and rounded in the smaller: pith relatively large, honey-combed or finally spongy. Buds solitary, sessile, ovoid, with about 5 ciliate scales. Leaf-scars alternate, minute and linear in the smaller type, but half-round or shield-shaped in the larger and then with a large bundle-trace: stipule-scars lacking. Leaves simple, short-stalked, minutely somewhat serrate.

Wintergreen "berries," which really are soft-walled capsules enclosed by a fleshy calyx, are sometimes brought into northern cities by the Indians.

Wintergreen and sweet birch are so similarly flavored as to give rise to the impression that oil of wintergreen and oil of birch contain identical aromatic substances. The principal constituent in each is said to be methyl salicylate, but the characteristic flavor is due to small quantities of an ester.

1. Bushy: twigs sparsely hairy or papillate: buds large. 2.
   With nearly simple short shoots from prostrate stems. 3.
2. Upright: leaves ovate, round-based. (1). G. Shallon.
   Spreading: leaves elliptical to obovate. G. Veitchiana.
3. Loosely hairy: leaves ovate, round-based. G. Myrsinites.
   Glabrate: leaves elliptical to obovate. (2). G. procumbens.

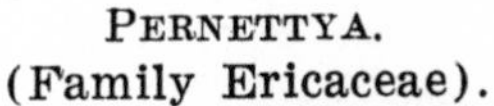

PERNETTYA.
(Family Ericaceae).

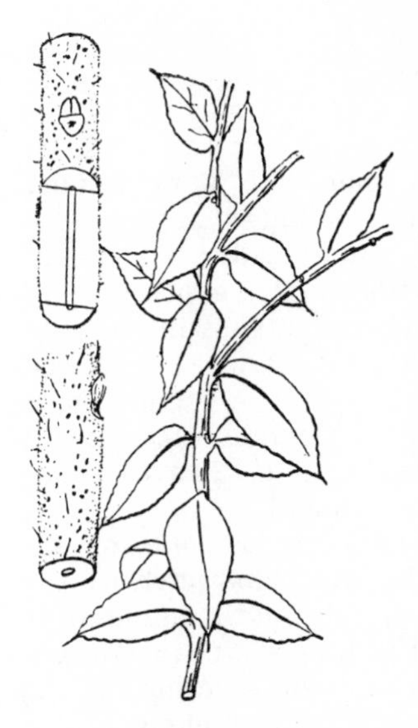

Small shrubs: evergreen. Twigs very slender, terete, more or less puberulent and sparsely stiff-hairy, at first green: pith minute, roundish, somewhat spongy. Buds small, solitary, sessile, ovoid or round, flattened, with 2 outer scales. Leaf-scars alternate, minute, obtusely 3-sided or crescent-shaped, low: bundle-trace 1: stipule-scars lacking. Leaves commonly twisted into one plane, small, simple, minutely somewhat toothed. Fruit axillary, commonly present in winter in the form of small berries.

The genus *Pernettya* is one of peculiar distribution: most of its species are of the North American highlands, but it is represented also in New Zealand. Reasons for believing that there was once a direct land connection between South American and New Zealand and Australia are brought together in an interesting volume by Scharff, on Distribution and Origin of Life in America.

1. Leaves ovate, pungently pointed. 2.
   Leaves lance-oblong. P. angustifolia.
2. Fruit red. (1). P. mucronata.
   Fruit white. P. mucronata alba.
   Fruit nearly black. P. mucronata nigra.

ARCTOSTAPHYLOS. Kinnikinnik. Red Bearberry.
(Family Ericaceae).

Dwarf northern shrubs, as here considered: evergreen. Twigs slender, somewhat 3- or 5-sided: pith small slightly angled, continuous. Buds solitary, sessile, ovoid, with about 3 exposed scales or the uppermost showing a larger number. Leaf-scars alternate, somewhat elevated, small, crescent-shaped: bundle-trace 1: stipule-scars lacking. Leaves spatulate, rather small.

The bearberry is one of the plants that are characteristically limited on the South and that in high latitudes occur in Europe and Asia as well as America. In an account of the biology of the region north of Saskatchewan and Alberta, published as No. 27 of North American Fauna, Preble states that the natives smoke the dried leaves of the bearberry, usually mixed with tobacco; and they are somewhat used medicinally.

Twigs puberulent, the bark finally exfoliating. A. Uva-ursi.

ARCTOUS. Mountain Bearberry.
(Family Ericaceae).

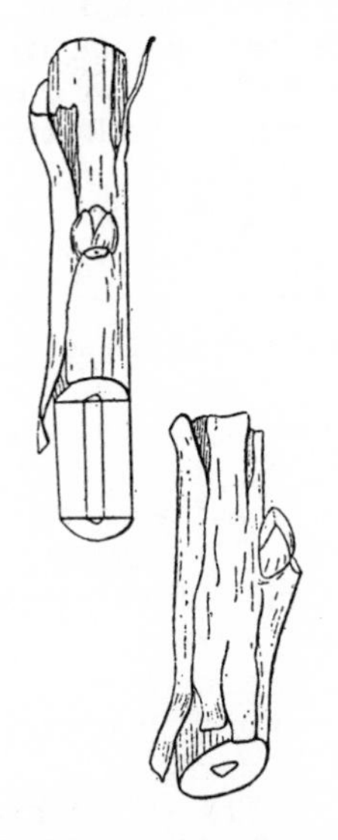

Low northern or alpine shrubs: deciduous. Twigs rather slender, subterete: pith minute, 3-sided, continuous. Buds solitary, sessile, ovoid, appressed, with about 3 exposed scales. Leaf-scars alternate, somewhat raised, small, crescent-shaped: bundle-trace 1: stipule-scars lacking. (*Mairania; Arctostaphylos*).

Though the fruits of *Arctostaphylos* are eaten by bears, as the scientific and popular names of the genus indicate, they do not appeal to the palate of even the average boy. Even the black bearberries, borne by *Arctous*, though pulpier and of pleasing appearance, are said to be nearly tasteless. Many botanists still place the deciduous bearberry in the genus *Arctostaphylos*.

Glabrous: bark quickly exfoliating. A. alpinus.

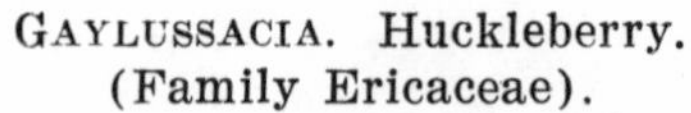

GAYLUSSACIA. Huckleberry.
(Family Ericaceae).

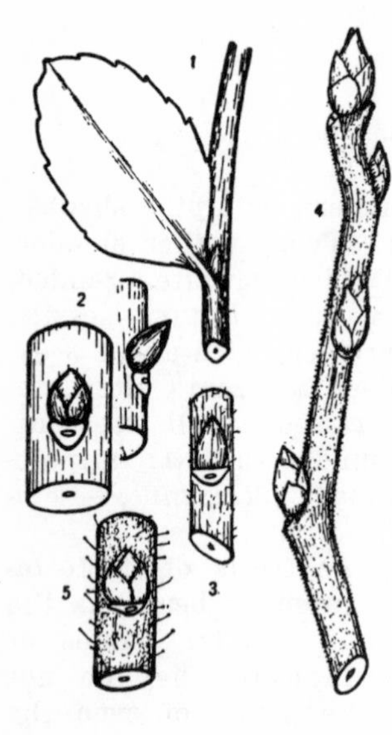

Shrubs: deciduous, or evergreen occasionally or in the South. Twigs slender, roundish: pith small, 3-sided or rounded, continuous. Buds solitary, sessile, ovoid, small, with 2 or some 4 or 5 exposed scales, the end-bud lacking. Leaf-scars alternate, low, crescent-shaped or 3-sided: bundle-trace 1: stipule-scars lacking.

Winter-characters of *Gaylussacia dumasa* are pictured by Schneider, f. 126.

The deciduous species of *Gaylussacia* and *Vaccinium* are not readily placed in the proper genus in winter, even though they may be told apart with some assurance. In this respect the genera resemble the group referred to under *Zenobia.* Because of their inferior ovary, these two genera and *Chiogenes* are believed by some botanists to constitute a family Vacciniaceae, distinct from the Aricaceae.

1. Evergreen: leaves serrulate. (1). G. brachycera.
   Deciduous, or the leaves entire and glandular-dotted if present. 2.
2. Glabrous: shoots glaucous. (Dangleberry). (2). G. frondosa.
   Twigs more or less pubescent. 3.
3. Buds with 2 or 3 exposed scales. (Black h.). (3). G. baccata.
   Buds with 4 or 5 exposed scales. 4.
4. Twigs puberulent but not villous. (Dwarf. h.). (4). G. dumosa.
   Twigs also with long glandular hairs. (5). G. hirtella.

VACCINIUM. Blueberry. Cranberry.
(Family Ericaceae).

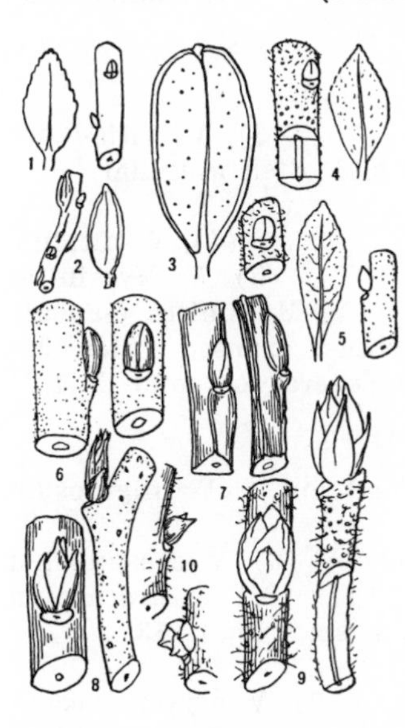

Shrubs, usually under 1 m. high, exceptionally trailing- or subarborescent: deciduous, or partly evergreen in the south, or some species evergreen. Twigs slender, very obscurely 3- or 5-sided or distinctly angled: pith small, nearly round, continuous. Buds small or minute, solitary, sessile, with 2 apparently valvate scales or the larger with some half-dozen scales, the end-bud deciduous. Leaf-scars alternate, small or minute, half-round or crescent-shaped, somewhat elevated: bundle-trace 1: stipule-scars lacking.

Winter-character references: — *Vaccinium Myrtillus*. Bösemann, 36; Schneider, f. 95. *V. Oxycoccos.* Bösemann, 36; Fant, 50. *V. uliginosum*. Bösemann, 36; Schneider, f. 95. *V. Vitis-Idaea*. Bösemann, 36; Fant, 49, f. 55. *Vaccinium* comprises the very different groups of trailing cranberries, sometimes segregated under the generic name *Oxyoccus*, low-bush cranberries, for which the name *Vitis Idaea* has been used, tree huckleberries, sometimes called *Batodendron*, squaw huckleberries, *Plycodium*, mountain cranberries, which Small segregates under the name *Hugeria*, and blueberries.

1. Trailing evergreens: leaves small (scarcely 5×15 mm.). 2.
   Bushy, tufted. 4.
2. Leaves entire, rather elliptical. (Cranberries). 3.
   Leaves serrate, somewhat ovate. (1). V. crassifolium.

3. Leaves very small (10 mm.), revolute. (2). V. Oxycoccos.
   Leaves larger (15 mm.). V. macrocarpon.
4. Low evergreens with small leaves. 5.
   Deciduous. 8.
5. Leaves blunt-mucronate, notched, dotted.
   (3). V. Vitis-Idaea.
   Leaves acute: twigs puberulent and often granular. 6.
6. Leaves prevailing oblanceolate and acute. 7.
   Leaves obovate and acuminate. (4). V. nitidum.
7. Leaves green on both sides. (5). V. Myrsinites.
   Leaves glaucous beneath. V. Myrsinites glaucum.
8. Buds oblong, appressed, with 2 obtuse exposed scales. 9.
   Buds ovoid or subglobose: scales several, or pointed. 15.
9. Twigs without angles. 10.
   Twigs conspicuously angled. 12.
10. Bark finely shredding: twiggy and low. V. uliginosum.
    Bark scarcely shredding. 11.
11. Scarcely a span high: tufted: slender. (6). V. caespitosum.
    Taller and stouter. V. erythrocarpum.
12. Dwarf and tufted, scarcely over a span high. 13.
    Taller and more bushy. 14.
13. Twigs slender: buds 1-1.5 mm. (7). V. erythrococcum.
    Twigs stouter: buds often 2 mm. long. V. oreophilum.
14. Twigs almost winged. V. parvifolium.
    Twigs only ribbed. V. ovalifolium.
15. Buds ovoid or oblong, ascending or appressed. 16.
    Buds subglobose or round-ovoid, divergent. 19.
16. Low shrubs. 17.
    Tall: twigs angled and warty. (8). V. corymbosum.
17. Twigs grooved above the buds, or angular. 18.
    Twigs nearly terete, very hairy. (9). V. canadense.
18. Twigs nearly smooth. V. pennsylvanicum.
    Twigs distinctly granular-warty. V. vacillans.
19. Modern or low shrub. (10). V. stamineum.
    Large shrub or small tree, often twiggy. V. arboreum.

CHIOGENES. Moxie Plum.
(Family Ericaceae).

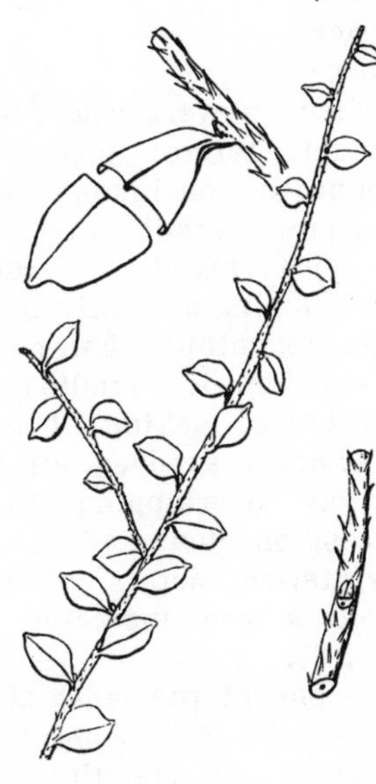

Low very delicate aromatic trailing shrubs: evergreen. Stems filiform, brown-chaffy, terete: pith minute. Buds solitary, sessile, ovoid, appressed, minute, with about 2 exposed scales. Leaf-scars alternate, low, minute, crescent-shaped: bundle-trace 1, scarcely discernible: stipule-scars lacking. Leaves small, subelliptical, acute, short-petioled, entire.

In some respects the creeping snowberry, as *Chiogenes* is called sometimes because of its white fruit, is the most attractive and dainty of our woody plants, and it is rarely seen except by close observers because of its habit of growth and its small size. The name capillaire given it by the French Canadians expresses well the delicacy of its stem. Like the wintergreen, it is pleasantly flavored.

Stem brown-chaffy: leaves slightly chaffy beneath.
C. hispidula.

CALLUNA. Heather.
(Family Ericaceae).

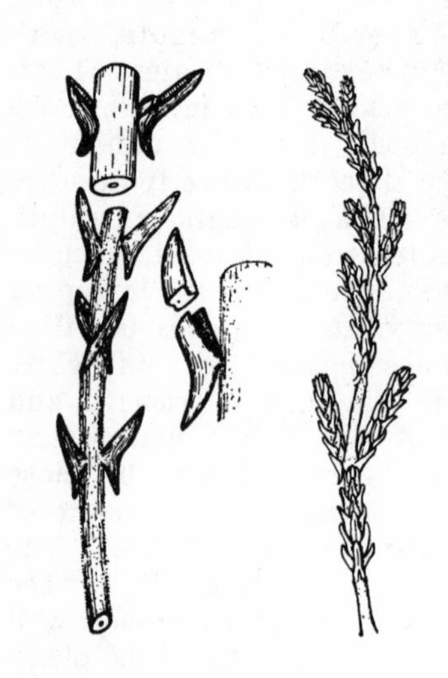

Small shrubs: evergreen. Twigs very slender, terete: pith very small, roundish, continuous. Buds small, solitary, sessile, angularly globose, with about 3 scales, usually developing promptly. Leaf-scars opposite, minute, half-round or crescent-shaped: bundle-trace 1: stipule-scars lacking. Leaves small, V-shaped, grooved on the keel, closely overlapping in 4 ranks except on elongated shoots.

The winter-characters of *Calluna vulgaris* are indicated by Bösemann, 33.

Heather, one of the most characteristic shrubs of European regions where soil sterility and mist meet, occurs in this country only along or near the northern Atlantic seaboard.

Twigs puberulent: leaves glabrous. C. vulgaris.

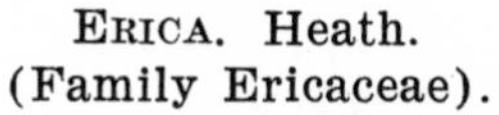

ERICA. Heath.
(Family Ericaceae).

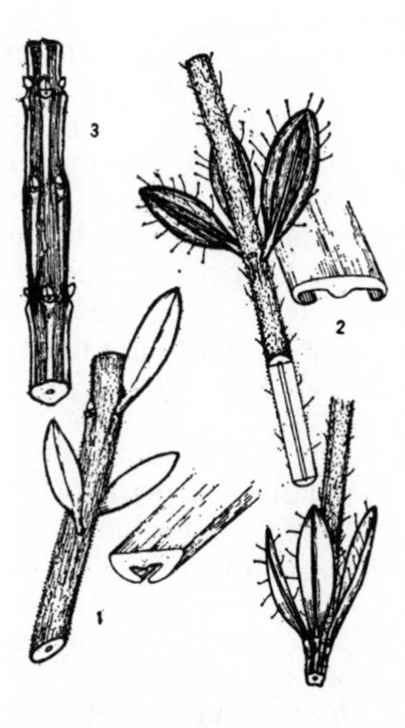

Typically, small bog shrubs: evergreen. Twigs very slender, more or less ridged below the leaves: pith very small, continuous. Buds minute, solitary, sessile, ovoid, with 2 or 3 exposed scales. Leaf-scars whorled, minute, half-round: bundle-trace 1: stipule-scars lacking. Leaves small, mostly, except the lowermost, very revolute or folded so that the edges meet down the back, rather longer than the internodes except on elongated shoots.

Winter-character references to *Erica Tetralix*:—Bösemann, 33; Fant, 52.

Like heather, the true heaths have barely secured a foothold in this country,—on the coast.

1. Leaves in whorls of 3. (1). E. cinerea.
   Leaves in whorls of four. 2.
2. Leaves glandular-bristly. (Bell heather). (2). E. Tetralix.
   Leaves not glandular. (3). E. carnea.

DIAPENSIA.

(Family Diapensiaceae).

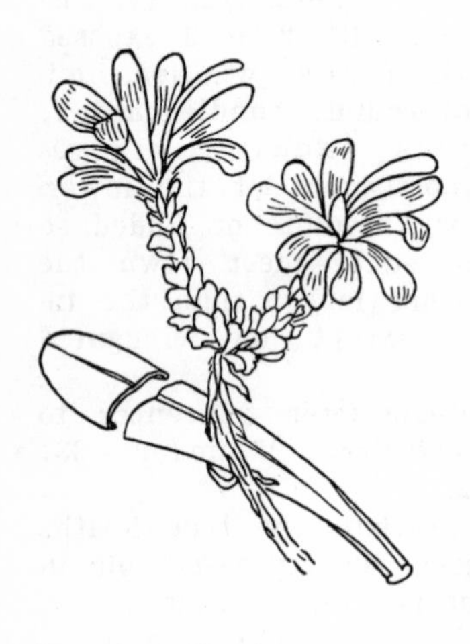

Dwarf matted high-northern shrub: evergreen. Stems slender, with shredding bark finally, but long covered by persistent leaf-remnants. Buds minute, naked, concealed by the bases of the leaves. Leaf-scars absent: stipule-scars or stipules lacking. Leaves alternate, spatulate, densely overlapping, somewhat recurving and revolute.

Kerner von Marilaun, one of the most popular exponents of adaptive teleology, mentions *Diapensia* in his charming Natural History of Plants as an illustration of Arctic plants characterized by the absence of pubescence restricting transpiration, in contrast with woolly plants of more southern and drier regions.

Glabrous, but the leaves minutely papillate. D. lapponica.

PYXIDANTHERA. Pyxie.
(Family Diapensiaceae).

Matted and trailing half-shrub of sandy pine barrens: evergeen. Stems slender, long covered by the persistent leaf-remnants. Buds minute, naked, concealed by the petioles. Leaf-scars absent: stipules or stipule-scars lacking. Leaves alternate or subopposite, oblanceolate, rather crowded, spreading or ascending.

The pyxie is counted among the most attractive plants of the New Jersey pine barrens, particularly as it flowers very early in the Spring. A special interest attaches to this region because in it, when Darwinian biology was new, Mrs. Mary Treat made many observations on the localized plants with which she was surrounded, and demonstrated the value and pleasure of a truly amateur interest in natural history in a series of contributions to The American Naturalist, the earlier volumes of which possess a readability which is rare in journals devoted to science.

Somewhat transiently white-hairy: leaves acute. P. barbulata.

Winter-characters of *Certatostigma plumbaginoides*, of the family Plumbaginaceae, much grown over walls, etc., in warm regions, are given by Schneider, f. 109.

BUMELIA. False Buckthorn.
(Family Sapotaceae).

Shrubs or small spreading trees with branch-spines: mostly deciduous. Twigs moderate, zigzag, often occurring as short leafy spurs: pith continuous, white or striped with brown. Buds small, hemispherical, sessile, sometimes branched or developing a collateral spine, with about 4 exposed scales. Leaf-scars alternate, triangular or crescent-shaped or shallowly U-shaped, somewhat raised: bundle-traces 3, sometimes subconfluent: stipule-scars lacking.

Winter-character reference·— *Bumelia lanuginosa.* Hitchcock (1), 4.

One of the first novelties to which a visitor to Mexico is introduced is the zapote or mamey sapote, the fruit of *Calocarpum mammosum* or *Lacuma mammosa;* and one of the sweetest of all fruits is the sapote chico, chicozapote, or sapodilla, the fruit of *Achras Sapota*, a tree which furnishes the too-familiar chicle chewing gum, of which large quantities are brought up by every fruit ship touching at Belize. A very readable account of these sapotaceous plants is given by Pititier in volume 18 of Contributions from the U. S. National Herbarium.

1. Subevergreen: leaves golden-satiny beneath. (1). B. tenax.
   Mostly deciduous: leaves not satiny if present. 2.
2. Glabrous: twigs black-purple. (2). B. lycioides.
   Somewhat tomentose: twigs red-gray. B. lanuginosa.

DIOSPYROS. Persimmon.
(Family Ebenaceae).

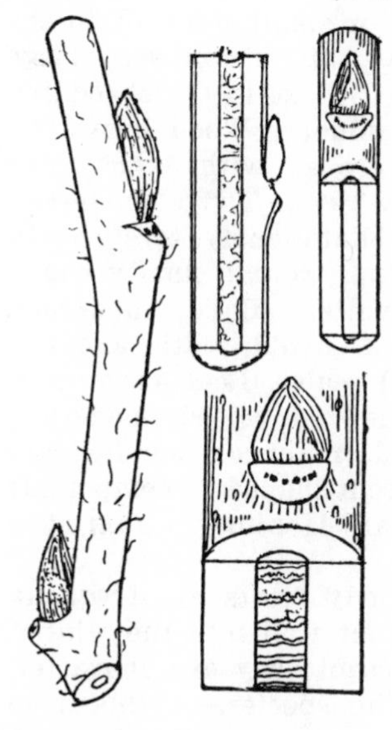

Shrubs or mostly moderate-sized trees: deciduous. Twigs moderate, terete, somewhat zigzag, red-brown, finally with evident lenticels: pith moderate, rounded, green becoming white, sometimes becoming spongy or even chambered between lace-like plates. Buds solitary, sessile, deltoid-ovoid, with 2 greatly overlapping scales, the end-bud lacking. Leaf-scars variable in position, 2-ranked on spreading branches, elsewhere 5-ranked or exceptionally sub-oppositely 4-ranked: half-elliptical, somewhat raised: bundle-trace 1, C-shaped: stipule-scars lacking.

Winter-character references:— *Diospyros kaki.* Shirasawa, 243, pl. 3. *D. Lotus.* Schneider, f. 117; Shirasawa, 243, pl. 3. *D. virginiana.* Brendel, pl. 3; Hitchcock (1), 5.

Few trees possess a more characteristic bark than the persimmon. The sometimes very regular squares into which it checks differentiate the mature tree from any other with which it is likely to occur. In contrast with this, it is unusually variable in leaf-position and in the structure of its pith, though no other tree possesses a combination of bud- and leaf-scar characters likely to be mistaken for those of *Diospyros.*

Twigs velvety or loosely hairy or glabrous: buds glabrous, blackish. D. virginiana.

HALESIA. Silver Bell. Pea-wood.
(Family Styracaceae).

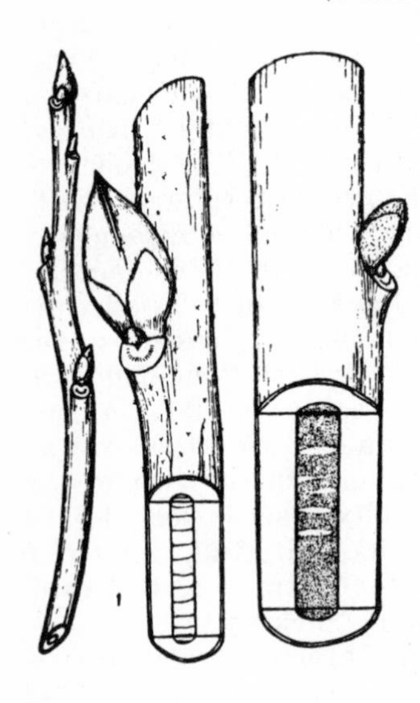

Shrubs or small trees, or in the mountains of Tennessee large trees, with striped shredding bark: deciduous. Wood brownish, diffused-porous with very fine medullary rays. Twigs moderate, at first stellate-scurfy, terete: pith rather small, round, finally chambered, white. Buds moderate, superposed, ovoid, with about 4 fleshy red scales. Leaf-scars alternate, somewhat raised, moderate, half-round, notched: bundle-trace 1, crescent-shaped, compound: stipule-scars lacking. (*Mohrodendron*).

The woody fruits are frequently persistent well into the winter. When present they are characteristic of the species,—4-winged in *H. carolina*, and 2-winged in *H. diptera*, which is not easily differentiated otherwise.

Winter-character references:—*Halesia carolina* (*H. tetraptera*). Schneider, f. 87. *H. corymbosa.* Shirasawa, 233, pl. 1. *H. hispida.* Shirasawa, 233, pl. 1.

The scaly trunk of a very large tree of *Halesia carolina* or *Mohrodendron carolinum* is pictured in connection with an account of the silver bells as timber trees (p. 601) in an instructive book on American Forest Trees, which consists substantially of articles published between 1905 and 1913 in the journal Hardwood Record, by Henry H. Gibson.

Glabrate: buds acute, slightly stalked. (1). H. carolina.
Puberulent: buds obtuse: pith less chambered. (2). H. diptera.

PTEROSTYRAX.
(Family Styracaceae).

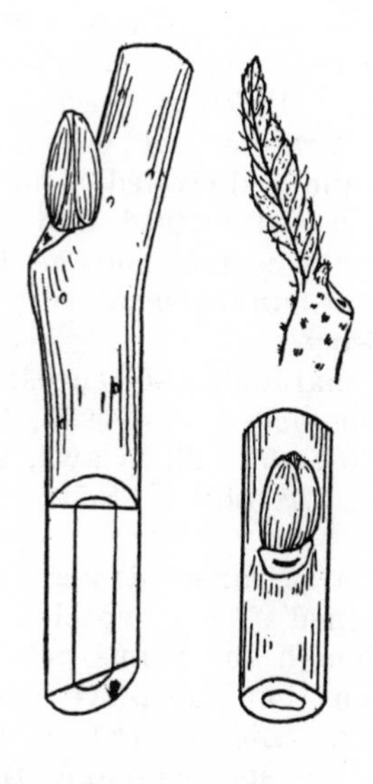

Shrubs, glabrescent or more or less microscopically stellate-scurfy: deciduous. Twigs rounded, rather slender: pith moderate, rounded, continuous, white. Buds moderate, sessile, usually solitary, the terminal elongated and hairy and naked, the lateral ovoid, glabrate, with 2 exposed scales. Leaf-scars alternate, 2-ranked, finally broadly crescent-shaped, somewhat raised: bundle-trace 1, indistinct: stipule-scars lacking.

Winter-character reference to *Pterostyrax hispida*: — Schneider, f. 87.

Pterostyrax is considered not generically different from *Halesia* by some botanists, and, as its generic name indicates, it bears winged fruits like *Halesia*. Though they do well in the South, its species are even less dependable in the North than the silver bells.

Twigs with quickly shredding gray bark. P. hispida.

STYRAX. Storax.
(Family Styracaceae).

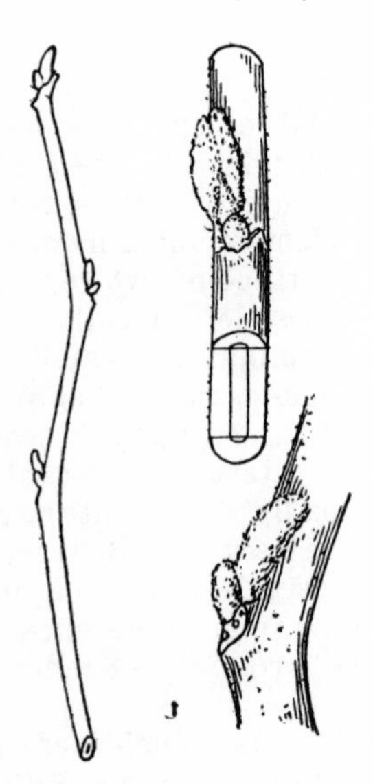

Shrubs: deciduous. Twigs rounded, rather slender, zig-zag, rough-scurfy: pith small, rounded, continuous, green. Buds small, sessile, naked, scurfy, superposed, the end-bud lacking. Leaf-scars alternate, 2-ranked, at first torn, narrow and shriveled, finally broadly crescent-shaped and less raised with a central more or less fragmented bundle-trace: stipule-scars lacking.

Winter-character references: — *Styrax japonica.* Shirasawa, 238, pl. 2. *S. Obassia.* Shirasawa, 238, pl. 2. *S. officinalis.* Schneider, f. 117.

The gum styrax of druggists is not obtained from species of *Styrax* though the genus gets its name from that substance which is produced by the Oriental equivalent, *Liquidambar orientale,* of our sweetgum which derives its specific name from the same substance.

1. Twigs very slender: buds short (scarcely 3 mm.). S. americana.
   Twigs stouter (2-3 mm.): buds rather long (4-6 mm.). 2.
2. Twigs 2 mm. thick: bark not exfoliating. (1). S. japonica.
   Twigs stouter (3 mm.): bark exfoliating. S. Obassia.

SYMPLOCOS. Sweet Leaf.
(Family Symplocaceae).

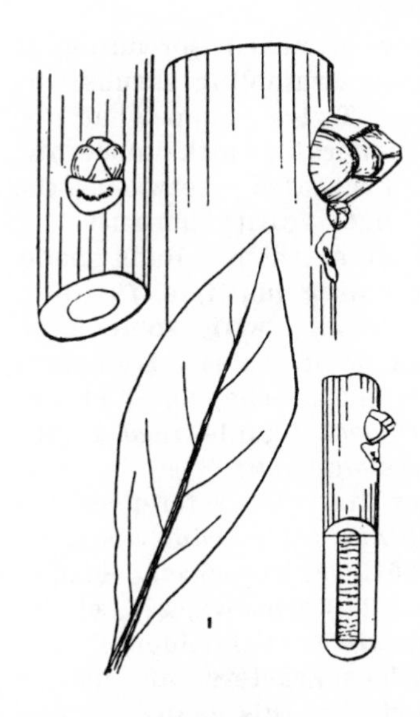

Shrub or small tree: tardily deciduous. Twigs moderate, terete: pith moderate, pale, chambered. Buds sessile, solitary or superposed, broadly conical, with about 4 scales. Leaf-scars alternate, half-round, low, bundle-trace a single crescent-shaped or transverse aggregate: stipule-scars lacking. Leaves when present oblanceolate, cuneately petioled, entire. (*Hopea*).

The chambered pith of *Symplocos*, which seems to have escaped the notice of special writers on the pith of trees, is mentioned and photographically illustrated in Hough's Handbook of the Trees of the Northern States and Canada, p. 381. The tree is evergreen in the southern part of its range, and holds its foliage until heavy frosts come elsewhere. It is sometimes called horse sugar because its sweetish leaves are eaten by stock after green herbage has generally disappeared in early winter.

End-bud absent: leaf-scars 2-ranked. S. paniculata.
End-bud present: leaf-scars more than 2-ranked.
(1). S. tinctoria.

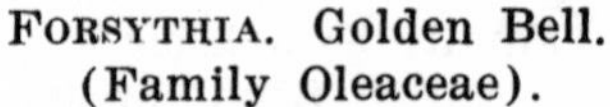

FORSYTHIA. Golden Bell.
(Family Oleaceae).

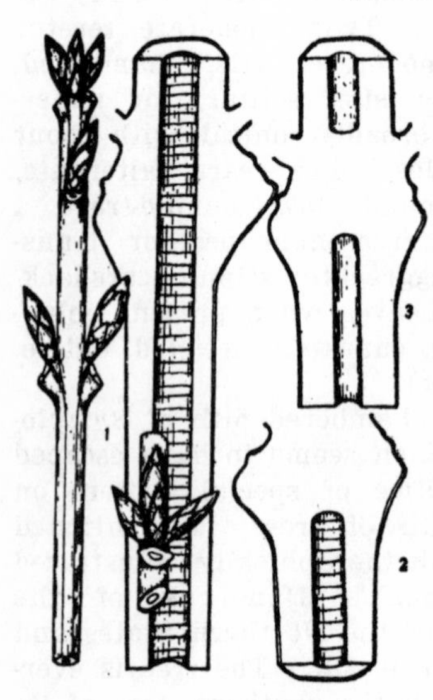

Loosely branched spreading or sometimes scrambling shrubs: deciduous. Twigs somewhat 4-sided, moderate: pith moderate, finally excavated between the nodes but continuous or chambered at them. Buds moderate, becoming multiple, fusiform though sessile, with some half-dozen pairs of scales. Leaf-scars opposite, shield-shaped, rather small, raised: bundle-trace 1: stipule-scars wanting.

Winter-character references: — × *Forsythia intermedia.* Schneider, f. 201. *F. suspensa.* Schneider, f. 201; Shirasawa, 277, pl. 12. *F. viridissima.* Schneider, f. 201. The pith-characters of species and hybrids of this genus are discussed by Koehne in Gartenflora for 1906, p. 199, f. 21.

1. Pith solid at the nodes. 2.
   Pith chambered throughout. (1). F. viridissima.
2. Pith chambered in the internodes. (2). × F. intermedia.
   Pith excavated between the nodes. (3). F. suspensa.

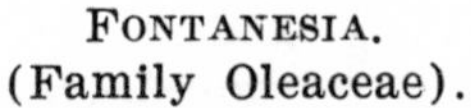

FONTANESIA.
(Family Oleaceae).

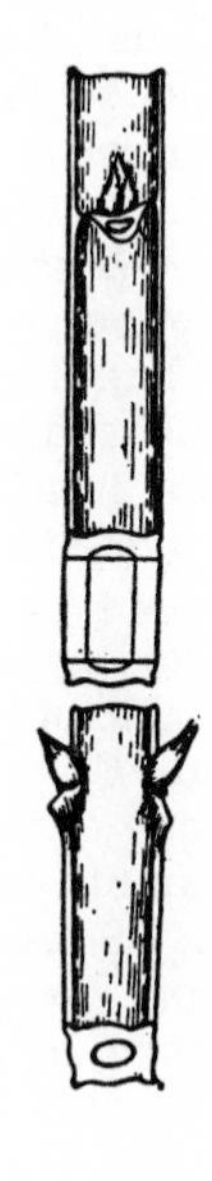

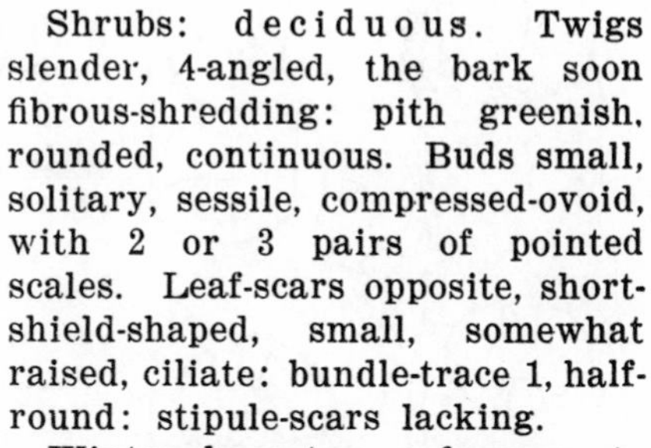

Shrubs: deciduous. Twigs slender, 4-angled, the bark soon fibrous-shredding: pith greenish, rounded, continuous. Buds small, solitary, sessile, compressed-ovoid, with 2 or 3 pairs of pointed scales. Leaf-scars opposite, short-shield-shaped, small, somewhat raised, ciliate: bundle-trace 1, half-round: stipule-scars lacking.

Winter-character reference to *Fontanesia phillyraeoides*:—Schneider, f. 205.

Fontanesias, like privets, are rather conspicuous among shrubs grown in the northern states in showing no autumnal coloration but holding their bright green foliage well through the fall,—a habit that dictates caution in unskilfully blending them in promiscuous planting.

Twigs and buds glabrous, brown. F. phillyraeoides.

FRAXINUS. Ash.
(Family Oleaceae).

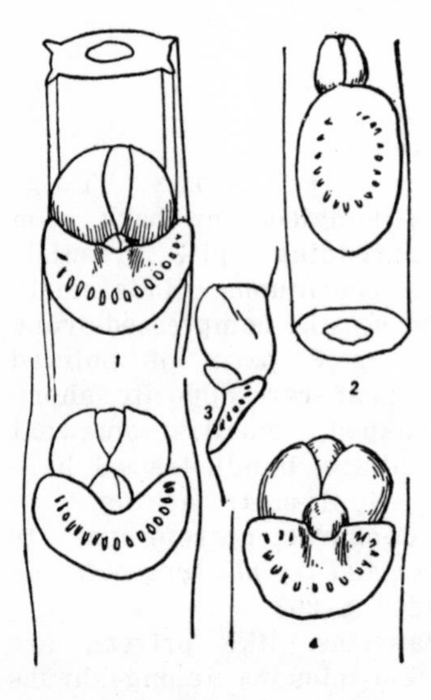

Trees: deciduous. Twigs rather stout, stiff and divergent, often squarish or compressed at the nodes: pith often 6-sided or lemon-shaped. Buds sessile, superposed with the lower somewhat covered by a narrow articular membrane, with 2 or 3 pairs of opposite scales, those of the end-bud often lobed. Leaf-scars opposite, half-round to subelliptical or broadly U-shaped, low: bundle-traces in an elliptical or C-shaped aggregate: stipule-scars lacking.

In a comparative study of reserve food materials in buds and surrounding parts published in volume 2 of the Memoirs of the Torrey Botanical Club, Halsted gives the ash as one example illustrating the accumulation of reserve starch in winter near the terminal bud. Schaar, in volume 99 of the Sitzungsberichte of the Vienna Academy, includes *Fraxinus* among genera which store food in their bud scales; and Goebel explains the color of the scales as due to the dried cell-contents of their scurf.

One species, *F. Ornus*, is spoken of sometimes as the manna ash because when wounded it exudes a sugary substance called by this name. A tree "boxed," somewhat as a pine is for turpentine, is pictured in Baillon's Dictionnaire de Botanique, vol. 2, p. 643.

Winter-character references to *Fraxinus*:—*F. americana*. Blakeslee & Jarvis, 343, 556, pl.; Brendel, pl. 1; Denniston,

Pharm. Archiv., 1:6-13, pl. 3-4; Hitchcock (1), 3; Otis, 212; Schneider, f. 198. *F. Bungeana.* Schneider, f. 197. *F. Bungeana pubinervis.* Shirasawa, 274, pl. 11. *F. excelsior.* Blakeslee & Jarvis, 343, 558; Bösemann, 61; Fant, 40, f. 37; Schneider, f. 198; Ward, 1:14, f. 6, 118, f. 59; Willkomm, 46, f. 80; Zuccarini, 9, pl. 5. *F. lanceolata* (*F. viridis*). Blakeslee & Jarvis, 343, 558; Brendel, pl. 1; Hitchcock (1), 3, (3), 16, (4), 137, f. 81-82; Otis, 216. *F. longicuspis.* Shirasawa, 274, pl. 11. *F. nigra* (*F. sambucifolia*). Blakeslee & Jarvis, 343, 560, pl.; Brendel, pl. 1; Otis, 220. *F. oregana.* Schneider, f. 197. *F. Ornus.* Bösemann, 62; Schneider, f. 198; Willkomm, 47, f. 81. *F. parvifolia.* Schneider, f. 197. *F. pennsylvanica* (*F. pubescens*). Blakeslee & Jarvis, 343, 558, pl.; Brendel, pl. 1; Hitchcock (1), 3, (3), 16; Otis, 214. *F. quadrangulata.* Brendel, pl. 1; Hitchcock (1), 3; Otis, 218. *F. Sieboldiana.* Shirasawa, 274, pl. 11.

1. Twigs acutely 4-angled: buds gray. (1). F. quadrangulata.
   Twigs not acutely angled or winged. 2.
2. Buds blue-black. 3.
   Buds brown. 7.
3. Leaf-scars vertically elliptical. (Black ash). (2). F. nigra.
   Leaf-scars half-round. 4.
4. Shrubby. F. excelsior nana.
   Trees. 5.
5. Not weeping. 6.
   Weeping. (Weeping ash). F. excelsior pendula.
6. Bark gray. (European ash). F. excelsior.
   Bark golden. (Golden-barked ash). F. excelsior aurea.
7. Leaf-scars deeply concave at top. 8.
   Leaf-scars nearly straight at top. 9.
8. Twigs very velvety. (Pumpkin ash). F. profunda.
   Twigs glabrate. (White ash). (3). F. americana.
9. Twigs glabrate. (Green ash). (4). F. lanceolata.
   Twigs velvety. (Red ash). F. pennsylvanica.

SCHREBERA.

(Family Oleaceae).

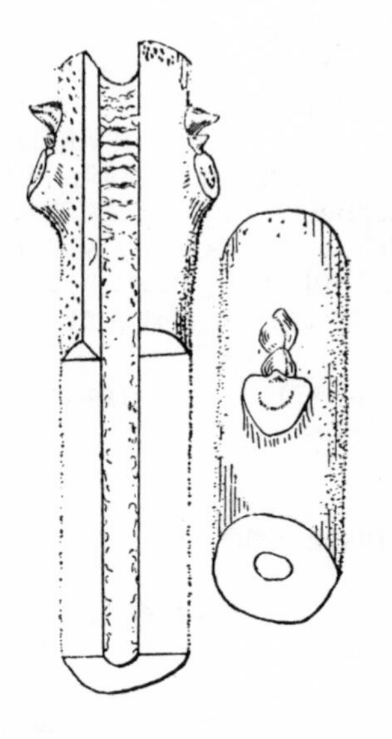

Tender trees: deciduous. Twigs slender, subterete though a little compressed and sometimes with slight decurrent lines at the nodes; pith moderate, round, white, spongily chambered at the nodes but disappearing between them. Buds small, with 2 overlapping ciliate scales. Leaf-scars opposite, obtusely shield-shaped, somewhat raised: bundle-trace 1, compound, crescent-shaped: stipule-scars lacking. (*Nathusia*).

The name of the genus *Schrebera*, which is botanically intermediate between *Forsythia* and *Syringa*, illustrates, like *Jamesia*, the conservative retention of names that have had often earlier but transient use. *Nathusia* is sometimes taken as the proper name for the present genus because the name *Schrebera*, first given it in 1798, had been used as early as 1791 for another genus not now considered to be tenable.

Twigs very minutely gray-puberulent. S. Saundersiae.

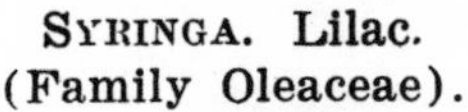

SYRINGA. Lilac.
(Family Oleaceae).

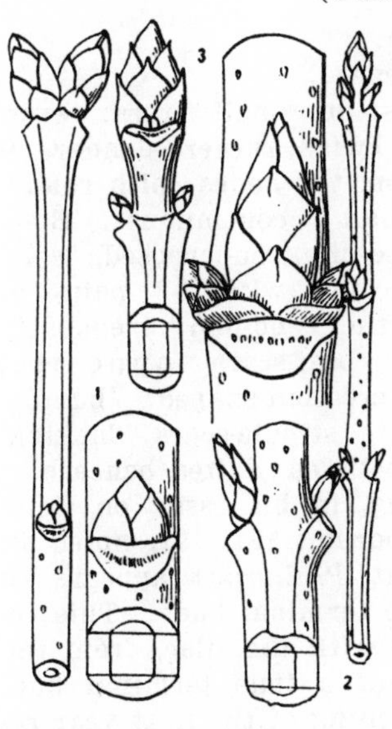

Shrubs, exceptionally tree-like: deciduous. Twigs moderate or slender, usually somewhat 4-lined or 6-sided: pith moderate, homogeneous, roundish, pale. Buds solitary or exceptionally collaterally multiple, sessile, ovoid, moderate, with about 4 pairs of scales, the end-bud frequently absent and the branches then forking. Leaf-scars opposite, crescent- or shield-shaped, raised, rather small: bundle-trace 1, transverse and compound: stipule-scars lacking.

Winter-character references: — *Syringa amurensis.* Schneider, f. 212. *S. chinensis.* Bösemann, 66; Schneider, f. 211. *S. japonica.* Schneider, f. 212; Shirasawa, 277, pl. 11. *S. josikaea.* Schneider, f. 211. *S. oblata.* Schneider, f. 210. *S. persica.* Bösemann, 66; Schneider, f. 211. *S. pubescens.* Schneider, f. 210. *S. vulgaris.* Bösemann, 66; Fant, 46, f. 51; Schneider, f. 210; Shirasawa, 277, pl. 11; Ward, 1:14, f. 5, 42, 157, f. 74; Willkomm, 46, f. 79; Zuccarini, 8, pl. 5.

1.	Buds subglobose, blunt.	S. amurensis.
	Buds ovoid. 2.	
	Buds subconical, acute. 3.	
2.	Lenticels prominent.	(3). S. villosa.
	Lenticels not prominent.	(1). S. vulgaris.
3.	Bud-scales fleshy.	S. chinensis.
	Buds quickly drying.	(2). S. persica.

PHILLYRAEA.
(Family Oleaceae).

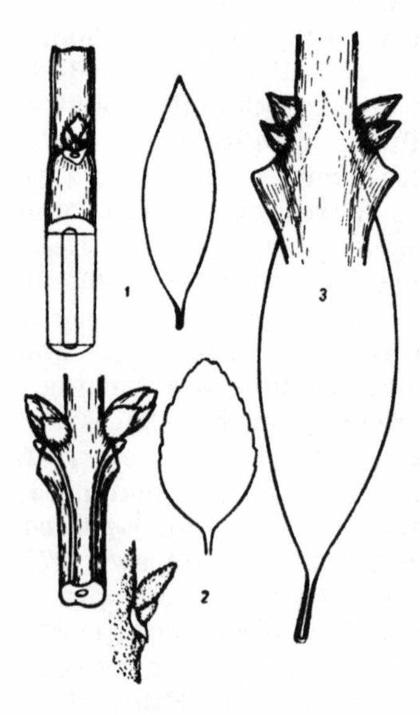

Shrubs or small trees: evergreen. Twigs rather slender, 4-lined from the nodes: pith roundish, small, continuous. Buds small, sessile, superposed, compressed-ovoid, with 1-3 pairs of scales, the end-bud frequently lacking. Leaf-scars opposite, raised, crescent-shaped: bundle-trace 1: stipule-scars lacking. Leaves petioled, dotted beneath.

Loefling, in his essay on Gemmae Arborum, 191, 197, noted in 1749 that *Phillyraea* appears to have two terminal buds. This results, as with the lilac, from the absence of a true terminal bud, the branching of the next year resulting from the development of the uppermost pair of axillary buds.

1. Exposed bud-scales 2, valvate. 2.
   Exposed scales 4 or 6: leaves lanceolate. (1). P. angustifolia.
2. Buds and twigs pubescent: leaves small, toothed. (2). P. media.
   Glabrous: leaves larger (8-10 cm.), entire. (3). P. decora.

OSMANTHUS. Fragrant Olive.
(Family Oleaceae).

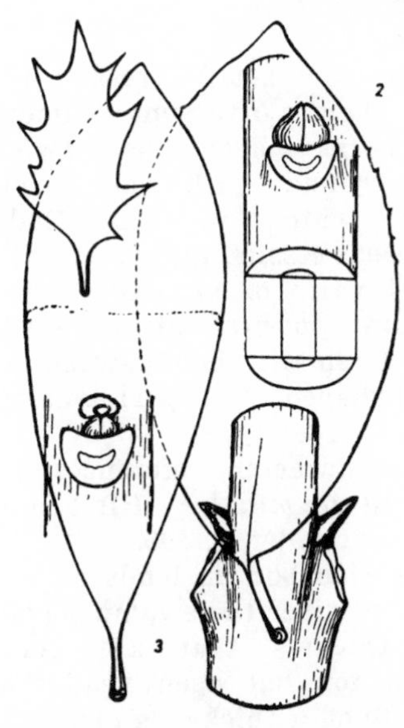

Shrubs or small trees: evergreen. Twigs moderately slender, rounded or 4-lined from the nodes: pith angular or roundish, pale, continuous. Buds small, sessile, sometimes superposed, with a pair of valvate scales. Leaf-scars opposite, broadly crescent-shaped, somewhat raised: bundle-trace 1, crescent-shaped: stipule-scars lacking. Leaves simple, coriaceous, sometimes pungently toothed.

Osmanthus Aquifolium bears considerable resemblance to an evergreen holly and is sometimes cultivated as a holly; but it may be recognized readily by its opposite leaves, those of *Ilex* being alternate. *O. fragrans*, like the related jessamines, emits an intense and penetrating fragrance which gives its common name to the genus.

1. Leaves small (5-7 cm.), typically toothed. (1). O. Aquifolium.
   Leaves larger, subentire. 2.
2. Leaves elliptical, somewhat denticulate. (2). O. fragrans.
   Leaves oblanceolate, entire, revolute. (3). O. americanus.

FORESTIERA. Swamp Privet.
(Family Oleaceae).

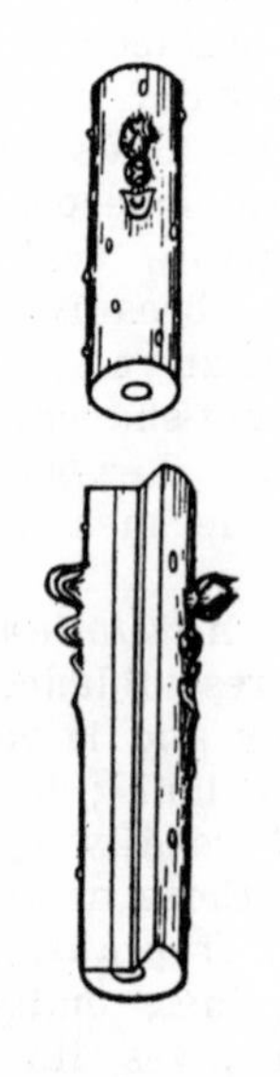

Shrubs or small trees with many short divergent almost spiny twigs: deciduous. Twigs slender, round: pith small, continuous, white, rounded. Buds superposed, sessile, globose, small, with 2-4 pairs of exposed scales. Leaf-scars opposite, shield-shaped, low and small: bundle-trace 1, crescent-shaped: stipule-scars lacking. (*Adelia*).

Winter-character references to *Forestiera acuminata*:—Hitchcock (1), 3; Schneider, f. 205.

In the rich bottom lands of the Mississippi river the swamp privet makes thickets that are very dense at top but open near the ground. Such a thicket is pictured (pl. 10) by S. M. Coulter in a discussion of various types of swamps in volume 15 of the Report of the Missouri Botanical Garden.

Twigs glabrous or puberulent, warty. F. acuminata.

CHIONANTHUS. Fringe Tree.
(Family Oleaceae).

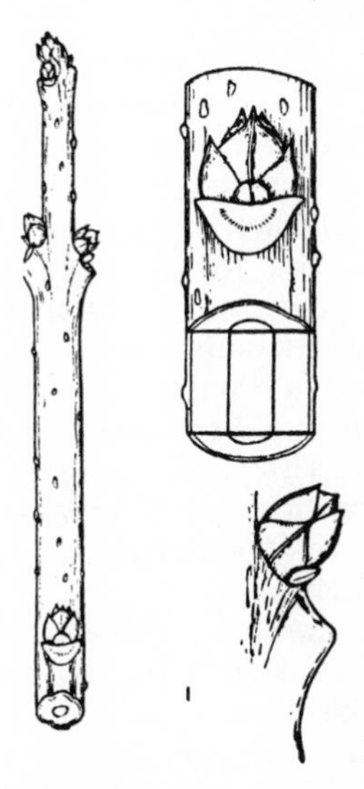

Shrubs or small trees: deciduous. Twigs moderate, more or less 4-sided: pith moderate, homogeneous, roundish, white. Buds often superposed, sessile, round-ovoid, rather small, with about 3 pairs of pungently pointed keeled scales. Leaf-scars opposite, crescent-shaped, raised, rather small: bundle-trace 1, transverse, compound: stipule-scars lacking.

Winter-character references: — *Chionanthus retusa.* Shirasawa, 274, pl. 11. *C. virginica.* Schneider, f. 205.

An excellent contrast between the woods of closely related genera is afforded by the cross sections of the strongly ring-porous wood of *Fraxinus* (p. 385), the weakly ring-porous wood of *Chionanthus* (p. 401) and the diffused-porous wood of *Forestiera* (p. 403), as illustrated in Hough's uniquely "photo-descriptive" Handbook of the Trees of the Northern States and Canada.

Buds ovoid, buff: scales short-pointed. (1). C. virginica.
Buds subconical, dark: scales often long-attenuate. C. retusa.

OLEA. Olive.
(Family Oleaceae).

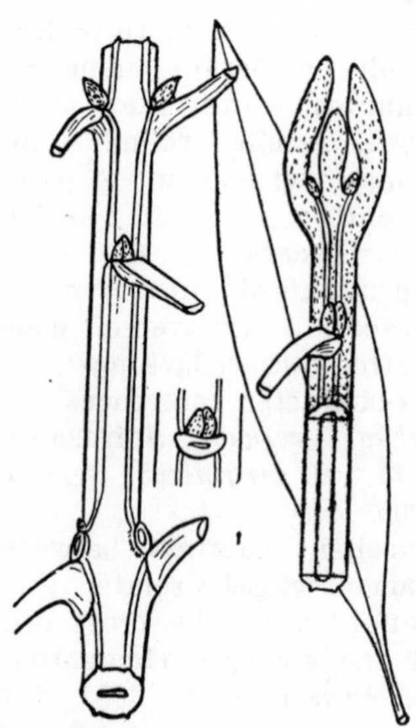

Small trees, sometimes with spiny twigs: evergreen. Twigs slender, more or less 4-lined from the nodes, or quadrangular, microscopically peltate-scurfy like the buds and the lower leaf-surface. Buds solitary, or occasionally 2 superposed, sessile, ovoid, naked but the valvate outer leaves simulating scales. Leaf-scars broadly crescent-shaped, little raised, small: bundle-trace 1, transverse: stipule-scars lacking. Leaves simple, entire.

Winter-character reference: — *Olea europaea Oleaster* (*O. Oleaster*). Bösemann, 49. Malpighi figured the buds of the olives as early as 1687, in his Opera Omnia, p. 22, pl. 9.

1. Spiny: leaves oblong, gray beneath. O. europaea Oleaster.
   Unarmed: leaves lanceolate, acute. 2.
2. Leaves gray beneath. (Common olive). O. europaea.
   Golden-scurfy. (Golden-leaved olive).
   (1). O. europaea chrysophylla.

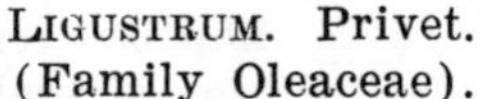

LIGUSTRUM. Privet.
(Family Oleaceae).

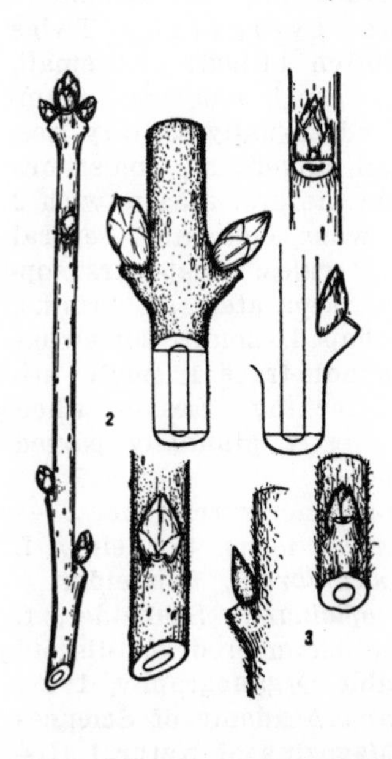

Shrubs: deciduous, but holding their foliage late, or more or less evergreen where winters are mild. Twigs slender, rounded, or 4-ridged below the nodes: pith moderate, white, homogeneous. Buds sometimes superposed, sessile, ovoid, small, usually with 2 or 3 pairs of exposed scales. Leaf-scars opposite or the pairs sometimes divided, crescent-shaped or transversely elliptical, raised, small: bundle-trace 1, transverse: stipule-scars lacking. Leaves, when present, simple, entire.

Winter-character references: — *Ligustrum Ibota.* Shirasawa, 276, pl. 11. *L. ovalifolium.* Schneider, f. 201. *L. vulgare.* Bösemann, 66; Fant, 44, f. 47; Schneider, f. 60, 201; Ward, 1:174, f. 86; Willkomm, 44, f. 78.

1. Scar as broad as bud: glabrous. (1). L. ovalifolium.
   Leaf-scars at first narrow: deciduous. 2.
2. Scales attenuate: twigs rather hairy. 3.
   Scales at most acute: twigs barely velvety. (2). L. vulgare.
3. Tall, with outcurving branches. 4.
   Low, with horizontal branches. (3). L. Ibota Regelianum.
4. Lenticels low: pubescence sometimes short. L. Ibota.
   Lenticels prominent: pubescence long. L. amurense.

JASMINUM. Jessamine.
(Family Oleaceae).

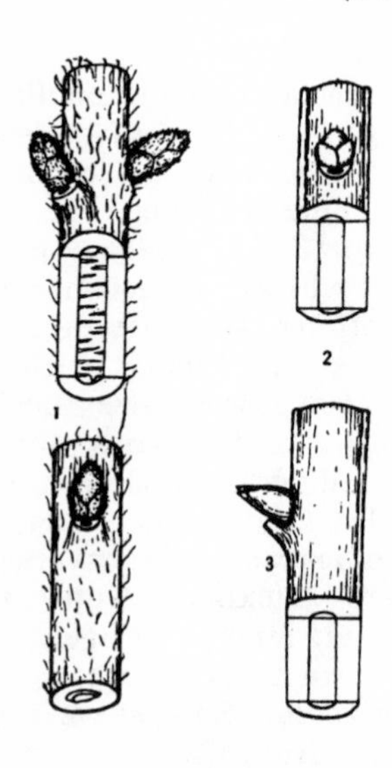

Shrubs, tender in the North, often scrambling or climbing: sometimes evergreen. Twigs slender, often 4-lined: pith small, roundish, continuous or chambered. Buds usually solitary, sessile, small, divergent, sometimes developing the first season, with 2 or 3 or, when elongated, several pairs of scales. Leaf-scars opposite, or separated in 4-ranks, crescent-shaped, small, somewhat raised; bundle-trace 1, small: stipule-scars lacking. Leaves, when present, mostly pinnately parted or compound.

Winter-character references: — *Jasminum fruticans.* Schneider, f. 115. *J. nudiflorum.* Schneider, f. 115. *J. officinale.* Schneider, f. 115. The chambered or discoid pith is noted by de Candolle, Vegetable Organography, 1:48; Foxworthy, Proceedings of the Indiana Academy of Sciences for 1903, 192; Morren, Annals and Magazine of Natural History, 4:84, ul. 2; and Solereder, Systematic Anatomy, 1:525.

1. Twigs terete: pith spongy, becoming chambered. 2.
   Twigs acutely 4-lined, glabrous: pith continuous. 4.
2. Very hairy: climbing. 3.
   Glabrate: loosely scrambling. J. officinale.
3. Pubescence white. J. Sambac.
   Pubescence rusty. (1). J. pubescens.
4. Buds globose, with broad blunt scales. (3). J. humile.
   Buds and their scales acute. (3). J. grandiflorum.

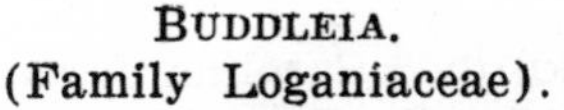

BUDDLEIA.
(Family Loganiaceae).

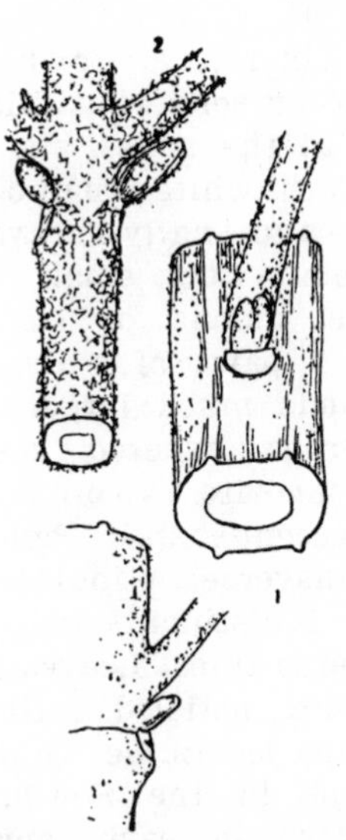

Soft-wooded shrubs or half-shrubs: deciduous. Stems more or less strongly 4-ridged, rather slender, puberulent or yellow-woolly or glabrescent: pith relatively large, white, continuous. Buds sessile, sometimes superposed and the upper commonly developing the first season, oblong, with a pair of exposed scales. Leaf-scars opposite, half-round or triangular, small, low: bundle-trace 1, roundish: stipule-scars transversely connected.

Winter-character reference to *Buddleia japonica*:—Schneider, f. 125.

Buddleias, which are coming into popularity for cultivation under glass as well as in the open, belong to a group of rather pithy and soft-wooded or suffruticose plants, untidy in winter unless cut back, of which *Vitex*, *Callicarpa* and *Caryopteris* are other examples.

Stems gray-puberulent: buds small. (1). B. Davidii.
Stems yellow-tomentose: buds larger (5 mm.). (2). B. nivea.

GELSEMIUM. Carolina Jessamine.
(Family Loganiaceae).

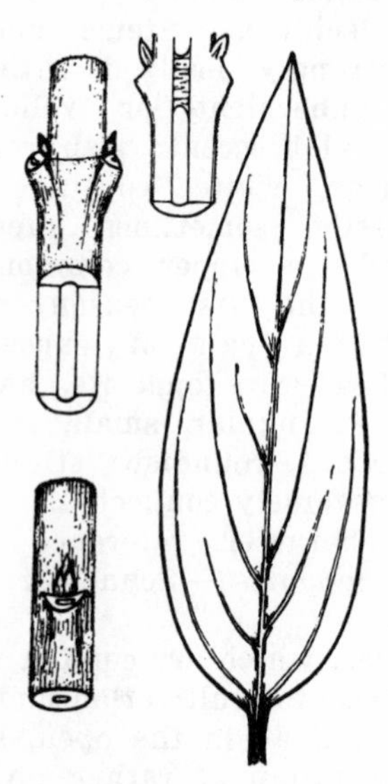

Woody twiners: evergreen. Stems terete or somewhat dilated and angled at the nodes, slender, branched: pith white, chambered at the nodes and finally excavated between them. Buds small, solitary, sessile, oblong or conical, with about 2 pairs of scales, or the flower-buds much larger and with numerous exposed scales. Leaf-scars opposite, somewhat elevated, crescent-shaped: bundle-trace 1, transverse: stipule-scars minute and indistinct, connected by a transverse line. Leaves lanceolate or ovate, petioled, entire.

The Carolina jessamine, which is tender except in the South, is very attractive in early spring when its fragrant yellow flowers expand. Its roots are of medicinal value. Strychnine is the product of another member, *Strychnos*, of the same family.

Stems purplish, puberulent. G. sempervirens.

CARISSA. Amatungulu.
(Family Apocynaceae).

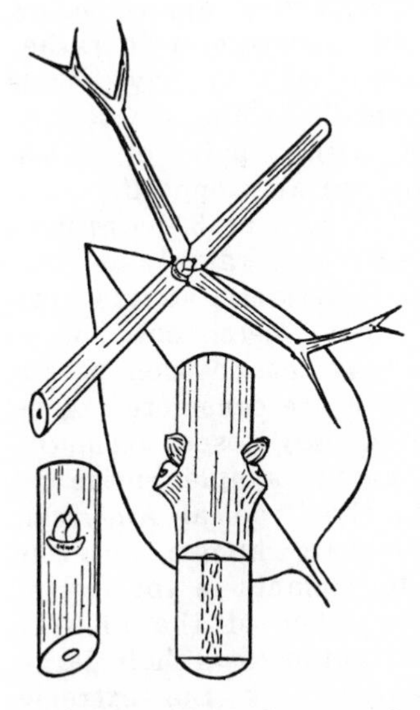

Shrubs with milky sap, usually with many forking axillary terete spines: evergreen. Twigs terete: pith moderate, spongy. Buds solitary, sessile, small, ovoid, with 1 or 2 pairs of exposed scales, or, when spines are present, these are above the axillary buds. Leaf-scars lacking. Leaves simple, entire.

Carissa Arduina, as *C. bispinosa* is usually called, is familiar in greenhouses and is grown out-of-doors in parts of the South for its large fragrant white flowers. The branches of its regularly forking spines are produced from the axils of small leaf-scars corresponding in arrangement to the opposite foliage leaves, the end-bud being abortive.

Glabrous: branches green, glossy: leaves deltoid-ovate.
C. bispinosa.

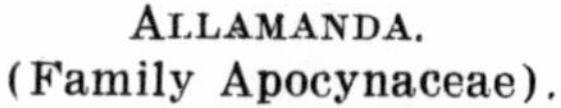

ALLAMANDA.
(Family Apocynaceae).

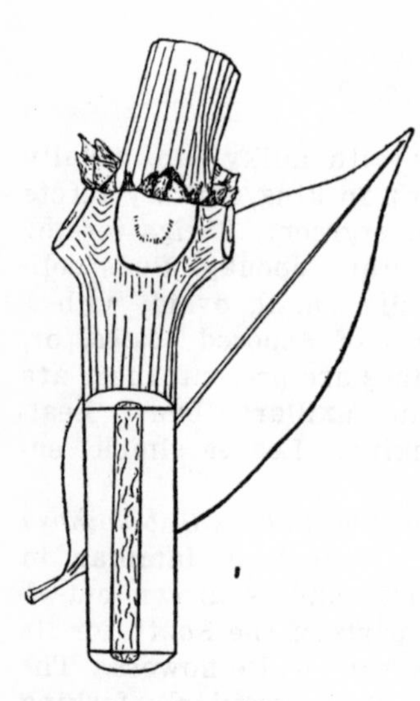

Tender usually scrambling shrubs with milky sap: evergreen. Stems green or reddened, obtusely somewhat angled below the leaves, moderate: pith rather large, roundish, spongy. Buds rather small, solitary, sessile, roundish, with 2 pairs of scales. Leaf-scars variably opposite or in whorls of 3 or 4 or 5, half-round or half-elliptical, raised: bundle-trace 1, indistinct: stipule-scars lacking, but persistent outer scales occupy the position of stipules, which are considered to be characteristically absent from the family. Leaves simple, entire.

Though the Tropical American allamandas are known only as conservatory plants in the North, in one or other of the distinct forms that are collectively named *A. cathartica*, their large yellow flowers are familiar everywhere. In the extreme South, they make effective and showy covering for trellises, etc.

1. Bushy. A. neriifolia.
   Climbing. 2.
2. Slender: flowers purple. A. violacea.
   Moderately stout: flowers yellow. (1). A. cathartica.

TRACHELOSPERMUM. Star Jasmine.
(Family Apocynaceae).

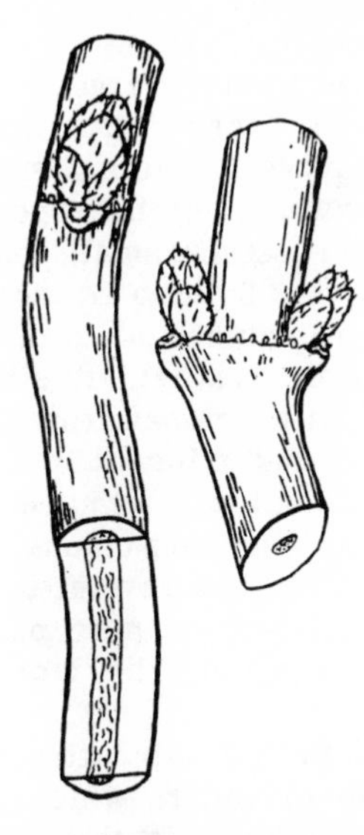

Tender twining shrubs with milky sap: evergreen. Stems terete, moderate, red-brown: pith round, spongy. Buds rather small, solitary, ovoid, sessile, appressed, with several fleshy scales. Leaf-scars opposite, raised, half-round or broadly crescent-shaped: bundle-trace 1, C-shaped: stipule-scars connected by a transverse line. Leaves elliptical to lanceolate, acute at both ends, entire. (*Rhynchospermum*).

The genus *Trachelospermum* is represented in the coastwise native flora from Delaware to Texas by the climbing dogbane, which is slightly woody. The star jasmine or jessamine—the Confederate jessamine of the reconstruction period of the South—gets its common name from its star-shaped very fragrant flowers. Like allamandas and bougainvilleas, it is grown often in bushy masses under glass, though a strong climber out-of-doors.

Leaves green, often granular beneath. T. jasminoides.
Leaves variegated with yellow. T. jasminoides variegatum.

NERIUM. Oleander.
(Family Apocynaceae).

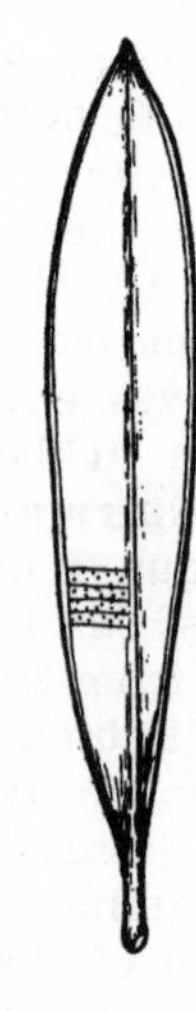

Shrubs or small trees with milky sap: evergreen. Twigs moderate, more or less 3-sided: pith moderate, irregular, spongy. Buds solitary, sessile, small, rounded with 2 or 3 exposed scales. Leaf-scars in whorls of 3 or opposite, broadly triangular, slightly notched, little raised, the axils tomentulose and fringed: bundle-trace 1, rounded: stipule-scars lacking. Leaves lance-oblong, entire, firm, slightly revolute, the lower surface with minute pubescent pits in which the stomata are grouped.

Notwithstanding its attractive flowers, the oleander, which has made itself at home in the Southwest, is regarded with disfavor as being poisonous. This aspect of the plant is presented by Wilson in Bulletin 59 of the Arizona Agricultural Experiment Station.

Branches green and puberulent, becoming glabrous.

N. Oleander.

PERIPLOCA. Silk Vine.
(Family Asclepiadaceae).

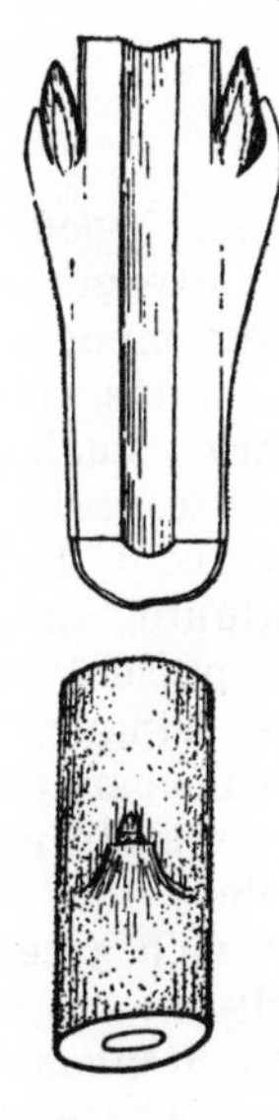

Soft-wooded twiners with milky sap: deciduous. Stems terete, moderate: pith round, excavated. Buds rather small, solitary, nearly concealed by the leaf-bases. Leaf-scars opposite, raised, shriveled or elliptical with a single crescent-shaped bundle-trace: stipule-scars lacking.

Winter-characters of *P. graeca* are figured by Schneider, f. 109.

Several herbaceous milkweeds are twining plants and become troublesome weeds when they get a foothold in orchards or beside fence-posts where it is hard to dislodge their strong perennial roots. The silk vine, which is the only woody representative of the family that is hardy well into the North, is a strong climber.

A technical distinction between the closely related families Apocynaceae and Asclepiadaceae is found in the powdery or granular pollen of the former and the coherent pollinia of the latter, familiar to every student of milkweed pollination and to every close observer of bees and other insects, to which the pollen masses become attached. In *Periploca* these pollinia are less firm than in most genera of the family. A typographic slip in one case has caused the apocynaceous pollen to be called glandular, tempting one to parallel Engelmann's impatient exclamation when what he wrote for glutinous pollen apeared in type as gelatinous, "but who ever heard of gelatinous pollen?"

Stems glabrescent from somewhat puberulent. P. graeca.

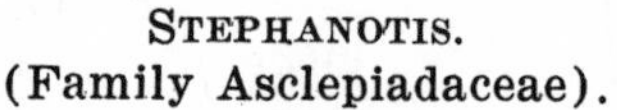

STEPHANOTIS.
(Family Asclepiadaceae).

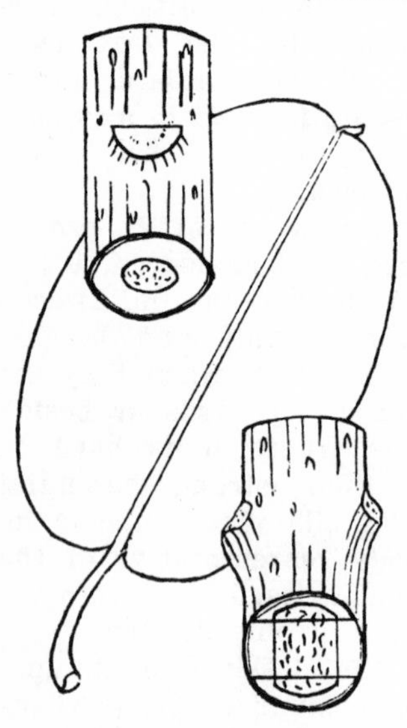

Tender twining woody plants with milky sap: evergreen. Stems somewhat 4-sided, moderate: pith angled, spongy. Buds (often suppressed) solitary, small, naked. Leaf-scars opposite, raised, half-round: bundle-trace 1, indistinct: stipule-scars minute and round, or the stipules present as small points. Leaves simple, entire, petioled, grooved near the apex, and with a few minute glands at top of the petiole.

Because of its rich green leaves and, particularly at night, very fragrant flowers, *Stephanotis* is a popular climber where the climate permits its cultivation.

No phase of out-of-doors botany exceeds in interest the study of pollen interrelations between flowers and certain groups of insects and Knuth's compendious Handbuch der Blütenbiologie affords a ready key to understanding many queer floral structures besides giving a meaning to those that are most familiar.

Glabrous: twigs green and glossy. S. floribunda.

CLERODENDRON.

(Family Verbenaceae).

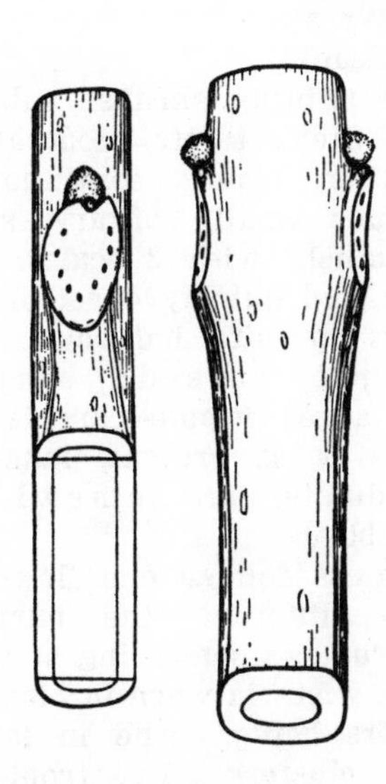

Soft-wooded loosely branched shrubs: deciduous. Twigs more or less obscurely 4-sided, moderate: pith relatively large, roundish, white, continuous. Buds small, superposed but the lower often concealed by the leaf-scar, and the upper developing the first season, round-ovoid, indistinctly few-scaled. Leaf-scars opposite or sometimes in whorls of 3, elliptical but the produced top notched, rather low: bundle-traces about 9, more or less aggregated in a U-shaped series: stipule-scars lacking.

Winter-characters of *Clerodendron trichotomum* are described and figured by Schneider, f. 191; and Shirasawa, 269, pl. 10.

Twigs gray-buff, glabrescent: buds violet. C. trichotomum.

Winter-characters of *Ehretia acuminata* are given by Shirasawa, 237, pl. 2; and of *E. serrata*, by Schneider, f. 84. The genus is placed in the family Boraginaceae.

PETRAEA. Purple Wreath.
(Family Verbenaceae).

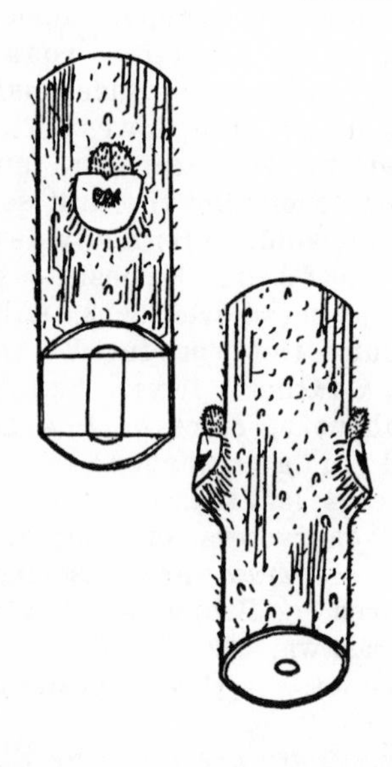

Tender twining shrubs: subdeciduous. Stems terete, moderate: pith rather small, continuous, pale. Buds small, solitary, sessile, roundish, with 2 scales, or an upper bud quickly developing. Leaf-scars opposite, half-round or shield-shaped, raised: bundle-trace 1, large: stipule-scars lacking. Leaves, if present, lanceolate, undulate, or somewhat toothed above.

Though its foliage and flowers are very different, the purple wreath produces something of the effect of a wistaria when in bloom, the flowers being borne in long hanging clusters. In tropical countries it is frequent as a covering of tree-trunks and hanging from the eaves of houses.

Somewhat pubescent: cortex cracking below. P. volubilis.

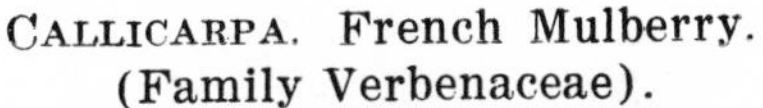

CALLICARPA. French Mulberry.
(Family Verbenaceae).

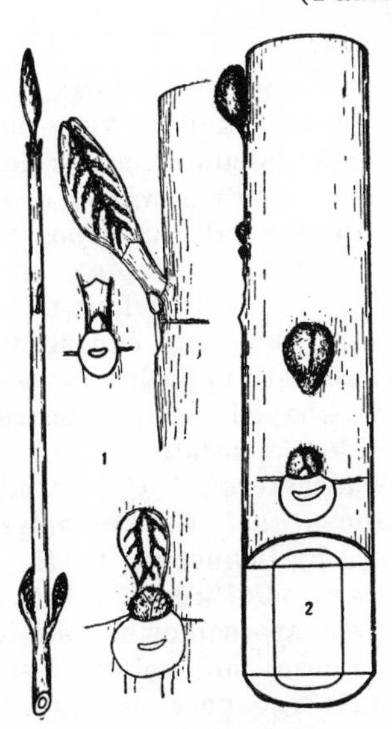

Rather small and soft-wooded shrubs: deciduous. Twigs round or obscurely 4-sided, slender, more or else stellate-scurfy: pith relatively large, rounded, white, continuous. Buds small, superposed, often distinctly stalked or the uppermost developing the first season, round or fusiform-oblong, naked or the smaller appearing to have 2 nearly valvate scales. Leaf-scars opposite or the pairs often irregularly separated in 4 ranks, broadly crescent-shaped: stipule-scars lacking.

Winter-character references:—*Callicarpa japonica.* Schneider, f. 191; Shirasawa, 269, pl. 10. *C. mollis.* Shirasawa, 269, pl. 10. *C. purpurea.* Shirasawa, 269, pl. 10.

1. Buds fusiform or oblong: twigs gray-buff. (1). C. japonica.
   Buds subglobose: twigs dingy straw-color. 2.
2. Twigs glabrescent. (2). C. purpurea.
   Twigs persistently scurfy. C. americana.

CARYOPTERIS.
(Family Verbenaceae).

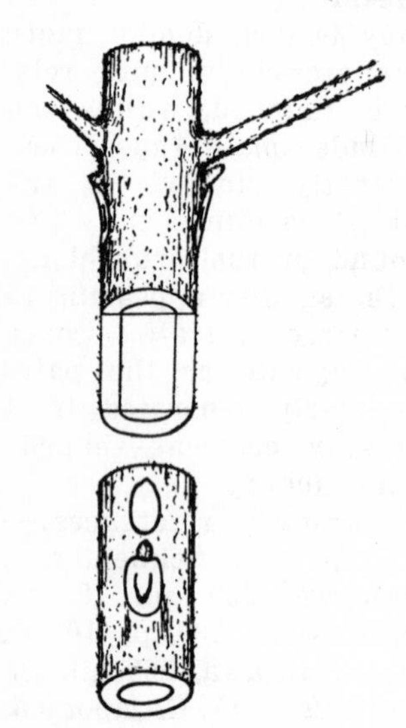

Small, soft-wooded shrubs: deciduous. Twigs round or very obscurely 4-sided, slender: pith relatively large, rounded, white, continuous. Buds small, superposed, the upper often developing the first season, round-conical, with 1 or 2 pairs of indistinct canescent scales. Leaf-scars opposite, broadly crescent-shaped: stipule-scars lacking. (*Mastacanthus*).

Winter-characters of *C. incana* (*C. Mastacanthus*, *C. sinensis*) are pictured by Schneider, f. 122.

Caryopteris, L*Callicarpa*,L *Vitex* and *Buddleia* are somewhat similar suffruticose or soft-wooded genera differing more in detail than in general winter appearance.

Twigs gray-puberulent. C. incana.

VITEX. Chaste Tree.
(Family Verbenaceae).

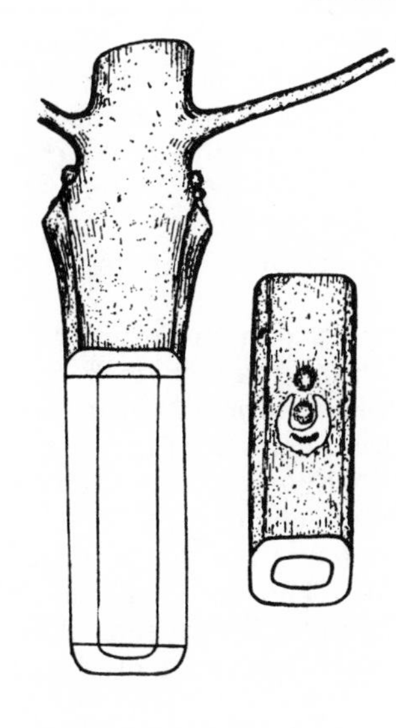

Soft-wooded peppery-aromatic shrubs or half-shrubs: deciduous. Stems compressed at the nodes, quadrangular with obtuse or flattened angles, rather slender: pith relatively large, more or less angled, white, continuous and homogeneous. Buds superposed, sessile or the upper commonly developing the first season, subglobose, the 1 or 2 pairs of leaf-rudiments or scales concealed in pubescence. Leaf-scars opposite, U-shaped, rather small, low; the surface usually torn and the solitary bundle-trace indistinct: stipule-scars lacking.

Winter-character references:—*Vitex Agnus-castus.* Schneider, f. 191. *V. Negundo.* Shirasawa, 270, pl. 10. *V. trifolia unifoliolata.* Shirasawa, 270.

Stems gray-puberulent. V. Agnus-castus.

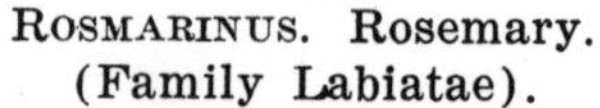

ROSMARINUS. Rosemary.
(Family Labiatae).

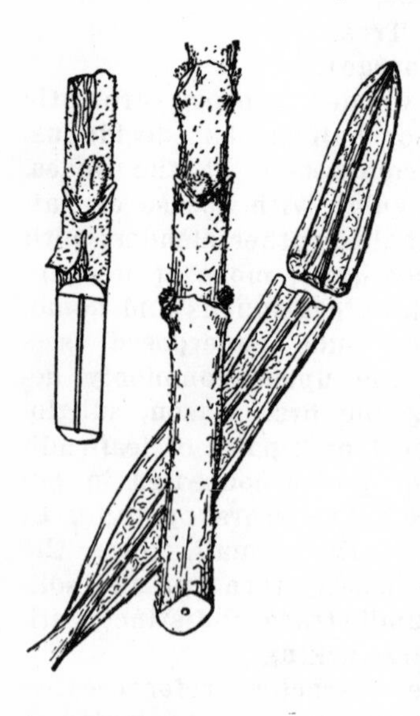

Small savory half-shrubs: deciduous. Twigs moderate, obscurely 4-sided: pith minute. Buds small, solitary, round and sessile or quickly becoming oblong and somewhat stalked or developing into leafy shoots. Leaf-scars opposite, deeply U-shaped. somewhat raised: bundle-traces 3, often not discernible: stipule-scars lacking.

Rosemary is one of a number of labiates that may or may not be considered as woody, according to one's predilection. Like sage, hyssop and thyme it is of more interest as a component of the kitchen garden than as a decorative plant. The fact that most such plants are herbaceous has given the word herbs an old-fashioned popular usage as their collective name.

Stellate-tomentulose: inner bark lace-like. R. officinalis.

Winter-character references to other suffruticose Labiatae:—*Hyssopus officinalis.* Schneider, f. 224. *Phlomis fruticosa.* Schneider, f. 224. *Salvia officinalis.* Schneider, f. 224. *Thymus vulgaris.* Schneider, f. 224.

LYCIUM. Matrimony Vine.
(Family Solanaceae).

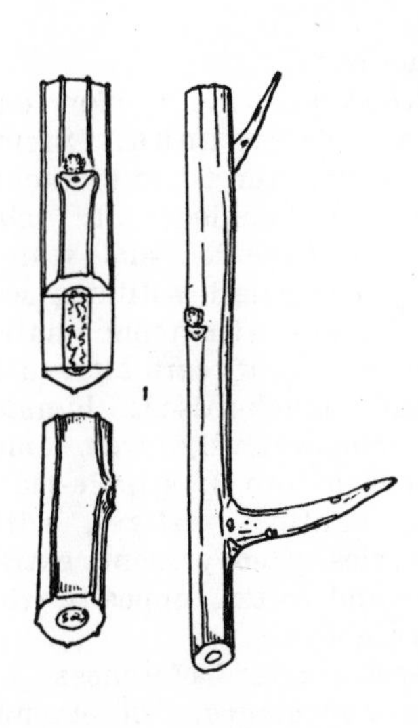

Spreading or (often high) scrambling shrubs with spinescent twigs: deciduous. Twigs slender, 5-angled, glabrous, often whitish or short-striate: pith moderate, spongy. Buds small and inconspicuously multiple, or developing into very dwarf aggregates, subglobose, indistinctly scaly. Leaf-scars alternate, crescent-shaped, small, somewhat raised: bundle-trace 1: stipule-scars lacking.

Winter-character references: — *Lycium chinense*. Shirasawa, 235. *L. halimifolium* (*L. barbarum* of common usage; *L. vulgare*). Bösemann, 51; Schneider, f. 83.

The bushy southwestern lyciums, in common with condalias, ceanothuses, etc., enter into the composition of chaparral.

1. Intricately branched bushes of the Southwest. 2.
   Loosely branched, sometimes scrambling. 3.
2. Twigs straight, gray. L. californicum.
   Twigs zig-zag, buff. L. parviflorum.
3. Wide-spreading or scrambling. (1). L. chinense.
   Bushy, with moderate shoots. 4.
4. Twigs red-brown, with fissured gray surface. L. pallidum.
   Twigs pale. 5.
5. Axils slightly hairy. (Garrambullo). L. Torreyi.
   Without hairs in the axils. 6.
6. Cultivated everywhere. (Matrimony vine). L. halimifolium.
   Wild, in the South. L. carolinianum.

SOLANUM.

(Family Solanaceae).

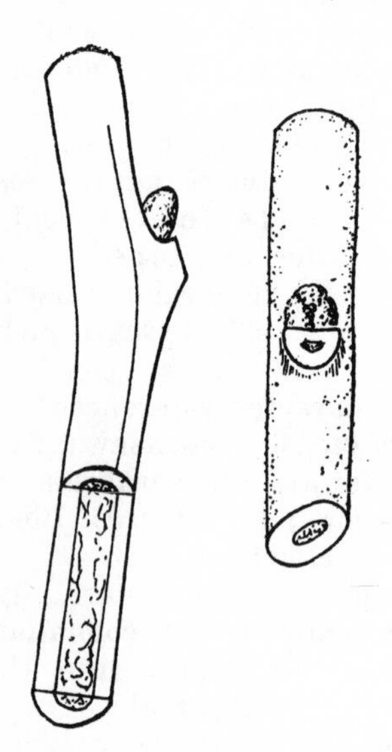

Soft-wooded twiners (for our purposes): deciduous. Stems rather slender, terete or tortuously somewhat 3-angled: pith relatively large, greenish and white, spongy. Buds small, solitary, sessile, subglobose, with about 4 hairy blunt scales. Leaf-scars alternate, half-round, much-raised: bundle-trace 1, comparatively large, sometimes broken into 3: stipule-scars lacking. Panticle-vestiges, with dried berries often present, extra-axillary and often opposite the leaf-scars above.

Winter-character references: — *Solanum Dulcamara.* Bösemann, 40; Fant, 12, f. 7; Schneider, f. 83.

Notwithstanding its rather succulent stem, the bittersweet is one of the hardiest climbers. Its berries are reputed poisonous if eaten and some of the most active alkaloids are derived from the Solanaceae; but the tomato, potato and egg plant are produced by species of the genus *Solanum* to which the bittersweet belongs.

Stems olivaceous, glabrate. (Bittersweet). S. Dulcamara.

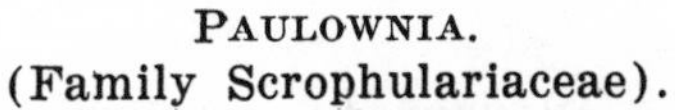

PAULOWNIA.
(Family Scrophulariaceae).

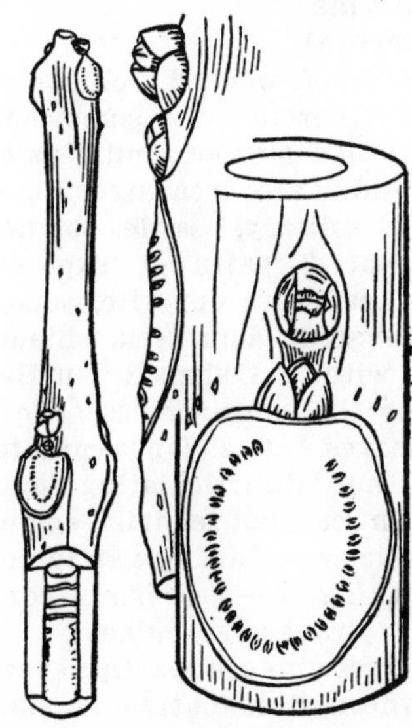

Moderate-sized trees: deciduous. Twigs stout, resembling those of *Catalpa*, compressed at the nodes: pith large, white, roundish, chambered or hollowed out between the nodes. Buds superposed, sessile, half-round, with about 4 exposed blunt scales, the end-bud lacking. Leaf-scars opposite, subelliptical, more or less notched at top, raised: bundle-traces many in a nearly closed and sometimes almost continuous ellipse: stipule-scars lacking. The rather large ovoid capsules persistent.

Winter-character references: — *Paulownia tomentosa* (*P. imperialis*). Schneider, f. 200; Shirasawa, 281, pl. 12.

The compact wood of *Paulownia* is said to be a favorite for making tea boxes in Japan, retaining the aroma of the tea well.

Paulowina tomentosa is not hardy in the northern interior where, if at all, it is seen usually in the form of strong large-leaved suckers from the persistent roots, but it is one of the conspicuous trees in front of the Smithsonian building in Washington, and has been used as a street tree as far north as Brooklyn near the coast.

Minutely velvety. (Imperial tree). P. tomentosa.

BIGNONIA. Cross Vine.
(Family Bignoniaceae).

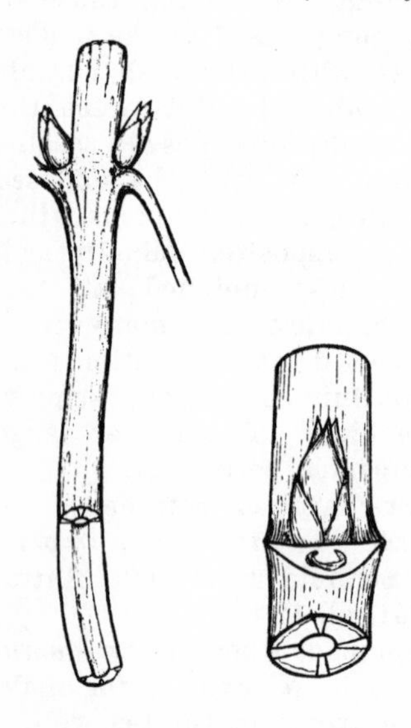

Rather soft-wooded climbers. Stems subterete or somewhat fluted, rather slender: pith pale, spongy and finally excavated. Buds moderate, solitary, sessile, oblong, with about 3 pairs of exposed scales. Leaf-scars opposite, somewhat elevated, depressed shield-shaped, with 1 C-shaped bundle-trace: or the more or less evergreen leaves, of 2 lance-cordate leaflets, not disarticulating and ending in coiling tendrils sometimes thickened at tip: stipule-scars lacking, the leaf-bases connected by transverse ridges.

The cross-vine is partly evergreen where it is native or successfully grown. Its common name refers to the intrusion of four large rays into its wood,—one of the many abnormalities that are seen in lianas, as high-climbing stems are called in the tropics. A comprehensive account of such stems is contained in Schenck's Beiträge zur Biologie und Anatomie der Lianen, published in 1893.

Glabrous except about the nodes. B. capreolata.

CAMPSIS. Trumpet Creeper.
(Family Bignoniaceae).

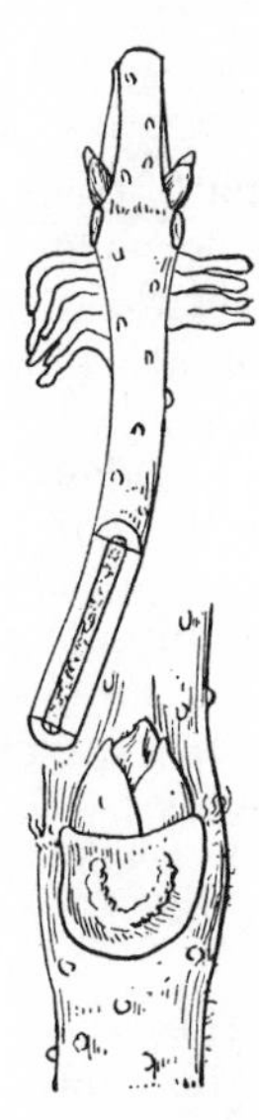

Straggling shrubs, usually climbing, often by aerial roots emitted in double bands from below the nodes: deciduous. Stems subterete, moderately slender, warty: pith pale, rounded, continuous or progressively disappearing from the nodes. Buds rather small, mostly solitary, sessile, triangular, compressed, ascending, with 2 or 3 pairs of exposed scales. Leaf-scars opposite, shield-shaped, low: bundle-trace 1, C-shaped, compound: stipule-scars lacking, but the leaf-scars connected by hairy transverse ridges. (*Tecoma*).

Winter-character references: — *Campsis chinensis*. Schneider, f. 200. *C. radicans*. Brendel, 28, pl. 1; Schneider, f. 200.

The trumpet creeper, which is native as far north as middle Illinois, is one of the most vigorous and tropical-appearing of hardy climbers. Its flowers are among the most brilliant and largest of those borne by such plants and, like most other American flowers with large red tubular flowers containing a great deal of nectar, are pollinated by humming birds whose visits afford another reason for planting such vines as this and the trumpet honeysuckle.

1. Glabrous, climbing. C. chinensis.
   Puberulent or scabrid. 2.
2. Climbing, with abundant roots. (1). C. radicans.
   Bushy. C. radicans speciosa.

CHILOPSIS. Desert Willow.
(Family Bignoniaceae).

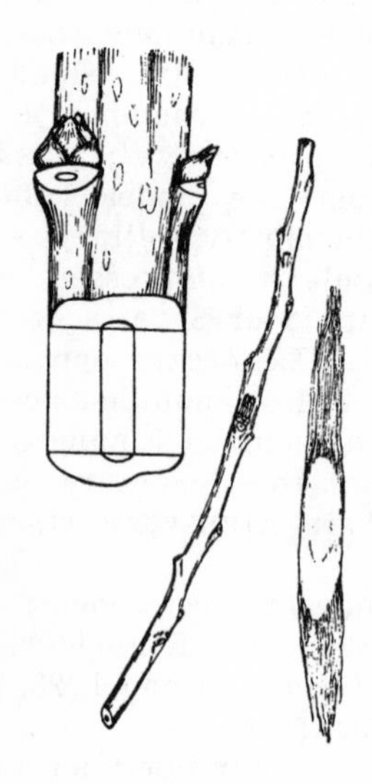

Shrub or small tree: deciduous. Twigs slender, ridged below the leaf-scars: pith rather small, rounded, continuous, white. Buds solitary, sessile, small, subglobose, with some 3 or 4 pointed scales swollen at base, the end-bud lacking. Leaf-scars 6-ranked, in whorls of 3 or in pairs, or scattered singly, small, half-elliptical, raised: bundle-trace 1, transverse: stipule-scars lacking. The long terete pods, with seeds ciliate at the ends as in *Catalpa*, persist in winter.

Chilopsis is the southwestern equivalent of the northeastern catalpas, and like them, though not in the same profusion, produces large and showy flowers. It is scarcely hardy north of St. Louis in the interior, and like the catalpa is of rather irregular open habit; but its slender willowy twigs and narrow leaves give it a grace entirely lacking to its coarser relative. Somewhat mealy: lentcels conspicuous. C. saligna.

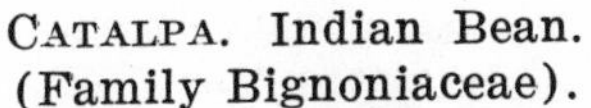

CATALPA. Indian Bean.
(Family Bignoniaceae).

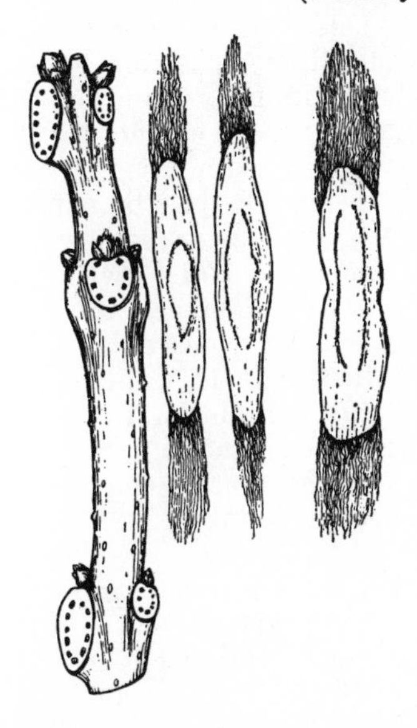

Small or moderate-sized trees: deciduous. Twigs stout, round: pith large, round, continuous, pale. Buds solitary, sessile, globose, with some half-dozen rather loose pointed scales, the end-bud lacking. Leaf-scars in whorls alternately of two large scars and one small scar, and one large scar and two small scars, round-elliptical, raised; bundle-traces a dozen or so, compound, in an ellipse: stipule-scars lacking. The long terete pods, with thin ciliate seeds, persist, and afford important specific characters.

Winter-character references: — *Catalpa bignonioides* (*C. syringaefolia; C. Catalpa*). Blakeslee & Jarvis, 562; Bösemann, 67; Brendel, 28, pl. 1; Otis, 226; Schneider, f. 15, 199. *C. ovata* (*C. Kaempferi*). Schneider, f. 179; Shirasawa, 280, pl. 12. *C. speciosa*. Blakeslee & Jarvis, 329, 562, pl.; Hitchcock (3), 16; Otis, 224; Schneider, f. 199.

1. Twigs and fruits (5 mm.) slender. (1). C. ovata.
   Twigs and capsules stouter. 2.
2. Capsules moderate (8 mm.): seeds pointed. (2). C. bignonioides.
   Capsules thick (10 mm.): seeds truncate. (3). C. speciosa.

TECOMA. Yellow Elder.
(Family Bignoniaceae).

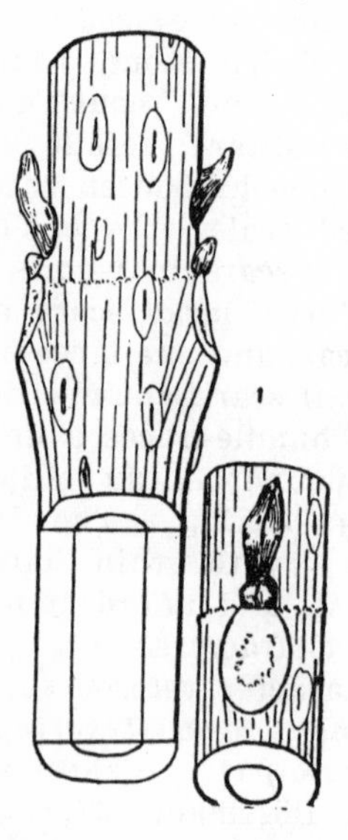

Soft-wooded shrubs or half-shrubs: deciduous. Stems somewhat quadrangularly compressed at the nodes, rather slender: pith relatively large, roundish, pale brown, continuous. Buds superposed with the upper somewhat stalked, flattened-ovoid, with 2 exposed scales. Leaf-scars opposite, elliptical, or concave at top, low: bundle-trace 1, compound, following the contour of the leaf-scar; stipule-scars lacking, but the leaf-scars transversely connected by puberulent lines. (*Stenolobium.*).

Numerous misunderstandings seem to have arisen as to the earlier generic limitations established in the Bignoniaceae, and the trumpet creeper, now called *Campsis*, is still known to most people as *Tecoma*, while these low bushy plants are coming to be known as species of *Stenolobium*. They are not hardy in the North, but their compound leaves and large yellow flowers give them an attractive appearance in the Southwest. Apparently they produce medicinally active organic compounds.

Glabrous: twigs brown, with orange lenticels. (1). T. stans.
Gray-tomentulose. T. mollis.

PINCKNEYA. Georgia Bark.
(Family Rubiaceae).

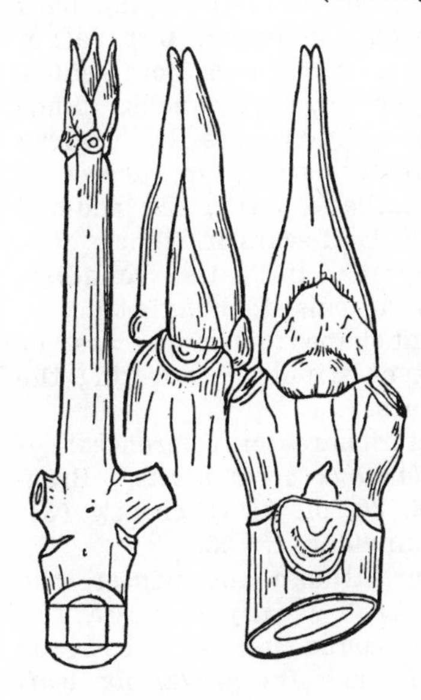

Shrubs, or somewhat arborescent: deciduous. Twigs rather stout, terete: pith round, very white, continuous. Buds solitary, sessile, ovoid and small or the terminal irregularly conical and enlarged, with 1 or 2 pairs of exposed scales. Leaf-scars opposite, crescent-shaped to angularly isodiametric, at first much raised: bundle-trace 1, crescent- or C-shaped, compound: stipule scars or membrane connecting the leaf-scars.

A century ago *Pinckneya pubens* possessed considerable repute in the South as a specific for malarial fevers. The common name Georgia bark comes from this use of the bitter bark. The genus is related to *Cinchona*, the source of quinine, and it was thought at one time that Peruvian or cinchona bark might find a rival in Georgia or pinckneya bark. Twigs from villous glabrescent. P. pubens.

CEPHALANTHUS. Button Bush.
(Family Rubiaceae).

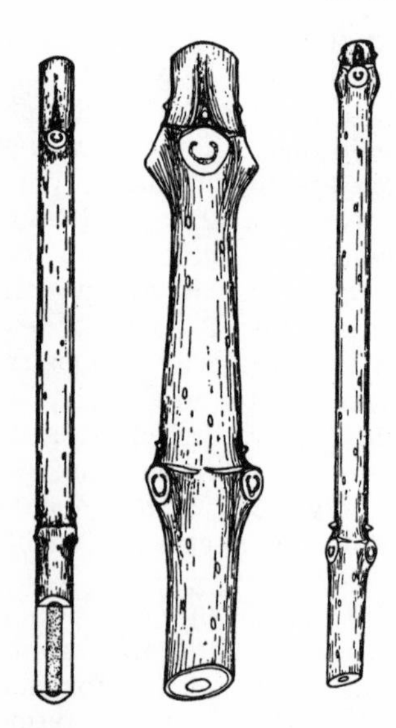

Rather slender openly branched shrubs: deciduous. Twigs round, slender, floriferous or dying back at the end, glabrous: pith rather small, more or less 4-or 6-sided, light brown, continuous. Buds mostly solitary, sessile, conical, indistinctly scaly, in depressed supra-axillary areas, the end-bud lacking. Leaf-scars in whorls of 3, or opposite in pairs, roundish, somewhat raised: bundle-trace 1, crescent-shaped: stipule-scars or persistent stipules connecting the leaf-scars.

Winter-character references: — *Cephalanthus occidentalis.* Brendel, 28, 30, pl. 1; Hitchcock (3), 16; Schneider, f. 223.

Even through the winter, the button bush usually carries at the ends of its branches some of the round inflorescence-heads that have given it its common name. Its prevailing leaf-arrangement appears to be whorled, but many plants with opposite leaf-scars are found. In this respect it parallels *Deutzia*, *Diervilla* and *Hydrangea*: but in these genera the opposite arrangment seems to be the more characteristic, and the whorled the exceptional.

Twigs reddish and glossy. C. occidentalis.

GARDENIA. Cape Jessamine.
(Family Rubiaceae).

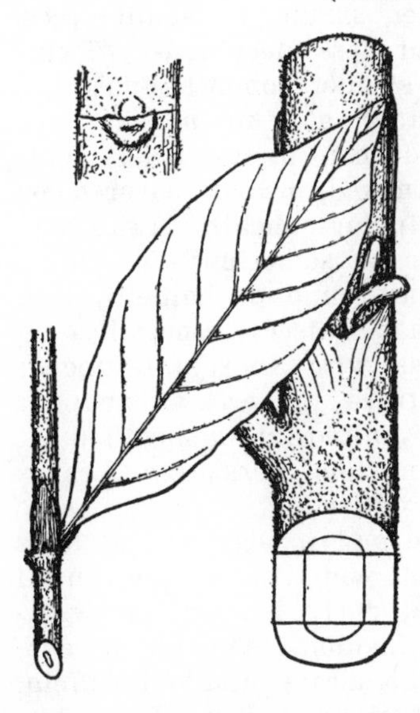

Shrubs: evergreen. Twigs moderate, rounded or finally 4-sided: pith relatively large, somewhat crenately angled, green, continuous. Buds small and naked within a supra-axillary sheath or with a single enveloping scale when terminal. Leaf-scars opposite or in whorls of 3, slightly raised, small, half-round; bundle-traces 7, the central one large and crescent-shaped. Leaves nearly sessile, with their stipules connate in a tube above each node.

The sheathing stipules of *Gardeni florida* are shown by Lubbock, On Buds and Stipules, f. 133.

Though gardenias are known in the North only as conservatory plants, their fragrant large white flowers are handled by florists to a considerable extent in winter. In the South they are favorite out-of-door plants. Unless the flowers are removed, they fail to fall promptly, and neglected plants become untidy as neglected perpetual-flowering roses do.

Twigs harsh-pubescent: leaves very glossy above.
G. jasminoides.

COFFEA. Coffee.
(Family Rubiaceae).

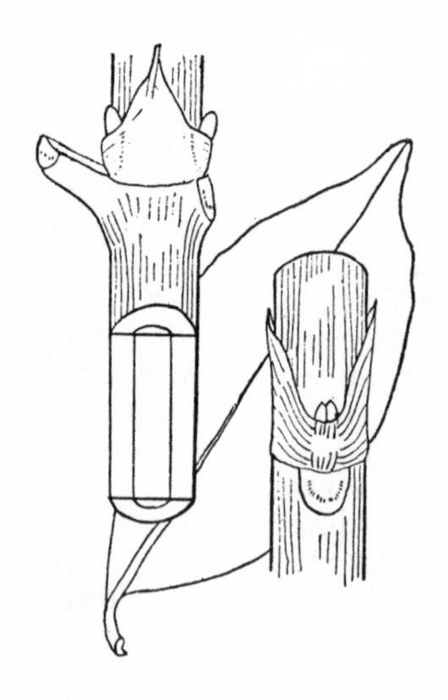

Tender shrubs or small trees, more or less deciduous. Twigs rather slender, somewhat flattened or dilated at the nodes: pith roundish, continuous, pale. Buds small, naked, nearly covered by the stipular sheath. Leaf-scars opposite or sometimes in whorls of 3, half-round or half-elliptical, somewhat raised, especially on branches with short internodes: bundle-trace 1, crescent-shaped: stipules united into a sheath about the stem, long persisting. Leaves simple, entire.

Coffee and tobacco are perhaps the most widely used unessential luxuries derived from the vegetable kingdom. Though it contains the active alkaloid caffein, now obtained largely from tea-leaves, it is not commonly conceded by those whose breakfast or dinner would be considered impossible without it that they are seeking the stimulus afforded by coffee, any more than those who follow the meal by tobacco admit that they are in quest of its sedative effect.

Glabrous: stipular-sheath 2-pointed. C. arabica.

DIPELTA.
(Family Caprifoliaceae).

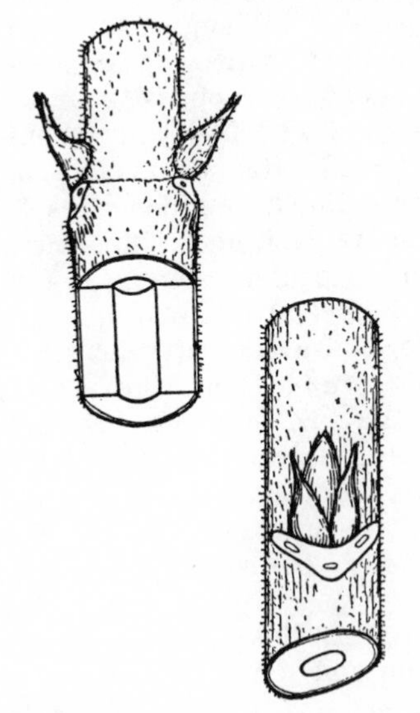

Shrubs with exfoliating bark: deciduous. Twigs rather slender, rounded: pith pale, moderate, becoming excavated between the nodes. Buds solitary, sessile, conical or ovoid, at first with 2 alternate scales but later becoming more open. Leaf-scars opposite, crescent-shaped or 3-lobed, moderate, low, transversely connected: bundle-traces 3: stipule-scars lacking.

Dipeltas, unlike weigelias, to which they are closely related and which are seen everywhere and have been in cultivation for a very long time, are rather tender, of recent introduction, and not commonly planted.

Twigs glandular-pubescent. D. ventricosa.

DIERVILLA.
(Family Caprifoliaceae).

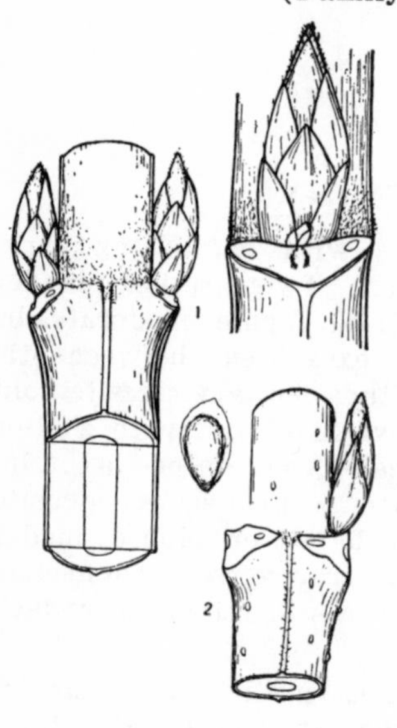

Shrubs: deciduous. Twigs terete, straw-colored or brownish, with 2 or 4 often crisp-puberulent ridges decurrent from the nodes, moderate: pith moderate, pale, continuous. Buds often superposed, sessile, oblong, appressed, with about 5 pairs of exposed scales. Leaf-scars opposite or occasionally in whorls of 3, crescent-shaped, moderate, connected by transverse lines: bundle-traces 3: stipule-scars lacking. The linear 2-valved capsules persist. (Includes *Weigelia*).

Winter-character references: — *Diervilla grandiflora*. Shirasawa, 279, pl. 12. *D. japonica*. Schneider, f. 216; Shirasawa, 279, pl. 12. *D. rosea*. Bösemann, 64. *D. sessilifolia*. Schneider, f. 216. *D. Lonicera* (*D. canadensis; D. trifida; Lonicera Diervilla*). Schneider, f. 216.

1. Lower scales very much shorter than the bud. 2.
   Lower scales nearly as long as the bud. (Asiatic). 4.
2. Twigs villous. D. rivularis.
   Twigs glabrescent or merely velvety. 3.
3. Twigs scarcely lined: capsule slender-beaked: sepals setaceous. D. Lonicera.
   Twigs 4-ridged: capsule with shorter beak and relatively short and broad sepals. (1). D. sessilifolia.
4. Calyx with an evident tube. D. florida.
   Sepals linear, distinct to the base. (2). × D. hybrida.

VIHURNUM. Arrow wood.
(Family Caprifoliaceae).

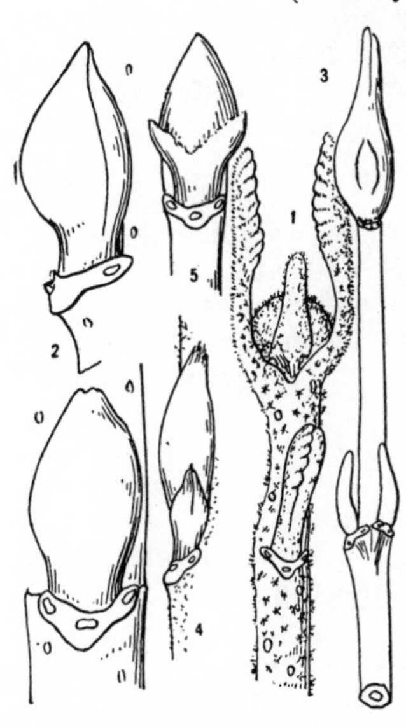

Shrubs or occasionally small trees: deciduous except for a few tender species. Twigs moderate or rather slender, more or less 6-sided: pith moderate, round or somewhat 6-sided, white or browning, continuous. Buds solitary or very exceptionally superposed, mostly stalked, ovoid, or oblong, without scales (1) or with a pair of mostly connate scales (2, 3), or with one (4, 5) or rarely several pairs of separate exposed scales. Leaf-scars opposite, crescent-shaped or exceptionally broad, sometimes ciliate at top, often raised and meeting or transversely connected: bundle-traces 3: stipule scars lacking.

Winter-character references: — *Viburnum dentatum*. Brendel, pl. 1. *V. dilatatum*. Shirasawa, 273, pl. 11. *V. furcatum*. Shirasawa, 269, pl. 10. *V. Lantana*. Bösemann, 57; Schneider, f. 192; Ward, 1:70, f. 49, 165, f. 80; Willkomm, 3, 9, 49, f. 88; Zuccarini, 28, pl. 15. *V. Lentago*. Brendel, pl. 1; Hitchcock (1), 3; Otis, 228; Schneider, f. 192. *V. Opulus*. Bösemann, 57; Fant, 45, f. 50; Lubbock, On Buds and Stipules; Schneider, f. 192; Shirasawa, 270, pl. 10; Ward, 1:168, f. 82; Willkomm, 9, 10, 11, 49, f. 87; Zuccarini 27 pl. 15. *V. phlebotrichum*. Shirasawa, 277, pl. 12. *V. prunifolium*. Hitchcock (1), 3. *V. Sieboldii*. Shirasawa, 273, pl. 11. *V. tomentosum*. Shirasawa, 273, pl. 11. *V. Wrightii*. Shirasawa, 274, pl. 11.

On winter-characters some species of *Viburnum* are easily

confused with *Cornus* and *Acer*, though in each genus some species stand out unmistakably as belonging to it. The native high-bush cranberry, *V. americanum*, not too easily distinguished in summer from its European counterpart, *V Opulus*, is believed by some nurserymen to differ from the later in golden rather than brown or reddish winter twigs.

1. Evergreen. 2.
   Deciduous. 6.
2. Leaves entire or denticulate: more or less pubescent. 3.
   Leaves usually distinctly toothed: glabrous. 5.
3. Leaves neither woolly nor impressed-veiny. 4.
   Leaves impressed-veiny, tomentose beneath. V. rhytidophyllum.
4. Glabrate or the leaves ciliate. V. Tinus.
   Hirsute. V. rigidum.
5. Leaves crenate: twigs slender. V. suspensum.
   Leaves serrate to subentire: twigs stouter. V. odoratissimum.
6. End buds naked, stellate-scurfy, like the twigs. 7.
   Buds scaly. 11.
7. Leaf-scars very broad: twigs glossy-purple. V. alnifolium.
   Leaf-scars narrow: twigs dull, usually brown. 8.
8. Dwarf: twigs slender (scarcely 3 mm.), glossy. V. Carlesii.
   Tall: twigs stouter (4-5 mm.). 9.
9. Twigs soon gray. V. macrocephalum.
   Twigs brownish straw-colored. 10.
10. Scurf at first dense: lenticels prominent. (1). V. Lantana.
    Scurf sparse: lenticels inconspicuous. V. cotinifolium.
11. Leaf-scars broad, meeting. V. Sieboldii.
    Leaf-scars relatively narrow. 12.
12. Scales closely valvate or connate as a closed sac. 13.
    Outer scales parted, mostly short. 22.
13. Buds ovoid-globose, green, or red. 14.
    Buds typically subovoid, stellate-scurfy. V. tomentosum.
    Buds oblong or flask-shaped, mostly appressed, scurfy. 17.

14. Dwarf. 15.
 Tall. 16.
15. Buds round-ovoid: native. V. pauciflorum.
 Buds oblong-ovoid: cultivated. V. Opulus nanum.
16. Twigs glabrous. (2). V. Opulus.
 Twigs more or less bristly. V. Sargentii.
17. Buds very red-scurfy. V. rufidulum.
 Buds brown, becoming lead-colored. 18.
18. Twigs often short, rigidly spreading: buds smooth. 19.
 Twigs mostly elongated and flexuous. 20.
19. Southern: buds very small. V. obovatum.
 Northern: buds nearly as in the next. V. prunifolium.
20. Buds smooth, quickly lead-colored. (3). V. Lentago.
 Buds rather loosely peltately brown-scurfy. 21.
21. Twigs dull: northern. V. cassinoides.
 Twigs rather glossy: southern. V. nudum.
22. Twigs and buds hispid. 23.
 Not hispid, though sometimes sparingly hairy. 24.
23. Twigs very hairy, rather stout (3-4 mm.). V. dilatatum.
 Twigs sparsely hispid, slender (2-3 mm.). V. erosum.
24. Bark freely exfoliating. V. molle.
 Bark not exfoliating. 25.
25. Buds stalked, rather small or slender. 26.
 Buds sessile, plump and rather large. 29.
26. Bud-scales 4: buds appressed. 27.
 Bud-scales often 6: buds plump, spreading. V. pubescens.
27. Lower scales short: twigs mostly pubescent.
 (4). V. acerifolium.
 Lower scales often reaching the middle of the bud. 28.
28. Twigs somewhat stellate-hairy. V. venosum.
 Twigs not stellate: scars ciliate. (5). V. dentatum.
29. Twigs purple. V. hupehense.
 Twigs olive, becoming gray. 30.
30. Lower scales nearly half the lenth of bud. V. theiferum.
 Lower scales nearly as long as bud. V. Wrightii.

SYMPHORICARPOS.
(Family Caprifoliaceae).

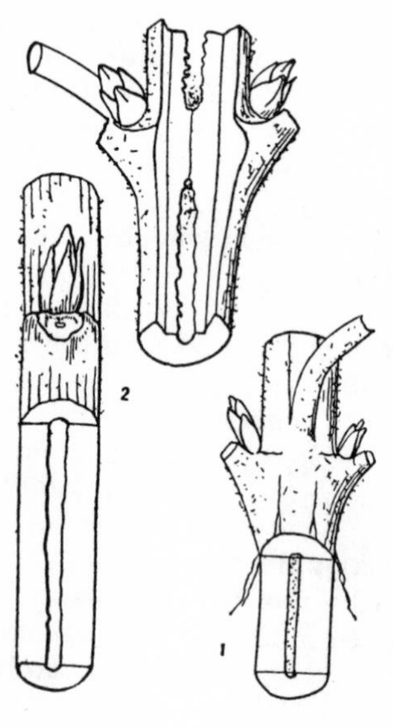

Rather small shrubs: deciduous. Twigs round, slender, more or less pubescent: pith small, round, somewhat brownish, usually excavated. Buds small, solitary or collaterally multiple or developing lateral branches the first season, ovoid-oblong, more or less compressed, sessile, with about 3 pairs of keeled scales. Leaf-scars opposite, half-round, small and mostly torn, raised, partly connected by transverse ridges: bundle-trace 1, indistinct: stipule-scars lacking.

Winter-character references: — *Symphoricarpos orbiculatus* (*S. vulgaris; Lonicera Symphoricarpos*). Hitchcock (3), 16, (4), 137, f. 80; Schneider, f. 196. *S. racemosa*. Bösemann, 66; Schneider, f. 196.

Like the related genus *Lonicera*, *Symphoricarpos* presents the phenomenon of two types of pith, excavated and continuous, in different groups of species that are referred to it; in this respect recalling *Jasminum*, some species of which have a continuous pith, while the pith is exquisitely chambered in others.

1. Pith continuous. (Coral berry). (1). S. orbiculatus.
   Pith excavated. (Snowberry). 2.
2. Buds small (2 mm. long): twigs glabrate. S. racemosus.
   Buds moderate (3 mm.): puberulent. (2). S. occidentalis.
   Buds large (4 mm.). (Hybrid snowberry). × S. Heyeri.

LONICERA. Honeysuckle.
(Family Caprifoliaceae).

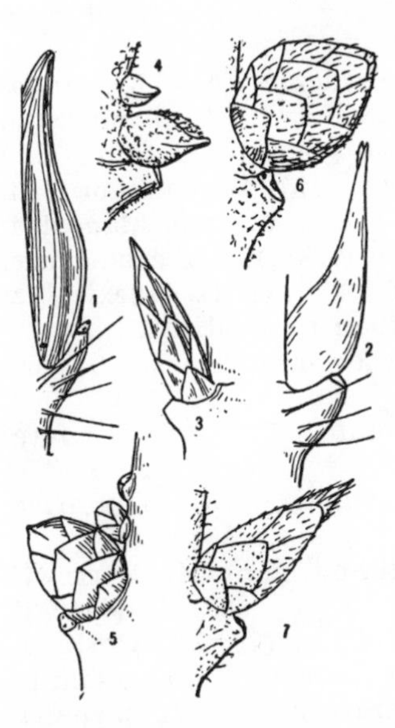

Bushes or woody twiners: deciduous or exceptionally partly or wholly evergreen. Twigs rounded, mostly slender: pith moderate, pale or brown, in some groups excavated between the nodes. Buds often superposed with the lowermost largest or developing into an inflorescence the first season, sessile, variously shaped, with 2 to rather numerous 4-ranked scales. Leaf-scars opposite, crescent-shaped, small, on the narrowed extremities of raised bases that are more or less connected by transverse lines: bundle-traces 3: stipule-scars lacking.

Sometimes divided into several genera: *Caprifolium*, *Distegium*, *Xylosteum*, etc. References under *Leycesteria*, p. 358.

1. Bushy: buds often superposed. 2.
   Twining: buds solitary: pith excavated. 17.
2. Pith white, continuous. 3.
   Pith brown, excavated between the nodes. 12.
3. Buds with valvate lower scales. 4.
   Bud-scales parted, the lower mostly short. 7.
4. Buds flattened, closely appressed, elongated. 5.
   Buds flask-shaped, ascending, elongated. 6.
   Buds short, spreading. (Mountain fly-h.). L. caerulea.
5. Buds pale, long (10 mm.). (1). L. hispida.
   Buds brown, shorter (8 mm.). L. chaetocarpa.
6. Buds rather long (7 mm.). (2). L. Standishii.
   Buds moderate (5 mm.). L. fragrantissima.

7. Lower scales essentially as long as the bud. 8.
   Lower scales distinctly shorter than the bud. 10.
8. Inner bud-scales wooly. L. iberica.
   Buds glabrate. 9.
9. Twigs glabrous. (Swamp fly-honeysuckle). L. oblongifolia.
   Twigs mostly long-hairy, 4-lined. L. involucrata.
10. Buds short-ovoid or nearly globose, glabrate. 11.
    Buds distinctly elongated, grooved. (3). L. Maximowiczii.
11. Scales acuminate. L. gynochlamydea.
    Scales acute. (American fly-honeysuckle). L. canadensis.
12. Lower scales as long as the bud. (4). L. deflexicalyx.
    Lower scales distinctly shorter than the bud. 13.
13. Buds oblong or ovoid or subglobose: scales short-pointed. 14.
    Buds oblong-ovoid: scales long-pointed. L. nigra.
    Buds conical-fusiform, hairy. 16.
14. Twigs and buds glabrous. (Tartarian h.). (5). L. tatarica.
    Twigs pubescent. 15.
15. Buds somewhat puberulent, small and blunt. L. Morrowii.
    Buds gray-hairy, oblong or acute. (6). L. Maackii.
16. Twigs somewhat puberulent. (7). L. Xylosteum.
    Twigs with long as well as short hairs. L. chrysantha.
17. Stems red-brown, hairy: subevergreen. L. japonica.
    Stems gray or straw-colored. 18.
18. Often with long glandular hairs above. L. Periclymenum.
    Not glandular-hairy. 19.
19. Rough or papillately hairy. L. hirsuta.
    Essentially glabrous, often glaucous. 20.
20. More or less evergreen. (Trumpet h.). L. sempervirens.
    Deciduous. 21.
21. Buds oblong, many-scaled. (Woodbine). L. Caprifolium.
    Buds ovoid, the lower scarcely surpassing their lowest scales. 22.
22. Scales narrowly triangular, pointed. L. glaucescens.
    Scales ovate, abrupt. L. dioica.

LINNAEA. Twinflower.
(Family Caprifoliaceae).

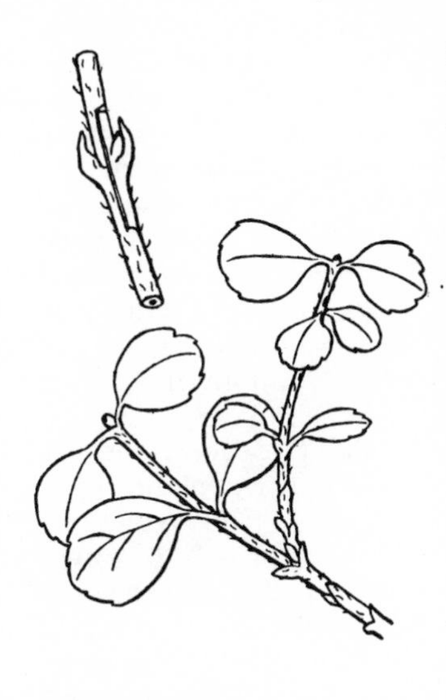

Low trailing and rooting shrubs with finally exfoliating red-brown bark: evergreen. Twigs almost filiform, terete: pith minute. Buds solitary, sessile, oblong, appressed, minute and concealed by the dilated petiole, with 2 valvate scales. Leaf-scars opposite, much raised and shriveled, the single bundle-trace obscured: stipules or stipule-scars lacking. Leaves small, obovate-orbicular, crenate, their petioles meeting transversely.

Winter-characters of *Linnaea borealis* are given by Bösemann, 37; and Fant, 51.

Though the American twinflower, *Linnaea borealis americana*, or *L. americana*, differs characteristically from its European representative, typical *L. borealis*, the distinction is not readily made out except when flowers are present.

Sparingly white-hairy. L. borealis.

Linnaea presents the seeming anomaly of a genus dedicated to himself by its author. Under international convention the nomenclature of flowering plants dates from the publications of the great author of the binominal system of designating plants. *Linnaea* was published by Linnaeus in his Genera Plantarum in 1737, and embodied in his Species Plantarum in 1753. He appears to have been extremely fond of the dainty little plant; but his friend Gronovius, and not he, named it in his honor.

LEYCESTERIA.
(Family Caprifoliaceae).

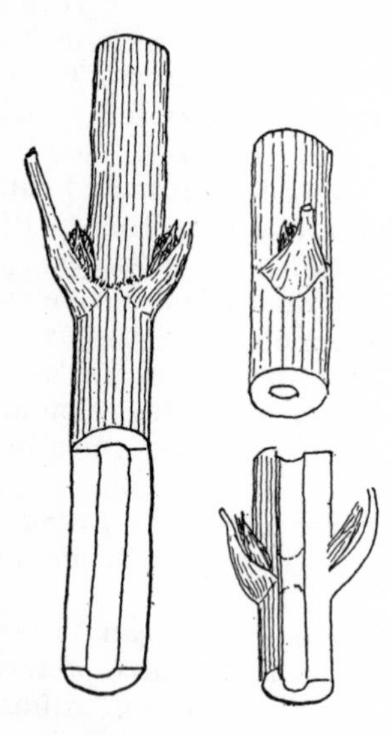

Soft-wooded small shrubs or half-shrubs: deciduous. Twigs rather slender, round: pith moderate, excavated. Buds solitary, slightly stalked, oblong, with 1 or 2 pairs of exposed scales, the outer attenuate. Leaf-scars opposite, minute, crescent-shaped, much raised so as to equal the bud, with a connecting cross-line: bundle-traces 3, indistinct: stipule-scars lacking.

Though tender, *Leycesteria* is a very attractive little plant when in fruit.

Winter-characters of *Leycesteria formosa* are pictured by Schneider, f. 202.

Glabrate and slightly glaucous.
L. formosa.

Winter-character references to *Lonicera*: — *L. alpigena.* Bösemann, 42; Schneider, f. 204; Willkomm, 11, 48, f. 85; Zuccarini, 23, pl. 13. *L. caerulea.* Bösemann, 42; Fant, 43, f. 45; Schneider, f. 203; Shirasawa, 273; Willkomm, 3, 48, f. 84; Zuccarini, 24, pl. 13. *L. Caprifolium.* Bösemann, 41; Schneider, f. 204; Ward, 1:163, f. 79; Willkomm, 11, 48, f. 86. *L. gracilipes.* Shirasawa, 273, pl. 11. *L. Morrowii.* Shirasawa, 272, pl. 11. *L. nigra.* Bösemann, 42; Schneider, f. 203; Willkomm, 47, f. 83. *L. Periclymenum.* Bösemann, 41; Fant, 43, f. 44; Schneider, f. 204; Ward, 1:163, f. 78; Willkomm, 11. *L. tatarica.* Bösemann, 42; Schneider, f. 203. *L. Xylosteum.* Bösemann, 42; Fant, 43; Schneider, f. 204; Willkomm, 11, 47, f. 82.

KOLKWITZIA.
(Family Caprifoliaceae).

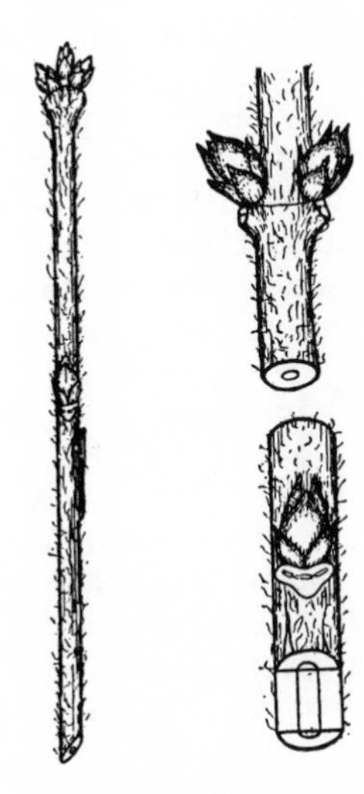

Shrubs with exfoliating bark: deciduous. Twigs round, at first villous: pith small, round, white, continuous. Buds solitary, sessile, ovoid, with 3 or 4 pairs of scales. Leaf-scars opposite, crescent-shaped or triangular, raised, connected by transverse lines: bundle-traces 3, or more or less confluent transversely: siptule-scars lacking.

Only the one species of *Kolkwitzia*, related to *Abelia*, is known. From twig and bud characters it is likely to be taken for a bushy honeysuckle with solid pith, or, if its 3 typically distinct bundle-traces seem to blend in a single long trace, for a privet or some similar oleaceous shrub.

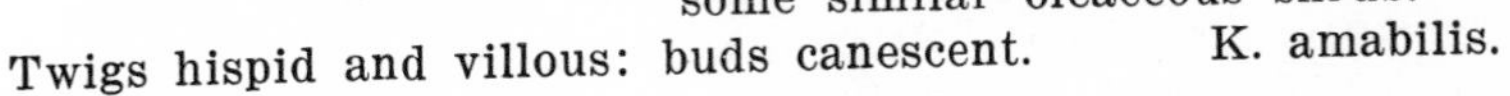

Twigs hispid and villous: buds canescent. K. amabilis.

ABELIA.
(Family Caprifoliaceae).

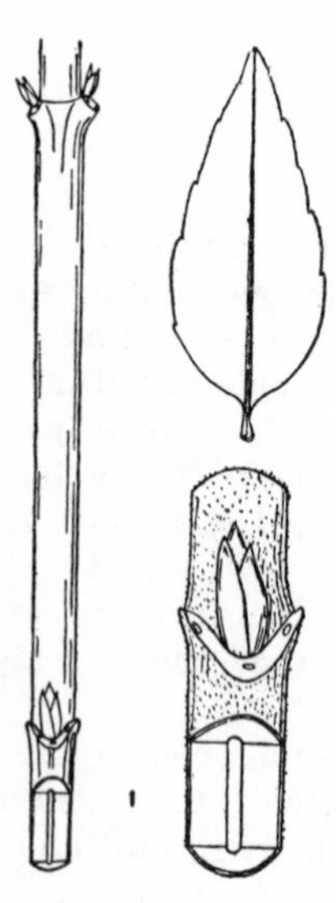

Rather small and soft-wooded shrubs: typically deciduous in the North. Twigs round or somewhat 4-sided, very slender, puberulent: pith small, excavated. Buds small, solitary, sessile or somewhat developing the first season, ovoid, with about 2 pairs of rather loose scales. Leaf-scars opposite, or on shoots in 3's and 4's U-shaped, somewhat raised, with connecting cross-line: bundle-traces 3: stipule-scars lacking.

Winter-character references: — *Abelia rupestris.* Schneider, f. 196. *A. serrata.* Shirasawa, 281, pl. 12.

As far north at least as Washington, where it is used effectively at the foot of the steps west of the Capitol, *Abelia* is one of the most attractive of compact small-leaved shrubs, and flowers well into the autumn. The most comprehensive analysis of the species of this genus, as of other genera cultivable in cool-temperate climates, is given in Schneider's Handbuch der Laubholzkunde, which, like his Dendrologische Winterstudien, is adequately and skilfully illustrated.

1. Half-evergreen: leaves small, ovate. 2.
   Truly deciduous. A. chinensis.
2. Leaves small (under 2.5 cm.). A. floribunda.
   Leaves medium (3-4 cm.). (1). A. grandiflora.
   Leaves large for the genus (4-5 cm.). A. triflora.

SAMBUCUS. Elder.
(Family Caprifoliaceae).

Open shrubs, or exceptionally arborescent: deciduous. Twigs more or less 6- or 8- or 10-sided or angled, stout: pith very large and soft, continuous. Buds solitary or multiple, the larger somewhat stalked and occasionally developing the first year, ovoid or the smaller depressed, with 3-5 pairs of scales: end-bud mostly lacking. Leaf-scars opposite or exceptionally in whorls of 3, broadly crescent-shaped or 3- or 4-sided, large, low, more or less transversely connected: bundle-traces 3 or 5 or 7: stipule-scars usually lacking.

Winter-character references: — *Sambucus canadensis.* Brendel, 28, pl. 1; Hitchcock (3), 16, (4), 137, f. 77-79. *S. nigra.* Bösemann, 65; Fant, 45, f. 49; Schneider, f. 20, 202; Ward, 1:58, f. 75; Willkomm, 9, 49, f. 89. *S. racemosa.* Bösemann, 65; Schneider, f. 202; Willkomm, 4, 7, 50, f. 90. *S. racemosa Sieboldiana.* Shirasawa, 277.

1. Pith white: buds rather small (4 mm.), often superposed. 2.
   Pith brown: bundle-traces mostly three. 3.
2. Lenticels moderate. (1). S. canadensis.
   Lenticels very numerous and prominent. S. nigra.
3. Buds rather small, often multiple. S. racemosa.
   Buds large (10 mm.), solitary. S. pubens.

BACCHARIS. Groundsel Tree.
(Family Compositae).

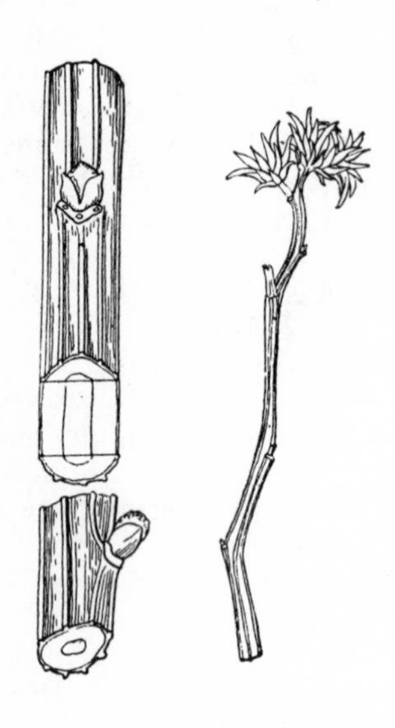

Openly bushy soft-wooded shrubs with resin-passages in the wood, etc.: tardily deciduous. Twigs slender, about 8-ridged, for a long time green: pith small, crenulate, pale, continuous. Buds rather small, solitary, sessile, nearly globose, with about 4 exposed scales, all or all but the outermost encased in hardened greenish resin. Leaf-scars alternate, small, angularly crescent-shaped, slightly raised, decurrent in ridges from the angles: bundle-traces 3: stipule-scars lacking. Inflorescence or its vestiges often present as rather small composite heads or their involucres.

Winter-characters of *Baccharis halimifolia* are indicated by Schneider, f. 77.

Twigs minutely puberulent, or glabrescent. B. halimifolia.

Winter-character references to other, rather suffruticose, Compositae: — *Artemisia camphorata* and *A. tridentata.* Schneider, f. 102. *Aster* (or *Amphiraphis*) *albescens.* Schneider, f. 102. *Chrysanthemum indicum.* Schneider, f. 77. *Gutierrezia euthamiae.* Schneider, f. 77. *Iva frutescens.* Schneider f. 98.

REFERENCES.

Blakeslee, A. F. & C. D. Jarvis. New England trees in winter. (Bulletin no. 69, Storrs Agricultural Experiment Station, pp. 307-576, with many half-tone illustrations). 1911 References are to this edition. The work was reissued under the title Trees in winter by the Macmillan Company of New York in 1913.

Blakeslee, A. F. & C. D. Jarvis. The identification of trees. Storrs, Conn. 1913. Pp. 195-209.—A separate issue of the keys from the Macmillan edition of Trees in winter.

Bösemann, F. A. Deutschlands Gehölze im Winterkleide. Pp. 91, ff. 17. Hildburghausen. 1884.

Brendel, F. The tree in winter. (Bulletin no. 1, Illinois Museum of Natural History, pp. 26-32, 73-76, 4 pl.). 1876.

Fant, C. G. Sveriges träd och buskar i vinterdrägt. Pp. 56, pl. 11. Stockholm. 1872.

Frank, A. B. Pflanzen-Tabellen. Leipzig, 1869. Pp. 169-176 consist of keys to woody plants in winter.

Hitchock, A. S. (1). Key to Kansas trees in their winter condition. Pp. 6, pl. 1. (Biennial Report of the Kansas Board of Agriculture). 1893. (2). A key to the woody plants of Manhattan based upon twig characters. Pp. 1-8. Manhattan, Kansas, 1901. (3). The woody plants of Manhattan in their winter condition. Pp. 20. Manhattan. 1893. (4). The opening of the buds of some woody plants. (Transactions of the Academy of Science of St. Louis. 6:133-141, 4 pl.). 1893.

Huntington, A. O. Studies of trees in winter. Boston, 1901. Pp. xxiv + 198, with many beautiful photographic illustrations of habit and bark.

Illick, J. S. Pennsylvania Trees. 4 ed. Harrisburg. 1923.

Otis, C. H. Michigan trees. (University Bulletin, University of Michigan, n. s. vol. 14, no. 16). Pp. xxxii + 246, with illustrations of all of the species. Ann Arbor. 1913.

Palmer, E. L. Woody plants in winter. (Cornell Rural School Leaflet. vol. 17, no. 3. 1924).

Sargent, F. L. Key to common deciduous trees in winter and key to common woods. Cambridge, Massachusetts. 1903.

Schneider, C. K. Dendrologische Winterstudien. Pp. vi + 290, ff. 224. Jena. 1903.

Shirasawa, H. Die japanischen Laubhölzer im Winterzustande. (Bulletin of the College of Agriculture, Imperial University, Tokio. 2:229-300, pl. 5-17—renumbered, and referred to in the text, as 1-13). 1895.

Trelease, W. (1). Juglandaceae of the United States. (Report of the Missouri Botanical Garden. 7:25-46, pl. 1-25). 1896. Pp. 28-45 and pl. 13-15 and 23-25 deal with winter characters. (2). The sugar maples, with a winter synopsis of all North American maples. (Report of the Missouri Botanical Garden. 5:88-106, pl. 4-16). 1894. Pp. 100-105 and pl. 4-7, 9, 11, 12 and, especially, 14-16 are concerned with winter-characters. (3). Classification of the black oaks. (Proceedings of the American Philosophical Society. 51:167-171, pl. 10-13). 1912.

Walser, E. Der Baum im Winter. Pp. 47, with a series of loose determination-tables. Bern. 1894.

Ward, H. M. Trees, vol. 1, Buds and twigs. Cambridge. 1904. Pp. xiv + 271, frontispiece and ff. 136.

Wiegand, K. M. & F. W. Foxworthy. A key to the genera of woody plants in winter. Pp. 33. Ithaca, New York. 1904.—2 ed. 1906.—3 ed. 1908.

Willkomm, M. Deutschlands Laubhölzer im Winter. Pp. ii + 60, ff. 106. Dresden. 1859. References are made to the third edition, published in 1880.

Zuccarini, J. G. Charakteristik der deutschen Holzgewächse im blattlosen Zustande. Pp. 32, pl. 18. München. 1829.

GLOSSARY.

Abortive. Undeveloped, rudimentary.

Abscission. The falling of leaf, twig-tip, etc, from a clean-cut scar, by a self-healing wound.

Acuminate. Pointed, with a line-of-beauty curve.

Acute. Sharp-pointed, in contrast with obtuse and acuminate.

Adnation. Growing together of different members.

Adventitious. Not in the usual place (buds that have remained undeveloped so that they are no longer evidently axillary, or that really originate elsewhere, as on a root).

Aerial roots. Roots produced above ground, often used for climbing (ivy).

Aggregated. Joined together, confluent, as applied to bundle-traces.

Alternate. One at a node, as applied to leaf-scars.

Amplexicaul. Encircling the stem (magnolia stipules, nandina leaves).

Analogous. Of comparable function but different origin.—See physiology.

Angiosperms. Plants that mature their seeds within the pistil. They constitute the dominant vegetation of today.

Appressed. Not spreading, as applied to buds, hairs, etc.

Approximated. Brought near to one another, as applied to buds.

Arboreous. Tree-like.

Arborescent. Becoming small trees.

Arcuate. Arched, bent like a bow.

Armed. With spines (barberry, Japanese quince) or prickles (brambles). Leaves that are pungent at tip or around the margin (holly), are not included in this limited definition.

Aromatic. Fragrantly scented, at least when broken.

Articular-membrane or tegment. A membrane consisting of the thin enlarged base of the petiole, on which the leaf-scar occurs (mock orange, locust).

Ascending. Between spreading and appressed, as applied to buds.

Attenuate. Narrowly drawn out, in contrast with acute.

Auricled. With small projections at base (leaf of heather).

Axil. The angle above a leaf: the point above a leaf-scar.

Axillary. In the axil.

Balsam. A fragrant gum.

Balsamiferous or balsamifluous. Producing or exuding balsam.

Bark. The rough outer part of the cortex; loosely used for the entire cortex.

Bast. The fibrous part of the cortex. Technically, the phloem or part of the fibro-vascular bundles of higher plants that contains sieve-cells.

Beaked. Ending in a beak or prolonged point.

Berry. A fleshy fruit, usually small.

Bi-. Twice, or doubly (bipinnate: bibracteate).

Bract. A modified leaf of an inflorescence. Several bracts form an involucre.

Bracteate or bracted. With bracts.

Branch. One of the coarser divisions of a trunk or main stem: loosely, any division of the stem.

Branch-spine. The same as twig-spine.

Bristly. With stiff hairs.

Broken. Not continuous, as applied to bundle-traces.

Bud. The rudimentary or resting end or branch of a stem: usually referring to the stage in which the growing tips pass the winter or dry season; also applied to undeveloped flowers or flower-clusters. Scaly buds are protected by modified leaves or stipules. Naked buds lack such special protection. Usually one bud occurs in each axil or angle above a leaf, but these often branch and collateral buds, standing side by side, are thus produced: in some plants (walnut, honeysuckle) several buds occur one above the other (superposed) in an axil.

Bundle-traces. The points on a leaf-scar where woody strands passed from the stem into the leaf; their number and position afford good winter-distinctions, and usually they are constant in number and position for a given species. Some entire families are characterized by the number of their bundle-traces: 1 in Myrtaceae and Ericaceae, 2 in Ginkgoaceae, etc. In long narrow leaf-scars their number is usually greater in the species with longer scars (3 to 5 in maple). Frequently the common number 3 is increased by the fragmentation or division of one or all into a corresponding number of groups of aggregated traces (species of maple, Juglandaceae, elm). In Oleaceae, which frequently have 1 transversely elongated bundle-trace, this may be transformed into a nearly closed ellipse, either uninterrupted or broken at rather short intervals. Rather exceptionally, numerous bundle-traces occur scattered over the leaf-scar, as in oak.—See, further, foliar gaps.

Burl. A knot or woody growth of very irregular grain, usually because of the continued activity of many slowly developing buds or branch-rudiments.

Buttressed. With supporting wings (mahogany trunk).

Caducous. Falling away early (bud-scales of clethra).

Calyx. The outer floral envelope, consisting of sepals.

Canes. The long shoots of blackberry, grape, etc.

Canescent. Ash-colored, with gray hairs.

Capsule. A dry dehiscent fruit (rose-of-sharon, mock orange).

Cataphyls. Scales or leaf rudiments on the lower part of a stem.

Catkin. The simple elongated flower-cluster of willow, etc.

Cauliflorous. Flowering on the trunk or on specialized spurs from it or from the larger branches (redbud, cacao).

-celled. Referring to the number of seed-cavities in a fruit.

Chaffy. With flattened hairs (chiogenes); thin and chaff-like (coca scales).

Chambered. With cavities separated by plates or disks, as applied to pith; discoid.

Ciliate. Hairy on the margin, like the eyelids.

Cladophylls or cladodia. Leaf-like flattened branches which serve the purpose of foliage (ruscus).

Cladoptosis. See abscission.

Clasping. Growing around; amplexicaul.

Climber. A plant which raises its foliage by supporting itself on surrounding objects, either by twining or coiling about them (bittersweet), by the aid of tendrils(greenbrier, Virginia creeper) or aerial roots (ivy), or by scrambling over them without either coiling or having such specialized organs of attachment (rose).

Coiling. Twining: winding about a support.

Collateral. Side-by-side (buds of silver maple in winter).

Composite. Compound: the common name of a member of the Compositae.

Compound. Of several distinct parts (tamarind leaf; bundle-traces of some maples; branched buds).

Compressed. Flattened from the sides, as applied to nodes or buds.

Cone. The characteristic scaly fruit of larch and cypress.

Confluent. Blending together, not easily distinguishable apart, as applied to bundle-traces.

Connate. Grown together (ephedra scales; gardenia stipules; weigelia sepals).

Continuous. Not broken by chambers or spongy: solid as applied to pith.

Cordate. Heart-shaped in the conventional sense.

Coriaceous. Firm and leathery.

Corky. Soft and springy, like bottle-cork (bark of Ohio buckeye).

Corky-ridged. With elongated warts or ridges on the bark (twigs of bur-oak, sweet gum, rock elm).

Corolla. The inner floral envelope, consisting of petals.

Corrugated. Closely grooved (stem of moonseed).

Cortex. The rind or outer covering of a stem; techncially it lies outside of the vascular bundles, which constitute the stele.

Cottony. Much the same as woolly, with white hairs.

Creeping. Prostrate and spreading over the ground.

Crenate. Scalloped; with rounded teeth.

Crenulate. Finely crenate.

Crisped. Wavy on the margin (leaves of laurel); short and curly when aplied to pubescence.

Cuticle. The outermost layer of the epidermal cell walls.

Deciduous. Falling away (leaves of elm in contrast with the persistent or evergreen leaves of ivy; terminal bud of ailanthus in contrast with the persistent end-bud of false cedar). Deciduous leaf-scars occasionally form at the top of a leaf-cushion which later falls away (cercidiphyllum, cornus, garrya, hamamelis).

Decompound. Repeatedly compound.

Decurrent. Continued down the stem in a ridge or wing, as applied to leaf-bases.

Decussate. With the pairs successively over the gaps of those below (leaf-scars of maple).

Dehiscent. Opening to discharge the seeds (fruit) or pollen (anther).

Deliquescent. Breaking up into fine branches (white elm).

Deltoid. Triangular, with equal sides.

Dentate. Toothed, the teeth spreading.

Denticulate. Finely dentate.

Denuded. Naked through loss of pubescence, epidermis, etc.

Depressed. Shortened, as applied to round buds or fruits.

Diaphragmed. With firmer plates at the nodes (grape) or between them (tulip tree), as applied to continuous pith.

Dicotyledonous. Belonging to or characteristic of Dicotyledoneae, one of the two main groups of Angiosperms.

Diffused-porous. Wood in which the ducts are scattered and neither larger nor more numerous in the spring wood than in that formed in summer (willow, basswood). Contrasted with ring-porous.

Digitate. Spreading like the fingers, the leaflets leaving the petiole at one point (stauntonia), as applied to compound leaves. The same as palmate.

Dingy. Neither white nor brightly colored, as applied to pubescence.

Disarticulating. Falling away by abscission, leaving a clean-cut scar, as with most leaves, many flowers, some twig-tips, etc.

Discoid. The same as chambered, when applied to pith.

Disk. An enlarged tip, as applied to tendrils (Boston ivy).

Distichous. Two-ranked.

Divergent. The same as spreading.

Divided. Deeply lobed (leaves): compound (bundle-traces).

Dorsal. Of or on the back of a leaf, etc.

Dotted. With lighter or darker spots or blackened hairs or glands, usually on the lower leaf-surface, as here used.

Downy. Pubescent with soft short straight hairs.

Drupe. A stone-fruit (cherry). Many "berry-like" fruits are technically small drupes,—even that of the huckleberry.

Duct. A water-passage in the wood; a trachea or vessel: easily seen in oak which is ring-porous, and walnut which is diffused-porous. The size and distribution of ducts afford usable means of distinguishing between bits of wood.

Dull. Not glossy.

Dwarf-shoots. The same as spurs.

Elbowed. Bent, like an arm at the elbow (crape myrtle bud).

Ellipsoid. Elliptical in section, like a football.

Emergences. Appendages other than hairs, of root, stem or leaf.

End-bud. The growing tip normally terminating a stem or its developed branches: sometimes transformed into a flower (magnolia) or inflorescence (lilac), or cast off early in the season (linden), or killed in winter (bramble).

Endogenous. Inside-growing. Applied formerly to stems of Monocotyledoneae, which have the wood in fibers scattered through the stem.

Entire. Neither toothed nor lobed, as applied to leaves.

Epidermis. The outer layer of cells covering a leaf or a young twig; often detached from the latter as a thin gray pellicle.

Epiphyte. A plant growing on another without being a parasite (conservatory orchids), or on a rock or tree-trunk (mosses, lichens). Contrasted usually with plants rooted in the soil; sometimes with parasites.

Epitrophic. More nourished and developed on the upper side (horizontal branches of linden)—See hypotrophic.

Erect. Contrasted with spreading, appressed, prostrate, etc.

Evanescent. Quickly disappearing.

Evergreen. Holding or constituting green foliage through the winter.

Excavated. Hollowed out, as applied to pith, making the stem fistulous.

Exfoliating. Peeling away (bark of canoe birch).

Exogeneous. Outside growing. Applied formerly to the stems of Dictoyledoneae and Gymnospermae, which have the wood in a zone between pith and bark and add to it by annual growth.

Extra-axillary or supra-axillary. Above rather than in the axil.

Falcate. Sickle-shaped (leaves of mature blue gum).

Fascicled. Clustered, like leaves on a spur of barberry.

Fastigiate. With upright branches (Lombardy poplar).

Fibrous-flaking. Flaking in narrow shreds (bark of osage orange).

Filiform. Thread-like and slender (chiogenes stem).

Fimbriate. Fringed: perhaps more properly with a torn membrane.

Fissured. Torn lengthwise, as applied to bark, or to pith, for which the more general term spongy is used.

Fistulous. Hollow, with excavated pith (honeysuckle stem).

Flaking. Shredding, but with short fragments.

Fleshy, or succulent. Not hard and woody (stem); not dry (fruit, bud-scales).

Floriferous, florigerous. Flower-bearing or producing flowers.

Fluted. Corrugated or ridged lengthwise.

Foliage. Collectively, the leaves of a plant: the green expanded organs in which carbon from the air is combined into organic compounds.

Foliage-sprays. Twigs that finally fall away carrying the small leaves with them,—sometimes at end of the first season (tamarisk), sometimes after several years (arbor vitae).

Foliar-gaps or lacunae. Breaks between those vascular bundles of the stem which run continuously from one internode into another. Through these breaks certain bundles of the stem pass out into the leaves to constitute the network of veins through which these organs are supplied with water absorbed by the root and conducted to them through the stem. An admirable illustrated paper on the anatomy of the node as an aid in the classification of angiosperms is published by Sinnott in The American Journal of Botany for July 1914.

Follicle. A small dry fruit opening down one edge (ninebark).

Fragmented. Not continuous, as applied to bundle-traces.

Fringed. Ciliate with glands or scales rather than fine hairs, as here used.

Fusiform. Spindle-shaped (buds of beech).

Gametes. Sex-cells: egg and sperm.

Gamophyllous. Of united leaves;—gamopetalous when these are petals, gamosepalous when they are sepals.

Glabrate. Nearly glabrous.
Glabrescent. Becoming glabrous.
Glabrous. Not hairy; without trichomes.
Glands. Secreting organs (resin-glands of sweet bay,—nectar-glands of cherry laurel, oil-glands of orange). Leaf-teeth and stipules often end in minute glands.
Glandular-bristly. With stiff gland-tipped hairs.
Glandular-ciliate. Fringed with small glands.
Glandular-pubescent. With gland-tipped hairs.
Glaucous. With white or bluish bloom (box elder twig).
Globose. Shaped like a globe; spherical.
Granular. Minutely roughened.
Gritty. Containing hard particles (pith of aucuba).
Gum. A rather fluid resin, as loosely used.
Gummy. Sticky, as applied to sap.
Gymnosperms. Plants that have naked seeds, not enclosed in a pistil. With angiosperms, they constitute the flowering plants or seed-plants.
Habit. General appearance or mode of growth.
Hairs. Superficial outgrowths; trichomes: sometimes flat and scale-like (rhododendron), sometimes of rays like the spokes of a wheel, when they are spoken of as stellate (deutzia), sometimes round plates attached in the middle, when they are spoken of as peltate (oleaster).
Hairy. Pubescent: often used when the hairs are rather long.
Half-shrub. A suffruticose or soft-wooded plant.
Hardy. Used in the horticultural sense, enduring winter-cold.
Harsh. Rough to the touch, as applied to pubescence.
Head. A round or flat cluster of sessile flowers.
Heath-like. Fine-stemmed and low, rather simple, with persistent leaves.
Herbaceous. Not woody; in contrast with lignified.
Hispid. With stiff bristly hairs.

Homogeneous. Without firmer plates or grit, as here used for pith: composed entirely of living cells, as applied by Gris.

Homologous. Of comparable morphological origin.—See morphology.

Honeycombed. Finely spongy (pith of wintergreen).

Horrid. Used in the classical sense.

Hypotrophic. More nourished and developed on the lower side (horizontal branches of yew)—See epitrophic.

Imbricated. Overlapping like shingles.

Impressed-veiny or venulose. With sunken veins or veinlets.

Incipient. Beginning or developing.

Indefinite or indistinct. Not readily made out: usually because very small or hairy (bud-scales), or because overgrown by a corky layer (bundle-traces).

Indehiscent. Not opening, as applied to fruits.

Inequilateral. With unequal sides: the same as oblique when applied to leaves or leaflets.

Inferior. Applied to a flower or fruit in which the pistil appears to bear the calyx around its side (witch hazel) oı top (apple).

Inflorescence. A flower cluster.

Inflorescence-scar. The scar from which a flower-cluster has fallen.

Infra-. Below.—Infra-axillary, below the axil or leaf (gooseberry prickle); infraspinal, below the spine (bougainvillea bud).

Internode. The part of a stem between two nodes.

Intricate. Much branched with entangled branches.

Involucrate. With an involucre or cluster of bracts.

Involucre. A cluster of modified leaves about a flower-cluster.

Isodiametric. As broad as high.

Junctures. The same as winter nodes. The points at which one season's growth is succeeded by the next: they comprise the interrameal region of Gris.

Keel. A ridge on the back of a leaf or bud-scale.

Knees. Pointed or dome-like outgrowths from cypress roots. rising above the water.

Lacunae. See Foliar-gaps.

Lanceolate. Shaped like a lance-head, as applied to leaves.

Lateral. Applied to all but the truly terminal bud.

Leaf. The foliage appendages of the stem, though not always serving as foliage: sometimes metamorphosed into a spine (barberry) or tendril (clematis) or reduced to a scale (tamarisk). Leaves originate at and mark the nodes or joints of the stem. Buds normally occur in the angles or axils above leaves and are correspondingly alternate, opposite or whorled on the stem.

Leaf-axis. The same as rachis.

Leaf-cushion. A raised base on which the leaf-scar sometimes appears.

Leaf-scars. Scars from which leaves have fallen. They usually occur characteristically either singly (alternate) or paired (opposite) or in groups of more than 2 (whorled) at each node. Leaf-scars differ greatly in size and shape, and offer some of the best winter-characters. The points where woody strands passed up into the leaf are usually evident, and are called bundle-traces. Typical leaf-scars are essentially at the level of the stem; but they are raised on a pronounced base or leaf-cushion in some cases, or the buds are covered by an articular membrane in others.

Leaf-spine. A spine metamorphosed from a leaf.

Leaflet. One of the divisions of a compound leaf.

Legume. A pod: characteristic fruit of the pea family.

Lenticels. Wart-like prominences breaking through the bark of most young twigs (elder, cherry).

Lignified. Woody, in contrast with herbaceous.

Linear. Long and narrow (leaves); nearly straight (leaf-scars).

Lined. Rather lightly ridged or ribbed.
Lobed. Divided rather deeply, as applied to leaves.
Lucky-nuts or knots. A name sometimes given by children to woody structures imbedded in the bark of beech, olive, etc. They represent loosely attached rudimentary branches and are comparable with burls.
Matted. Growing in very compact tufts, or so as to form a low close cover to the ground.
Medullary rays. The plates radiating between pith and cortex in exogenous stems. Like pith, they serve for the storage of reserve food,—usually starch as may be demonstrated by a drop of iodine on the end of a twig cut in winter.
Member. A morphological part of a plant: root, stem, leaf.
Membranaceous. Thinner and less firm than coriaceous.
Metamorphosis. Conversion of a member of the plant body into an organ differing in function from its usual form: tendril of grape (stem) or clematis (leaf) and aerial roots of poison ivy (root) as organs of climbing; spine of red haw (stem) or barberry (leaf), or pea-tree (leaf rachis) as organs of protection; cladodia of butcher's broom (stem), green roots of some conservatory orchids, etc., as foliage.
Midrib. The strong main vein of a leaf.
Milky. Colored, usually white, as applied to sap.
Moniliform. Resembling a necklace of beads (sophora fruit).
Monocotyledonous. Belonging to or characteristic of Monocotyledoneae, one of the two main groups of angiosperms.
Morphology. The science of form in living things, classifying their parts as members from the view-point of origin and development. However they may differ in function, members that are morphologically of like origin are homologous one with another.
Mucronate. With a short stiff abrupt point.
Mucronulate. Minutely mucronate.

Multiple. Applied to several buds in or over an axil, instead of the customary single or solitary bud.

Naked. Without specialized scales, as applied to buds.

Nectar-glands. Glands that secrete the sugary fluid nectar: common in flowers; characteristic of the petioles of cherries, the under surface of leaves of the cherry-laurel, the calyx of paeonies, etc.

Netted-veined. Much the same as reticulate.

Nodal. At or pertaining to a node.

Node. The part of a stem marked by a leaf, or a pair or whorl of leaves.

Nodose. Swollen into joints.

Nutlets. Small hard fruits or their parts, or the stones of a small drupe.

Ob-. Used as a prefix to indicate inversion: obcordate in contrast with cordate, oblanceolate, etc.

Oblique. Not immediately over the leaf-scar (mulberry bud): not equal-sided at base (tamarind leaflet).

Obliquely opposite. Sometimes said of normally opposite leaves with some pairs broken (ash, etc.).

Oblong. Between elliptical and linear in shape.

Obscure. Not easily made out, as applied to buds, bundle-traces, etc.

Obtuse. Blunt, in contrast with acute.

Ochreae. Sheathing stipules, or their near equivalent, of Polygonaceae.

Odd-pinnate. Pinnate with a terminal or odd leaflet: contrasted with abruptly pinnate.

Odoriferous. Much the same as aromatic but of questionable fragrance.

Olivaceous. Brownish or yellowish green, like a pickled olive.

Opposite. Two at a node, as applied to leaf-scars.

Organ. A physiological part of a plant, considered with reference to the work it does rather than its morphological origin.

Osier-like. Long and lithe (shoots of willow or dogwood).
Ovate. Shaped like the section of an egg.
Ovoid. Egg-shaped.
Palmate. The same as digitate. Contrasted with pinnate.
Panicle. A branched cluster of stalked flowers (lilac).
Panicled. In panicles.
Papery. Firm but thin, as applied to leaves.
Papillate. Much the same as granular, the granules more elevated.
Papillately hairy. With short thick hairs, or hairs from papillae.
Parted. Much the same as divided, when applied to leaves or stipules.
Pedicel. The stalk of an individual flower in a flower-cluster.
Pedicel- or peduncle-scar. The scar from which a flower or flower-cluster has fallen.
Peduncle. The stalk of a flower-cluster, or of a solitary flower.
Pellucid-dotted or punctate or glandular. With translucent dots when held to the light (orange leaf).
Peltate. Attached to a stalk nearly by its center (scales of oleaster).
Percurrent. With the main trunk continued through to the top: contrasted with deliquescent.
Persistent. Not deciduous, as applied to leaves: not disappearing, as applied to pith, pubescence, epidermis, etc.
Petals. Modified leaves forming the inner floral envelope.
Petiole. The leaf-stalk; rarely (nandina) persistent after the rest of the leaf has fallen.
Petioled or petiolate. With a petiole: stalked, as applied to leaves.
Petiolule. The petiole or stalk of a leaflet.
Phyllodia. Dilated petioles taking the place of foliage (acacia).

Phyllotaxis. Leaf-arrangement: alternate, or separate in 2, 3, 5 or 8 ranks, on many plants; opposite, or in groups of 2, in others; whorled, or in groups of more than 2, in still others.

Physiology. The science of function in living things, classifying their parts as organs with respect to the work they perform. Organs of unlike morphological origin are analogous to one another.—See metamorphosis; morphology.

Pinna. One of the divisions of a pinnate leaf.

Pinnate. Like the plume of a feather: having the leaflets along a rachis, as applied to compound leaves (tamarind). Contrasted with digitate or palmate.

Pinnule. A leaflet of a bipinnate or decompound leaf.

Pistillate. Producing pistil, or seed-organ, but not stamens (ear of corn, "female" cottonwood).

Pith. The central part of a dictolyedonous or exogenous stem, surrounded by the woody cylinder: usually continuous and of uniform texture, or gritty or surrounded by cells different from those at the center, or exceptionally with plates of firmer cells, or diphragms, at the nodes (paper mulberry, grape) or at intervals between them (tupelo) though otherwise continuous; rather commonly with cavities like a sponge (evonymus), or entirely excavated or disappearing, at least between the nodes (honeysuckle) so as to make the stem fistulous; not infrequently chambered between persistent thin plates or disks (walnut) when it is spoken of sometimes as discoid.

Pithy. Sometimes used in the sense of having large pith and little wood.

Pod. A dry dehiscent seed-vessel: capsule, legume, follide.

Pointed. The general equivalent of acute, acuminate or mucronate.

Pollen. The male cells or microspores produced by flowers.

Pome. An apple-fruit, with a papery or bony core at center and crowned by sepals or scars from which they have fallen. Many "berry-like" fruits are really small pomes (cotoneaster).

Preformed. Already with definite shape or structure (leaves within the bud).

Prehensile. Clasping, coiling in response to touch (tendrils).

Prickle. A pungent outgrowth of a stem or leaf, not representing a modified form of either member (rose).

Prominent. Standing out, usually in the literal sense.

Pruinose. Encrusted with wax, very glaucous (bayberry fruit).

Puberulent. Minutely pubescent.

Pubescence. Collective name for the hairs of a plant.

Pubescent. With hairs, in contrast with glabrous: sometimes used to designate the presence of soft short hairs in contrast with villous, hispid, etc.

Punctate. Marked with small points: dotted.

Pungent. With a sharp hard point: acrid in taste or odor.

Raceme. An elongated unbranched cluster of stalked flowers.

Racemed or racemose. In racemes.

Rachis. The axis along which the leaflets of a pinnate leaf are arranged (tamarind).

Rachis-spine. A spine metamorphosed from a leaf-rachis.

Ranks. As applied to leaf-scars, the longitudinal series in which these are arranged on the stem; usually 2, 3, 5 or 8 when they are alternate, and twice as many as the scars at a node when these are opposite or whorled; also applied to bud-scales.

Receptacle. The part of a stem that bears the floral organs or, when enlarged, the flower (cashew apple) or flowers (fig).

Reduced. Smaller or simpler than usual, as commonly applied.

Resin. A hardening gum, as loosely used.

Resin-warts or glands. Glands that secrete resin (bayberry, black birch).

Resiniferous or resinifluous. Exuding or producing resin.

Reticulate. Netted, usually referring to veins of a leaf.

Retrorsely hairy. With hairs directed downward on stem or leaf.

Revolute. With the margins rolled back, as applied to leaves.

Ring-porous. Wood in which the ducts first formed in the season are larger or more crowded or both than those formed in summer (oak).

Root-climber. A plant climbing by aid of aerial roots.

Rudiment. Beginning of an undeveloped member. Contrasted with vestige.

Rugulose. Minutely rugose or wrinkled.

Savory. Smelling like thyme.

Sap. As here used, the fluid that flows from a freshly cut leaf-stalk or twig.

Scabrous. Rough to the touch.

Scale. As usually employed, a reduced leaf, as in winter buds, ruscus, etc.: one of the parts of a cone of the larch, etc.: a flattened (rhododendron) or peltate (elaeagnus) hair.

Scarious. Thin, dry and papery.

Scattered. Not in any of the usual definite groups, as applied to leaves, bundle-traces, etc.

Scrambling-plants. Climbers that neither coil nor produce aerial roots or tendrils (rose).

Scurfy. Scaly rather than hairy.

Sepals. Modified leaves forming the outer floral envelope.

Serrate. Saw-toothed: the teeth pointed upward.

Serrulate. Serrate with fine teeth.

Sessile. Not stalked.

Setaceous. Bristle-like, very narrow.

Sheathing. Forming a (frequently tubular) sheath (sea grape stipules).

Shield-shaped. Of the conventional shield-form (leaf scar of cyrilla): peltate (scale-chaff of oleaster).

Shredding. Falling away in shreds (bark of grape).

Shrub. A woody plant not becoming a tree: usually the equivalent of the colloquial word bush, which also excludes climbers.

Silky. With soft appressed hairs.

Simple. Not compound, of one part (ivy leaf; maple bundle-traces).

Sinuate. With wavy margin, as applied to leaves.

Smooth. Not roughened, not warty: wrongly used for glabrous.

Soft-wooded. Suffruticose, not fully lignified, as here used.

Spatulate. Oblong with the upper part rather abruptly widened.

Spermatophytes. Seed-plants: flowering plants.

Spine. A specialized pungent form of the leaf (barberry) or its stipules (locust) or rachis (pea-tree); or of a twig (hawthorn). Contrasted with prickle.

Spinescent. Turning into spines.

Spirally arranged. Leaves or their equivalent that are neither opposite nor whorled and not 2-ranked.

Spongy. Porous, suggesting a sponge, as applied to pith.

Spreading. Not closely appressed to the twig (buds) or the surface (hairs); horizontal as applied to branches.

Spur. A dwarf-branch, as applied to twigs (larch, birch), often bearing the flower-buds (pear).

Stalked. Elongated perceptibly below the lowest scales, as applied to buds (alder).

Staminate. Producing stamens or pollen-organs, but not pistil (tassel of corn, "male" cottonwood).

Standard. In horticulture, a small tree commonly produced by grafting a weeping or dwarf form on a trunk of the desired height.

Star-shaped or stellate. With several arms radiating from a center (hairs of deutzia; pith of oak in cross section).

Staring. Widely spreading, as applied to hairs, etc.

Stellate-scurfy. Scurfy with star-shaped hairs or scales.

Stem. The trunk and its branches: one of the three fundamental parts of a higher plant,—root, stem and leaf.

Sterigmata. The raised bases from which some small leaves fall (spruce).

Stipular. Pertaining to or derived from stipules.

Stipulate. Provided with stipules.

Stipule-scars. Scars from which stipules have fallen; sometimes forming a ring around the twig (magnolia), or very unequal (elm); usually small.

Stipule-spines. Spines metamorphosed from stipules.

Stipules. Small basal outgrowth of a leaf; sometimes serving as bud scales (beech), or spines (locust); usually otherwise represented by scars, if at all, in winter. The relation of stipules to the nodal anatomy of plants is considered by Sinnott and Bailey in The American Journal of Botany for November 1914.

Stolon. A stem that arches over and roots at the tip (blackcap).

Stoloniferous. Producing stolons.

Stomata. The "breathing-pores" of a leaf.

Stone. The hard inner part of a drupe or stonefruit (cherry).

Stratified. In horizontal layers (foliage of red haw and tupelo).

Striate. Striped, usually by alternating ridges and grooves.

Sub-. Often used as a prefix in the sense of nearly:—subacute, subsessile, etc.

Subtending. Standing below.

Succulent. Fleshy (stem of ocotillo; scales of hawthorn).

Suckers. Adherent disks on tendrils (Boston ivy); also applied to new stems that originate underground (poplar), or to canes (rose).

Sulcate. Grooved.

Sunken. In depressions (buds of coffee-nut or buttonball).

Supernumerary. Beyond the usual number (superposed or collateral buds).

Superposed. One above the other (buds of coffee-nut).

Suppressed. Undeveloped or rudimentary, when applied to buds, etc.

Surpassing. Sometimes used in the sense of longer than.

Tender. In the horticultural sense of not enduring winter cold.

Tendril. A climbing organ metamorphosed from leaf (clematis), stipule (smilax) or stem (grape).

Terete. Round in cross-section as though rolled between the fingers, as applied to twigs, capsules, etc.

Teretely. In a terete manner.

Ternate. Compound or decompound with 3 divisions (nandina leaf).

Thorn. The same as spine.

Tomentose. Woolly.

Tomentulose. Microscopically tomentose or woolly.

Toothed. With the margin cut into, but not deeply enough for lobing, as applied to leaves.

Torsion. Twisting. It frequently gives a false impression of the number of ranks in which leaf-scars stand. Leaves of privet, pernettya and many other plants lie in one plane through curving of their petioles, though they orignate on the stem in 4 ranks.

Torulose. Much the same as moniliform: necklace-like.

Tracheae. The ducts or vessels of wood; chains of elongated cells the cross partitions between which have more or less completely disappeared.

Tracheides. Short pitted or spirally thickened cells replacing tracheae as water channels in the wood of most gymnosperms.

Trailing. Slender-stemmed, prostrate on the ground.

Transverse. Used sometimes in the sense of transversely lengthened.

Transversely joined leaf-scars. Those of a pair or whorl connected by a ridge or line running around the twig.

Tree. A woody plant, usually of large size or with a single trunk when smaller. Contrasted with shrub, but not easily separated in definition, as sumach, witch hazel and many other plants show.

Trichomes. The same as hairs.

Trifoliolate. Of 3 leaflets, as applied to compound leaves.

Truncate. Abruptly cut off (seed of hardy catalpa; petiole of fendlera; leaf-scar of sorbaria).

Truncately. In a truncate manner.

Trunk. The main stem or axis of a tree.

Tube. The lower tubular part of a gamophyllous calyx or corolla, etc.

Tuberculate. Warty.

Twig-spine. A spine metamorphosed from a twig.

Twigs. The finer or finest branches of a stem.

Twiggy. Used in the sense of having many divergent twigs.

Twinned-hairs. Two-armed appressed hairs (dogwood).

Unarmed. Without either spines or prickles,—though the leaves may have pungent teeth or tip as in holly.

Unifoliolate. Really compound, though of only one leaflet (leaf of barberry or orange).

Uniform. Neither diaphragmed nor gritty, as here applied to pith.

Urceolate. Urn-shaped in the conventional sense, with the neck contracted.

Valvate. Meeting by the edges but not overlapping.

Valves. The parts into which a capsule finally breaks.

Vascular bundles. The strands, chiefly woody, of root, stem or leaf.

Veinlets. The finer or finest veins of a leaf.

Veins. The woody bundles of a leaf,—often called nerves when they run rather distinctly from its base to tip.

Veiny. Usually meaning with conspicuous veins.

Velvety. Downy: pubescent with short spreading hairs.

Venulose. Finely veiny.

Vernation. Arrangement of leaves in the bud.

Verticillate. Whorled.

Vessels. Ducts, or tracheae.

Vestiges. The remnants of disappearing parts. Contrasted with rudiments of unformed parts.

Villous. With long spreading hairs.

Vine. A climbing or trailing plant, in popular usage.

Warty. With rounded warts or tubercles (twig of elder). Contrasted with granular, where the roughening is fine.

Weeping. With drooping branches, as used horticulturally.

Whorled. Three or more at a node, as applied to leaf-scars.

Winged. With thin border or appendage (leaf-scar of some maples, twig of some spindle-trees, petiole of orange).

Wood. Technically, the xylem or part of the fibro-vascular bundles of higher plants that contains ducts or tracheides, in contrast with the bast or phloem which contains sieve-cells.

Wood-parenchyma. Tissue accompanying fibers, ducts and tracheides, in wood.

Woody fibers. As here used loosely, the vascular bundles.

Woolly. With long curved tangled hairs.

Zig-zag. Bent back and forth at the nodes.

INDEX

MANUAL OF THE TREES OF NORTH AMERICA

by Charles Sprague Sargent

The greatest dendrologist America has ever produced was without doubt Charles Sprague Sargent, Professor of Arboriculture at Harvard and Director of the Arnold Arboretum in Boston until his death in 1927. His monumental "Manual of the Trees of North America," incorporating the results of 44 years of original research, is still unsurpassed as the most comprehensive and reliable volume on the subject. Almost every other book on American trees is selective, but this one assures you of identifying any native tree; it includes 185 genera and 717 species of trees (and many shrubs) found in the United States, Canada, and Alaska. 783 sharp, clear line drawings illustrate leaves, flowers, and fruit.

First, a 6-page synoptic key breaks trees down into 66 different families; then, an unusually useful 11-page analytical key to genera helps the beginner locate any tree readily by its leaf characteristics. Within the text over 100 further keys aid in identification. The body of the work is a species by species description of leaves, flowers, fruit, winterbuds, bark, wood, growth habits, etc., extraordinary in its fullness and wealth of exact, specific detail. Distinguishing features of this book are its extremely precise locations and distributions; flower and leaf descriptions that indicate immaturity variations; and a strong discussion of varieties and local variants.

Additional useful features are a glossary of technical terms; a system of letter keys classifying trees by regions; and a detailed index of both technical and common names (index, glossary, and introductory keys are printed in both volumes.) Students and teachers of botany and forestry, naturalists, conservationists, and all nature lovers will find this set an unmatched lifetime reference source. "Still the best work," Carl Rogers in "The Tree Book."

Unabridged and unaltered reprint of the 2nd enlarged 1926 edition. Synopsis of Families. Analytical Key of Genera. Glossary. Index. 783 illustrations, 1 map. Total of 982pp. 5⅜ x 8.

T277 Vol I Paperbound **$2.25**
T278 Vol II Paperbound **$2.25**
The set **$4.50**

FRUIT KEY AND TWIG KEY TO TREES AND SHRUBS

FRUIT KEY TO NORTHEASTERN TREES
TWIG KEY TO THE DECIDUOUS WOODY PLANTS OF EASTERN NORTH AMERICA

by W. M. Harlow

(Professor of Wood Technology, College of Forestry, State University of New York, Syracuse)

Bound together for the first time in one volume, these handy, accurate, and easily used keys to fruit and twig identification are the only guides of their sort with photographs—over 350 of them, of nearly every twig and fruit described—making them especially valuable to the novice.

The fruit key (dealing with both deciduous trees and evergreens) begins with a concise introduction, explaining smiply and lucidly the process of seeding, and identifying the various organs involved: the cones and flowers, and their component parts and variations. Next, the various types of fruits are described—drupe, berry, pome, legume, follicle, capsule, achene, samara, nut—and fruiting habits, followed by a synoptic summary of fruit trees.

The introduction to the twig key tells in plain language the process of growth, and its relation to twig morphology through leaf scars, branch scars, buds, etc. For the benefit of the unwary, poison-ivy, poison-oak, and poison-sumac are immediately and fully described.

Identification in both books is easy. There is a pair of alternative descriptions of each aspect of the specimens. Your choice of the fitting one leads you automatically to the next proper pair. At the end of the chain is the name of your specimen and, as a double check, a photograph. More than 120 different fruits and 160 different twigs are distinguished.

This exceptional work, widely used in university courses in botany, biology, forestry, etc., is a valuable tool and instructor to the naturalist, woodsman, or farmer, and to anyone who has wondered about the name of a leafless tree in winter, or been intrigued by an interestingly shaped fruit or seed.

Over 350 photographs, up to 3 times natural size. Bibliography, glossary, index of common and scientific names, in each key. Total of xvii + 126pp. 5⅝ x 8⅜. Two volumes bound as one. T511 Paperbound **$1.35**

INSECT LIFE AND NATURAL HISTORY

by J. W. Frost

This very unusual book is a middle-level account of the immense empire of insects and their ways. Although it is used in scores of biology classes throughout the world, it is also an unexcelled browsing or self-study work, full of solid information presented in a most engaging manner.

Professor Frost, who is one of the country's foremost entomologists, presents insects, not as subjects for classification alone, but as living beings, with habits, life cycles, interraltions with other forms of life, and remarkable abilities and deficiencies. Beginning with the biological position of insects throughout the world, he then discusses the origin and distribution of insects, types and classification, the process of metamorphosis and other stages in the life cycle, morphology, insect color, sound, behavior, social life, insects of prey, parasites, insects in relation to plants, subterranean insects, aquatic insects, and similar topics of importance. Very interesting sections are also included on insects as subjects for art, literature, and music, insects as human food, and insects and civilization.

Although Professor Frost's book is thorough and impeccably accurate, it is delightful reading, packed with of startling facts about insects and their ways. You will read about insects that change color at will; insects that feign death; insects that live in hot springs up to 150° moth larvae that construct diving suits for themselves; short circuit beetles that bore through lead electric cables; butterflies whose wing radiation can expose photographic plates; fireflies that flash in unison; insects that live by running after ants and snatching food from their mandibles; insects that are driven by instinct to fly to their death in the snows of Mount Everest, and countless other facts about insects in their relations to each other and to man.

"Distinclty different, possesses an individuality all its own; well-organized, clearly presented, scholarly and pleasing," Journal of Forestry. "Well written, stimulating," Quarterly Review of Biology.

Formerly titled "General Entomology," 1300 item classified bibliography. Appendix with 13 keys enabling you to identify insects. Over 700 illustrations. Index. x + 524pp. 5⅝ x 8⅜.

Paperbound $2.50